INTRODUCTION TO THE THEORY OF QUEUES

UNIVERSITY TEXTS IN THE MATHEMATICAL SCIENCES

Introduction to the
Theory of Queues

LAJOS TAKÁCS

Associate Professor of Mathematical Statistics
Columbia University

NEW YORK   OXFORD UNIVERSITY PRESS   1962

To Dalma

PREFACE

The aim of this book is to give an introduction to the probabilistic treatment of mass servicing. We deal with different models which can be applied successfully to the theory of telephone traffic, airplane traffic, road traffic, storage, operation of dams, serving of customers, operation of particle counters, and others. Our interest is chiefly in the time-dependent or transient behavior of these processes. The bulk of this book is based on the author's recent research work. The most important auxiliary theorems which are frequently used in the text may be found in the Appendix. There are a few problems for solution to help the reader to become familiar with the methods used here. The solutions are given at the end of the book. At the end of each chapter there is a bibliography which includes the references in that chapter as well as other papers which the author recommends to the reader. The numbering of the formulas starts anew in each section. The formulas mentioned in any one section indicate formulas of the same section unless otherwise stated.

We should say a few words about the investigation of the time dependence of the processes occurring in this book. If we introduce a sufficient number of auxiliary parameters, then every process can be treated as a Markovian one. However, the use of this method leads to a complicated mathematical treatment and it is often necessary to impose superfluous restrictions on the processes. Instead, we exploit the fact that the processes in question possess regeneration points and thus we can apply the theory of recurrent processes. Blackwell's theorem* is particularly useful for the investigation of the limiting behavior of these processes.

This book is not a complete monograph of the theory of queues, but the methods which we consider most important are presented here. By using these methods one can approach several types of queueing processes not discussed in this book. In several cases the

---

* *D. Blackwell:* A renewal theorem. Duke Math. J., 15 (1948), 145–50.

solution of queueing problems results in an apparently complicated formula; but fortunately we are living in an age of electronic computers, when complicated formulas in the old-fashioned sense can easily be handled.

Finally I should like to thank Professor Herbert Robbins for reading the manuscript of this book and for suggesting linguistic improvements.

New York   L. Takács
March 1961

CONTENTS

INTRODUCTION TO THE THEORY OF QUEUES

INTRODUCTION

1. The mathematical model of queues

In the wider sense the theory of queues deals with the investigation of the stochastic law of different processes arising in connection with mass servicing in cases when random fluctuations occur. Here are some examples of such processes.

TELEPHONE TRAFFIC PROCESS. Calls are arriving at a telephone exchange according to a certain stochastic law. There are a fixed number of available lines. If a call finds a free line then a connection is realized. The lengths of the holding times are random variables. If all the lines are busy, then the incoming call is lost. Of course, there are some variants of this system. For instance, there may be a waiting facility and if all the lines are busy then a new call joins the waiting line and awaits its turn. In this case we speak about a waiting system. If the waiting facility has a limited capacity then we speak about a combined waiting and loss system.

MASS SERVICING PROCESS. Let us suppose that customers are arriving at a counter according to some probabilistic law. There are one or more servers. The customers will be served by the servers in the order of their arrival (or in a random manner, or by the principle "last come first served," etc.). If every server is busy then the customers join the queue or waiting line. Generally the service times are random variables. We speak about a single server queueing process if there is one server, and a many server queueing process if there is more than one server. If every customer is served immediately on his arrival, then we speak about a queueing process with infinitely many servers.

Several queueing processes belong to this category. For example, the process of calls in a telephone exchange, the reading of messages in a telegraph office, the moving of equipment in the production line, the landing of airplanes at an airport, the arrival of ships in a harbor, railway traffic, road traffic, and others. Many processes which seem to have very little to do with queues are in fact closely related to queueing processes. For instance, the fluctuation of the size of the stock in a warehouse is similar to the fluctuation of the size of a queue. Even the operation of a dam can be described as a queueing process.

SERVICING AUTOMATIC MACHINES. The following problem is particularly interesting. A group of automatic machines is serviced by several repairmen. Normally the machines work continuously; however, at any time a machine may break down and need servicing. If a machine breaks down it will be serviced immediately when there is an idle repairman. If every repairman is busy then a waiting line is formed. The times required for servicing the machines are random variables.

THE PROCESS OF PARTICLE COUNTING. Particles arrive at a counting device according to some probabilistic law. In consequence of the inertia of the device, not all particles will be recorded. The process of the registrations has special importance. This process can be discussed in a way similar to the queueing processes.

Throughout this book we shall apply the expressions 'customers' and 'servers' to all these processes. Every conceivable process can always be described in this terminology. For instance, in the case of the telephone traffic process the calls, lines, and holding times are replaced by customers, servers, and service times respectively.

The mechanism of the queueing processes is very simple. Customers are arriving at a counter according to a certain probabilistic law (Poisson input, Erlang input, Palm input, etc.). The customers will be served by one or more servers following a certain principle (service in order of arrival, random service, priority service, last come first served, batch service, etc.). The service times are random variables governed by a given probabilistic law. After being served, the customers depart.

Of course, there are several variants of the above-mentioned queueing processes, e.g. queueing with balking, queue with repeated arrivals, queueing with feedback, queue with batch arrivals. Further, it is interesting to investigate the interaction of different queues, e.g. queues in parallel, queues in series.

The three most important characteristics in the theory of queues are as follows.

The *waiting time* of each customer.

The *busy period*, that is, the time interval during which one or more servers are busy.

The *queue size*, that is, the number of customers in the system.

The waiting time concerns the customers, the busy period concerns the servers, and the queue size concerns the design of the system, e.g. the size of the waiting room or the waiting facility in telephone exchanges.

The theory of queues, like the theory of probability, gives abstract models which are applied in many different fields. One of the most important models is as follows.

Customers arrive at a counter at the instants $\tau_1, \tau_2, \ldots, \tau_n, \ldots$ The customers will be served by m servers in the order of their arrival. Let us denote by χ_n the service time of the nth customer and write $\theta_n = \tau_{n+1} - \tau_n$. It is supposed that the inter-arrival times $\{\theta_n\}$ and the service times $\{\chi_n\}$ are independent sequences of identically distributed, positive random variables with distribution functions $\mathbf{P}\{\theta_n \leqq x\} = F(x)$ and $\mathbf{P}\{\chi_n \leqq x\} = H(x)$, respectively. Such a queueing process can be described by the triplet $[F(x), H(x), m]$.

Denote by $\eta(t)$ the *virtual waiting time* at the instant t; i.e. $\eta(t)$ is the time that a customer would wait if he joined the queue at the instant t.

The virtual waiting time $\eta(t)$ can also be interpreted as follows: $\eta(t)$ is the time at the instant t needed to complete the serving of all those customers who joined the queue before t. In this case we say that $\eta(t)$ is the *occupation time* of the server at the instant t.

Denote by $\xi(t)$ the *queue size* at the instant t, i.e. the number of customers waiting or being served at the instant t. We say that the system is in state E_k at the instant t if $\xi(t) = k$.

Let us denote by $\tau_1', \tau_2', \ldots, \tau_n', \ldots$ the instants of the successive departures.

Further define $\eta_n = \eta(\tau_n - 0)$, i.e. η_n is the waiting time of the nth customer, and let $\xi_n = \xi(\tau_n - 0)$ and $\zeta_n = \xi(\tau_n' + 0)$, i.e. ξ_n is the queue size immediately before the nth arrival and ζ_n is the queue size immediately after the nth departure.

In what follows we shall be interested in the transient behavior of the stochastic processes $\{\eta(t)\}$ and $\{\xi(t)\}$ and that of the stochastic sequences $\{\eta_n\}$, $\{\xi_n\}$ and $\{\zeta_n\}$.

There is a huge literature on the asymptotic behavior of different types of queueing processes but only a few papers deal with their time dependent or transient behavior.

An extensive bibliography of the theory of queues by *A. Doig* (1957) contains more than six hundred papers, most of which deal with stationary queues. The theory of stationary queues is very important because most of the queueing processes are ergodic; that is, starting from any initial state, the process tends toward equilibrium irrespective of the initial state. In the state of equilibrium the process shows only statistical fluctuation with no tendency to a certain state. Many queueing processes rapidly approach equilibrium and this explains why one can apply with success the stationary approximation. However, the investigation of the transient behavior of queueing processes is also important, not only from the point of view of the theory but also in the applications.

We shall consider different particular cases of the queueing model $[F(x), H(x), m]$ and in addition we shall deal with telephone traffic processes, servicing of machines, and counter problems.

REMARK. The pioneer works on the theory of queues are those of *A. K. Erlang* (1917), *F. Pollaczek* (1930), and *A. Y. Khintchine* (1932). Many other works including the latest are mentioned in the bibliography at the end of each chapter. The most extensive bibliography of the theory of queues has been compiled by *A. Doig* (1957).

2. Input process

Throughout this book we shall consider the following type of input process. We shall suppose always that the time t ranges over the interval $[0, \infty)$. Let us denote by $\tau_1, \tau_2, \ldots, \tau_n, \ldots$ the arrival instants of the customers. We shall suppose that the inter-arrival times $\theta_n = \tau_{n+1} - \tau_n$ $(n = 0, 1, \ldots; \tau_0 = 0)$ are mutually independent, positive random variables with the distribution function

$$\mathbf{P}\{\theta_n \leq x\} = F(x) \qquad (n = 1, 2, \ldots).$$

In general the random variable $\theta_0 = \tau_1$ may have a distribution function

$$\mathbf{P}\{\tau_1 \leq x\} = \hat{F}(x)$$

which is different from $F(x)$. Generally $\hat{F}(x)$ depends on the initial state of the process.

In this case we say that the input process is a *recurrent process*.

If specifically we suppose that $\hat{F}(x) = F(x)$ and

$$(1) \qquad F(x) = \begin{cases} 1 - e^{-\lambda x} & \text{if } x \geq 0, \\ 0 & \text{if } x < 0, \end{cases}$$

then $\{\tau_n\}$ is said to be a *Poisson process*.

If $\hat{F}(x) = F(x)$ and

$$(2) \qquad F(x) = \begin{cases} 1 - \displaystyle\sum_{j=0}^{m-1} e^{-\lambda x} \frac{(\lambda x)^j}{j!} & \text{when } x \geq 0, \\ 0 & \text{when } x < 0, \end{cases}$$

then we say that $\{\tau_n\}$ is an *Erlang process*.

If $\hat{F}(x) = F(x)$ and $F(x)$ is arbitrary then we speak about a *Palm process*.

If we suppose that the average inter-arrival time $\beta = \displaystyle\int_0^\infty x \, dF(x)$ is finite and $\hat{F}(x) = F^*(x)$ where

$$(3) \qquad F^*(x) = \begin{cases} \dfrac{1}{\beta} \displaystyle\int_0^x [1 - F(y)] \, dy & \text{if } x \geq 0, \\ 0 & \text{if } x < 0, \end{cases}$$

then we speak about a *homogeneous recurrent process*.

We shall always use the following notation. The expectation

$$\phi(s) = \mathbf{E}\{e^{-s\theta_n}\} \qquad (n = 1, 2, \ldots)$$

always exists if $\Re(s) \geq 0$. This can be written also as

$$\phi(s) = \int_0^\infty e^{-sx} \, dF(x)$$

and is called the Laplace-Stieltjes transform of the distribution function $F(x)$. Knowing $\phi(s)$, the distribution function $F(x)$ can be determined uniquely.

The expectation

$$\beta = \mathbf{E}\{\theta_n\}$$

always exists (possibly $\beta = \infty$). β is the average inter-arrival time which can be written in the following form

$$\beta = \int_0^\infty x \, dF(x).$$

The variance of the inter-arrival time is defined by

$$\sigma_\beta^2 = \mathbf{E}\{(\theta_n - \beta)^2\} = \int_0^\infty (x - \beta)^2 \, dF(x)$$

(possibly $\sigma_\beta^2 = \infty$).

We suppose that the arriving customers form a queue in the order of their arrival and wait for service.

3. Service mechanism

Generally we shall consider the case 'first come first served,' but we mention in advance that the queue size, the busy period, and the occupation time are independent of the system of serving and that the principle 'first come first served' may be replaced by the assumption that 'there is no idle server, if there is a customer in the waiting line.' We shall denote by m the number of servers.

The service times are supposed to be identically distributed, independent, positive random variables, independent of the input process. The service time of the nth customer will be denoted by χ_n. We shall define

$$\mathbf{P}\{\chi_n \leq x\} = H(x)$$

as the distribution function of the service times. The Laplace-Stieltjes transform of $H(x)$ is denoted by

$$\psi(s) = \mathbf{E}\{e^{-s\chi_n}\} = \int_0^\infty e^{-sx} \, dH(x)$$

which is convergent if $\Re(s) \geq 0$. The average service time will be denoted by

$$\alpha = \int_0^\infty x \, dH(x)$$

and the variance of the service time by

$$\sigma_\alpha^2 = \int_0^\infty (x - \alpha)^2 \, dH(x).$$

An important particular case is that in which the service time has an exponential distribution, i.e.

(1)
$$H(x) = \begin{cases} 1 - e^{-\mu x} & \text{if } x \geq 0, \\ 0 & \text{if } x < 0. \end{cases}$$

The exponential distribution has the following characteristic property. The probability that a service in progress at time t will terminate during $(t, t + x]$ is $H(x)$ irrespective of the past duration of the service. For, if χ denotes the service time having the distribution function $\mathbf{P}\{\chi \leq x\} = H(x)$, then, under the condition that the past duration of the service is u, the remaining service time has the distribution

$$\mathbf{P}\{\chi \leq u + x \mid \chi > u\} = \frac{\mathbf{P}\{u < \chi \leq u + x\}}{\mathbf{P}\{\chi > u\}} = \frac{H(u+x) - H(u)}{1 - H(u)} = H(x).$$

In this particular case $\psi(s) = \mu/(\mu + s)$, $\alpha = 1/\mu$ and $\sigma_\alpha^2 = 1/\mu^2$.

If the service time has the distribution function $H(x)$ defined by (1), then the probability that a service in progress at time t will terminate during $(t, t + \Delta t]$ is

$$H(\Delta t) = \mu \, \Delta t + o(\Delta t),$$

where $o(\Delta t)/\Delta t \to 0$ as $\Delta t \to 0$. If at time t exactly k services are in progress and their lengths are independent of each other and have the same distribution function $H(x)$ defined by (1), then the probability that one service terminates during $(t, t + \Delta t]$ is

$$\binom{k}{1} H(\Delta t)[1 - H(\Delta t)]^{k-1} = k\mu \, \Delta t + o(\Delta t)$$

and the probability that more than one service terminates during $(t, t + \Delta t]$ is $o(\Delta t)$.

Another important particular case is when the service time has a gamma distribution, i.e.

(2)
$$H(x) = \begin{cases} 1 - \sum_{j=0}^{m-1} e^{-\mu x} \dfrac{(\mu x)^j}{j!} & \text{if } x \geq 0, \\ 0 & \text{if } x < 0. \end{cases}$$

In this case the service time can be considered as a sum of m independent random variables each of which has an exponential distribution. We can conveniently say that the service time consists of m phases, the lengths of which are independent random variables with distribution function (1).

4. A simple waiting time problem

The following example shows that surprising phenomena can occur in waiting time problems.

Suppose that at a given stop buses are arriving in accordance with a homogeneous recurrent process. The inter-arrival times have the distribution function $F(x)$ and β is the average inter-arrival time. What is the average waiting time of a passenger arriving at time t at the stop?

The answer usually given is $\beta/2$. But this is so only if buses run at exactly β-time intervals. The average waiting time depends on the variance of the inter-arrival times. The right answer is

$$\frac{\beta}{2} + \frac{\sigma_\beta^2}{2\beta},$$

where σ_β^2 is the variance of the inter-arrival time. If σ_β^2 is infinite, then the average waiting time is also infinite, in spite of the fact that the average inter-arrival time is finite.

Let us denote by $W_t(x)$ the probability that the waiting time is less than or equal to x at the instant t. If $\tau_1, \tau_2, \ldots, \tau_n, \ldots$ denote the instants of arrivals in the time interval $(0, \infty]$, then we can write

$$W_t(x) = \sum_{n=1}^{\infty} \mathbf{P}\{t < \tau_n \leq t + x < \tau_{n+1}\}$$

$$= \sum_{n=1}^{\infty} \int_t^{t+x} [1 - F(t + x - u)] \, d\mathbf{P}\{\tau_n \leq u\}$$

if $x \geq 0$. For, the waiting time is less than or equal to x if at least one bus arrives during $(t, t + x]$, and this event can occur in several mutually exclusive ways: the last bus arriving in the time interval

$(t, t + x]$ may be the 1st, 2nd, ..., nth, ..., one. Here

$$\sum_{n=1}^{\infty} \mathbf{P}\{\tau_n \leqq t\} = \frac{t}{\beta}$$

is equal to the expectation of the number of buses arriving in the time interval $(0, t]$.

Thus

$$W_t(x) = \frac{1}{\beta} \int_t^{t+x} [1 - F(t + x - u)]\, du = \frac{1}{\beta} \int_0^x [1 - F(y)]\, dy$$

irrespective of t. If $\sigma_\beta^2 < \infty$, then

$$\int_0^{\infty} x\, dW_t(x) = \frac{1}{\beta} \int_0^{\infty} x[1 - F(x)]\, dx = \frac{\beta^2 + \sigma_\beta^2}{2\beta},$$

and if $\sigma_\beta^2 = \infty$, then

$$\int_0^{\infty} x\, dW_t(x) = \infty.$$

Bibliography

[1] *E. Brockmeyer, H. L. Halstrøm and A. Jensen:* The Life and Works of A. K. Erlang. Trans. of the Danish Acad. of Technical Sci. No. 2 (1948), 1–277.

[2] *A. Doig:* A bibliography on the theory of queues. Biometrika, 44 (1957), 490–514.

[3] *A. K. Erlang:* Solution of some problems in the theory of probabilities of significance in automatic telephone exchanges. The Post Office Electrical Engineer's Journal, 10 (1917–18), 189–97.

[4] *A. Y. Khintchine:* Mathematical theory of a stationary queue (in Russian). Mat. Sbornik, 39, No. 4 (1932), 73–84.

[5] *F. Pollaczek:* Über eine Aufgabe der Wahrscheinlichkeitstheorie. Math. Zeit. 32 (1930), 64–100 and 729–750.

1

SINGLE SERVER QUEUEING PROCESSES

1. The time dependence of a single server finite queue with Poisson input and exponential service times

Customers arrive at a counter in accordance with a Poisson process of density λ. There is a single server. The service times are identically distributed, independent random variables with distribution function

$$(1) \qquad H(x) = \begin{cases} 1 - e^{-\mu x} & \text{if } x \geqq 0, \\ 0 & \text{if } x < 0. \end{cases}$$

Let us suppose that there is a waiting room with $N - 1$ places, i.e. the maximal number of customers in the system is N. If a customer finds exactly N customers in the system, then he goes away without being served.

Denote by $\xi(t)$ the queue size at the instant t. Under the given conditions $\{\xi(t)\}$ is a Markov process; that is, the future stochastic behavior of the process is uniquely determined by the present state and does not depend on the past of the process. The transition probabilities are defined by

$$P_{ik}(t) = \mathbf{P}\{\xi(t) = k \,|\, \xi(0) = i\} \qquad (i, k = 0, 1, \ldots, N).$$

The process $\{\xi(t)\}$ is said to be homogeneous since it has the property

$$\mathbf{P}\{\xi(t) = k \,|\, \xi(s) = i\} = P_{ik}(t - s) \qquad (0 \leqq s < t),$$

i.e. the transition probability depends only on the difference $t - s$.

The transition probabilities $P_{ik}(t)$ satisfy the so-called Chapman-Kolmogorov equation

$$(2) \qquad P_{ik}(t + s) = \sum_{j=0}^{N} P_{ij}(t) P_{jk}(s) \qquad (t > 0, s > 0).$$

This equation reflects the fact that the passage from E_i to E_k during time $t + s$ must occur via some intermediate state E_j at time t.

THEOREM 1. *If* $\lambda \neq \mu$ *then*

$$(3) \quad P_{ik}(t) = \frac{1 - \dfrac{\lambda}{\mu}}{1 - \left(\dfrac{\lambda}{\mu}\right)^{N+1}} \left(\frac{\lambda}{\mu}\right)^k$$

$$+ \frac{2}{N+1} \sum_{j=1}^{N} \frac{e^{-(\lambda+\mu)t + 2t\sqrt{\lambda\mu}\cos[j\pi/(N+1)]} \left(\dfrac{\lambda}{\mu}\right)^{(k-i)/2}}{\left[1 - 2\sqrt{\dfrac{\lambda}{\mu}}\cos\dfrac{\pi j}{N+1} + \dfrac{\lambda}{\mu}\right]}$$

$$\cdot \left[\sin\frac{ij\pi}{N+1} - \left(\frac{\lambda}{\mu}\right)^{\frac{1}{2}}\sin\frac{(i+1)j\pi}{N+1}\right]$$

$$\cdot \left[\sin\frac{kj\pi}{N+1} - \left(\frac{\lambda}{\mu}\right)^{\frac{1}{2}}\sin\frac{(k+1)j\pi}{N+1}\right],$$

and if $\lambda = \mu$ *then*

$$(4) \quad P_{ik}(t) = \frac{1}{N+1} + \frac{1}{N+1}\sum_{j=1}^{N}\frac{e^{-2\lambda t + 2\lambda t\cos[j\pi/(N+1)]}}{\left(1 - \cos\dfrac{\pi j}{N+1}\right)}$$

$$\cdot \left[\sin\frac{ij\pi}{N+1} - \sin\frac{(i+1)j\pi}{N+1}\right]$$

$$\cdot \left[\sin\frac{kj\pi}{N+1} - \sin\frac{(k+1)j\pi}{N+1}\right].$$

PROOF. The probability that exactly one customer arrives at the counter during the time interval $(t, t + \Delta t]$ is $\lambda\Delta t + o(\Delta t)$, and that more than one customer arrives $o(\Delta t)$. If $\xi(t) = i \geqq 1$ then the probability that one customer departs during the time interval $(t, t + \Delta t]$ is $\mu\Delta t + o(\Delta t)$ and that more than one departs is $o(\Delta t)$.

Using these facts we obtain that

(5) $\qquad P_{ik}(\Delta t) = a_{ik}\,\Delta t + o(\Delta t) \qquad$ if $k \neq i$

and

(6) $\qquad P_{ii}(\Delta t) - 1 = a_{ii}\,\Delta t + o(\Delta t),$

where

(7) $\qquad a_{00} = -\lambda, \quad a_{01} = \lambda;$

$a_{i,i-1} = \mu, \quad a_{ii} = -(\lambda + \mu), \quad a_{i,i+1} = \lambda \qquad (i = 1, 2, \ldots, N-1);$

$\quad a_{N,N-1} = \mu, \quad a_{NN} = -\mu \quad$ and $\quad a_{ik} = 0 \quad$ if $|k - i| > 1.$

By (2) we have

(8) $\qquad P_{ik}(t + \Delta t) = \sum_{j=0}^{N} P_{ij}(t) P_{jk}(\Delta t)$

or

(9) $\qquad P_{ik}(t + \Delta t) = \sum_{j=0}^{N} P_{ij}(\Delta t) P_{jk}(t).$

If we form the limit

$$\lim_{\Delta t \to 0} \frac{P_{ik}(t + \Delta t) - P_{ik}(t)}{\Delta t} = P'_{ik}(t),$$

replacing $P_{ik}(t + \Delta t)$ by (8) and (9) respectively and using (5) and (6), we obtain the following systems of differential equations

(10) $\qquad P'_{ik}(t) = \sum_{j=0}^{N} P_{ij}(t) a_{jk}$

and

(11) $\qquad P'_{ik}(t) = \sum_{j=0}^{N} a_{ij} P_{jk}(t).$

The initial condition is

$$P_{ik}(0) = \begin{cases} 1 & \text{if } k = i, \\ 0 & \text{if } k \neq i. \end{cases}$$

Let us introduce the following matrix notation. Let

$$\mathbf{P}(t) = \|\,P_{ik}(t)\,\| \quad (i, k = 0, 1, \ldots, N)$$

and

$$\mathbf{A} = \|\,a_{ik}\,\| \quad (i, k = 0, 1, \ldots, N),$$

where a_{ik} is defined by (7). In matrix notation the equation (10) is

$$\text{(12)} \qquad \mathbf{P}'(t) = \mathbf{P}(t)\mathbf{A}$$

and the equation (11) is

$$\text{(13)} \qquad \mathbf{P}'(t) = \mathbf{A}\mathbf{P}(t).$$

The initial condition is

$$\mathbf{P}(0) = \mathbf{I},$$

where $\mathbf{I} = \| \delta_{ik} \|$ $(i, k = 0, 1, \ldots, N)$ is the unit matrix. (δ_{ik} is the Kronecker symbol, $\delta_{ik} = 1$ if $k = i$ and $\delta_{ik} = 0$ if $k \neq i$.) Then we can write the solution to both (12) and (13) as

$$\mathbf{P}(t) = e^{\mathbf{A}t},$$

where the exponential of a matrix is defined as the element by element sum of the exponential series.

To find the solution $\mathbf{P}(t)$ we first mention the following general method.

Let us find the canonical decomposition of $\mathbf{A}$. If

$$\text{(14)} \qquad \mathbf{A} = \mathbf{H}\Omega\mathbf{H}^{-1},$$

where $\mathbf{H}^{-1}$ is the inverse matrix of $\mathbf{H}$, which exists if the determinant $|\mathbf{H}| \neq 0$, then

$$\text{(15)} \qquad \mathbf{P}(t) = e^{\mathbf{A}t} = \mathbf{H}e^{\Omega t}\mathbf{H}^{-1}.$$

To find (14), first of all let us determine the characteristic values of $\mathbf{A}$, that is, the roots in ω of the equation

$$\text{(16)} \qquad |\mathbf{A} - \omega\mathbf{I}| = 0.$$

Let

$$\mathbf{x} = \left\| \begin{matrix} \alpha_0 \\ \alpha_1 \\ \cdot \\ \cdot \\ \cdot \\ \alpha_N \end{matrix} \right\|$$

be a column vector and $\mathbf{y}' = \| \beta_0, \beta_1, \ldots, \beta_N \|$ be a row vector. The matrix equations

$$\mathbf{A}\mathbf{x} = \omega\mathbf{x}$$

and

$$\mathbf{y}'\mathbf{A} = \omega\mathbf{y}'$$

have solutions $\mathbf{x}$ and $\mathbf{y}'$ other than the zero vector if and only if ω is a characteristic value of the matrix $\mathbf{A}$. If the roots of the characteristic equation (16) are distinct then Ω can be represented as a diagonal matrix. Now we shall restrict ourselves to this special case. Let us denote by $\omega_0, \omega_1, \ldots, \omega_N$ the roots of the characteristic equation (16). Further denote by $\mathbf{x}_j$ and $\mathbf{y}'_j$ one of the right-hand and left-hand characteristic vectors belonging to the characteristic value $\omega = \omega_j$. If $j \neq k$ then we have $\mathbf{y}'_j\mathbf{x}_k = 0$ and by suitable normalization we can achieve $\mathbf{y}'_j\mathbf{x}_j = 1$ $(j = 0, 1, \ldots, N)$.

With this choice

$$\mathbf{H} = \|\mathbf{x}_0, \mathbf{x}_1, \ldots, \mathbf{x}_N\| \quad \text{and} \quad \mathbf{H}^{-1} = \begin{Vmatrix} \mathbf{y}'_0 \\ \mathbf{y}'_1 \\ \cdot \\ \cdot \\ \cdot \\ \mathbf{y}'_N \end{Vmatrix}$$

are inverse matrices, and by means of these matrices we can write

$$(17) \qquad\qquad \mathbf{A} = \mathbf{H}\Omega\mathbf{H}^{-1},$$

where Ω is the diagonal matrix

$$\Omega = \begin{Vmatrix} \omega_0 & 0 & \cdots & 0 \\ 0 & \omega_1 & \cdots & 0 \\ \cdot & \cdot & \cdots & \cdot \\ 0 & 0 & \cdots & \omega_N \end{Vmatrix}.$$

Accordingly if

$$\mathbf{x}_j = \begin{Vmatrix} \alpha_{0j} \\ \alpha_{1j} \\ \cdot \\ \cdot \\ \cdot \\ \alpha_{Nj} \end{Vmatrix} \quad \text{and} \quad \mathbf{y}'_j = \| \beta_{j0}, \beta_{j1}, \ldots, \beta_{jN} \|,$$

then by (15) we get

$$P_{ik}(t) = \sum_{j=0}^{N} e^{-\omega_j t}\alpha_{ij}\beta_{jk}.$$

If the non-null characteristic vectors $\mathbf{x}_j$ and $\mathbf{y}'_j$ are arbitrarily chosen, then we can write similarly that

(18) $$P_{ik}(t) = \sum_{j=0}^{N} C_j e^{-\omega_j t}\alpha_{ij}\beta_{jk},$$

where

(19) $$C_j = \frac{1}{\mathbf{y}'_j \mathbf{x}_j} = \frac{1}{\displaystyle\sum_{\nu=0}^{N} \beta_{j\nu}\alpha_{\nu j}}.$$

Now we shall apply the previous method to our special matrix $\mathbf{A} = \| a_{ij} \|$ defined by (7). First let us consider the equation

(20) $$\mathbf{A}\mathbf{x} = \omega\mathbf{x},$$

where

$$\mathbf{x} = \left\|\begin{array}{c} \alpha_0 \\ \alpha_1 \\ \cdot \\ \cdot \\ \cdot \\ \alpha_N \end{array}\right\|.$$

The matrix equation (20) is equivalent to the following system of linear equations

(21) $$-\lambda\alpha_0 + \lambda\alpha_1 = \omega\alpha_0$$

(22) $$\mu\alpha_{i-1} - (\lambda + \mu)\alpha_i + \lambda\alpha_{i+1} = \omega\alpha_i \qquad (i = 1, 2, \ldots, N-1)$$

(23) $$\mu\alpha_{N-1} - \mu\alpha_N = \omega\alpha_N.$$

We see immediately that if $\omega = 0$ then $\alpha_i = 1$ $(i = 0, 1, \ldots, N)$ is a solution of this system of linear equations. That is, $\omega_0 = 0$ is a characteristic value of $\mathbf{A}$ and $\alpha_{i0} = 1$ $(i = 0, 1, \ldots, N)$ are the components of a non-null characteristic vector $\mathbf{x}_0$ belonging to $\omega_0 = 0$.

The general solution of (22) is

(24) $$\alpha_i = \left(\frac{\mu}{\lambda}\right)^{i/2} (A \sin iy + B \cos iy) \qquad (i = 0, 1, \ldots, N),$$

where A and B are arbitrary constants and

$$\cos y = \frac{\lambda + \mu + \omega}{2\sqrt{\lambda\mu}}.$$

This can be proved as follows. The solution of the difference equation (22) is

$$\alpha_i = C_1 x_1^i + C_2 x_2^i,$$

where x_1 and x_2 are the roots in x of the equation

(25) $$\lambda x^2 - (\lambda + \mu + \omega)x + \mu = 0,$$

provided that the roots are distinct. The C_1 and C_2 are arbitrary constants. If we introduce a new variable y by

$$\cos y = \frac{\lambda + \mu + \omega}{2\sqrt{\lambda\mu}}$$

then the roots of (25) are

$$x_1 = \sqrt{\frac{\mu}{\lambda}} e^{y\sqrt{-1}} \quad \text{and} \quad x_2 = \sqrt{\frac{\mu}{\lambda}} e^{-y\sqrt{-1}}$$

and α_i can be written in the form of (24) if we write $B = C_1 + C_2$ and $A = (C_1 - C_2)\sqrt{-1}$.

The α_i defined by (24) satisfies (21) if

$$A = C\left(1 - \sqrt{\frac{\lambda}{\mu}} \cos y\right)$$

and

$$B = -C\sqrt{\frac{\lambda}{\mu}} \sin y,$$

where C is a constant. Choose $C = 1$ then

$$\alpha_i = \left(\frac{\mu}{\lambda}\right)^{i/2} \left[\sin iy - \left(\frac{\lambda}{\mu}\right)^{1/2} \sin (i+1)y\right].$$

This α_i satisfies (23) if and only if $\sin (N+1)y = 0$, that is,

$$y = \frac{j\pi}{N+1} \quad (j = 0, 1, \ldots, N).$$

If $y = 0$ then the roots x_1 and x_2 agree and this case is excluded. We know that $\omega_0 = 0$ is a characteristic root of the matrix $\mathbf{A}$ and accordingly the other characteristic roots are

$$(26) \quad \omega_j = 2\sqrt{\lambda\mu} \cos \frac{j\pi}{N+1} - (\lambda + \mu) \qquad (j = 1, 2, \ldots, N).$$

These characteristic values are distinct and so we can apply the above-mentioned method to determine $P_{ik}(t)$.

Now if a non-null characteristic vector belonging to ω_j is denoted by

$$\mathbf{x}_j = \left\| \begin{array}{c} \alpha_{0j} \\ \alpha_{1j} \\ \cdot \\ \cdot \\ \cdot \\ \alpha_{Nj} \end{array} \right\|$$

then according to the above considerations we may choose $\alpha_{i0} = 1$ $(i = 0, 1, \ldots, N)$ and for $j = 1, 2, \ldots, N$

$$(27) \qquad \alpha_{ij} = \left(\frac{\mu}{\lambda}\right)^{i/2} \left[\sin \frac{ij\pi}{N+1} - \left(\frac{\lambda}{\mu}\right)^{1/2} \sin \frac{(i+1)j\pi}{N+1} \right].$$

To determine the left-hand characteristic vector belonging to the different characteristic roots let us consider the equation

$$(28) \qquad\qquad\qquad \mathbf{y}'\mathbf{A} = \omega\mathbf{y}',$$

where we write $\mathbf{y}' = \| \beta_0, \beta_1, \ldots, \beta_N \|$. This is equivalent to the system of linear equations

$$(29) \qquad\qquad\qquad -\lambda\beta_0 + \mu\beta_1 = \omega\beta_0$$

$$(30) \quad \lambda\beta_{k-1} - (\lambda + \mu)\beta_k + \mu\beta_{k+1} = \omega\beta_k \qquad (k = 1, 2, \ldots, N-1)$$

$$(31) \qquad\qquad\qquad \lambda\beta_{N-1} - \mu\beta_N = \omega\beta_N.$$

Let us denote by $\mathbf{y}'_j = \| \beta_{j0}, \beta_{j1}, \ldots, \beta_{jN} \|$ a non-null characteristic vector belonging to ω_j. If $\omega = \omega_0 = 0$ then it is easy to see that $\beta_k = \left(\frac{\lambda}{\mu}\right)^k$ is a solution of the above linear equations and thus

$$\beta_{0k} = \left(\frac{\lambda}{\mu}\right)^k \qquad (k = 0, 1, \ldots, N).$$

If $\omega = \omega_j$ $(j \neq 0)$ then $\beta_k = \beta_{jk}$ is a non-null solution where

$$(32) \quad \beta_{jk} = \left(\frac{\lambda}{\mu}\right)^{k/2} \left[\sin\frac{kj\pi}{N+1} - \left(\frac{\lambda}{\mu}\right)^{1/2}\sin\frac{(k+1)j\pi}{N+1}\right]$$

$$(k = 0, 1, \ldots, N).$$

This can be proved as follows. The general solution of (30) similarly to (24) is

$$(33) \quad \beta_k = \left(\frac{\lambda}{\mu}\right)^{k/2}[A\sin ky + B\cos ky],$$

where

$$\cos y = \frac{\lambda + \mu + \omega}{2\sqrt{\lambda\mu}},$$

provided that the roots in question are different. If now $A = C\left(1 - \sqrt{\frac{\lambda}{\mu}}\right)\cos y$ and $B = -C\sqrt{\frac{\lambda}{\mu}}\sin y$, then (33) satisfies (29) too. Let us choose $C = 1$; then

$$\beta_k = \left(\frac{\lambda}{\mu}\right)^{k/2}\left[\sin ky - \sqrt{\frac{\lambda}{\mu}}\sin(k+1)y\right]$$

is a solution. This β_k satisfies (31) if $\sin(N+1)y = 0$, i.e. $y = j\pi/(N+1)$ $(j = 1, 2, \ldots, N)$. The case $y = 0$ is excluded. If $y = j\pi/(N+1)$ then $\omega = \omega_j$ and $\beta_k = \beta_{jk}$ as was stated above.

In the above treatment we did not normalize $\mathbf{x}_j$ and $\mathbf{y}'_j$ such that $\mathbf{y}'_j\mathbf{x}_j = 1$; therefore, we must determine

$$C_j = 1/\mathbf{y}'_j\mathbf{x}_j = 1/\sum_{\nu=0}^{N}\alpha_{\nu j}\beta_{j\nu}.$$

If $j = 0$ then

$$(34) \quad C_0^{-1} = \frac{1 - \left(\frac{\lambda}{\mu}\right)^{N+1}}{1 - \frac{\lambda}{\mu}} \qquad \text{when } \lambda \neq \mu$$

and

$$(35) \quad C_0^{-1} = N + 1 \qquad \text{when } \lambda = \mu.$$

If $j \neq 0$ then

$$(36) \qquad C_j^{-1} = \sum_{\nu=0}^{N} \left[\sin \frac{\nu j \pi}{N+1} - \left(\frac{\lambda}{\mu}\right)^{\frac{1}{2}} \sin \frac{(\nu+1)j\pi}{N+1} \right]^2$$

$$= \frac{N+1}{2} \left[1 - 2 \sqrt{\frac{\lambda}{\mu}} \cos \frac{\pi j}{N+1} + \frac{\lambda}{\mu} \right],$$

which can be proved by elementary transformations using the relations

$$\sum_{\nu=0}^{N} \cos \frac{2\nu j \pi}{N+1} = \sum_{\nu=0}^{N} \sin \frac{2\nu j \pi}{N+1} = 0.$$

Finally, $P_{ik}(t)$ is given by (18), which proves (3) and (4).

THEOREM 2. *The limiting probability distribution* $\lim_{t \to \infty} P_{ik}(t) = P_k^* \ (k = 0, 1, \ldots, N)$ *exists and is independent of the initial state. We have*

$$(37) \qquad P_k^* = \begin{cases} \dfrac{1 - \dfrac{\lambda}{\mu}}{1 - \left(\dfrac{\lambda}{\mu}\right)^{N+1}} \left(\dfrac{\lambda}{\mu}\right)^k & \text{if } \lambda \neq \mu, \\[6mm] 1/(N+1) & \text{if } \lambda = \mu. \end{cases}$$

PROOF. By using (18) we obtain that

$$\lim_{t \to \infty} P_{ik}(t) = C_0 \alpha_{i0} \beta_{0k} = C_0 \left(\frac{\lambda}{\mu}\right)^k,$$

where C_0 is defined by (34) and (35). For, $\omega_0 = 0$ and $\omega_1, \ldots, \omega_N$ are negative real roots.

REMARK 1. If $\lim_{t \to \infty} P_{ik}(t) = P_k^* \ (k = 0, 1, \ldots, N)$ exists, then we obtain by (10) that $\{P_k^*\}$ satisfies the equations

$$\sum_{j=0}^{N} P_j^* a_{jk} = 0 \qquad (k = 0, 1, \ldots, N)$$

and

$$\sum_{j=0}^{N} P_j^* = 1.$$

By solving this system of linear equations we can obtain $\{P_k^*\}$ also in this way.

REMARK 2. If we suppose that the initial queue size $\xi(0)$ is a random variable with distribution

$$(38) \qquad \mathbf{P}\{\xi(0) = k\} = P_k^* \qquad (k = 0, 1, \ldots, N)$$

defined by (37), then it is valid that

$$(39) \qquad \mathbf{P}\{\xi(t) = k\} = P_k^* \qquad (k = 0, 1, \ldots, N)$$

for all $t \geqq 0$. In this case we say that $\{\xi(t)\}$ is a *stationary stochastic process*.

This property can be proved as follows. We have generally that

$$\mathbf{P}\{\xi(t) = k\} = \sum_{i=0}^{N} \mathbf{P}\{\xi(0) = i\} P_{ik}(t)$$

and in the particular case (38)

$$\mathbf{P}\{\xi(t) = k\} = C_0 \sum_{i=0}^{N} \left(\frac{\lambda}{\mu}\right)^i P_{ik}(t) = C_0 \sum_{i=0}^{N} \sum_{j=0}^{N} \left(\frac{\lambda}{\mu}\right)^i C_j e^{-\omega_j t} \alpha_{ij} \beta_{jk}$$

$$= C_0 \sum_{j=0}^{N} C_j e^{-\omega_j t} \beta_{jk} \sum_{i=0}^{N} \alpha_{ij} \left(\frac{\lambda}{\mu}\right)^i = C_0 \beta_{0k} = C_0 \left(\frac{\lambda}{\mu}\right)^k = P_k^*$$

since by (27)

$$\sum_{i=0}^{N} \alpha_{ij} \left(\frac{\lambda}{\mu}\right)^i = \begin{cases} 0 & \text{if } j = 1, 2, \ldots, N, \\ 1/C_0 & \text{if } j = 0. \end{cases}$$

2. The time dependence of a single server queue with Poisson input and exponential service times

Customers arrive at a counter in accordance with a Poisson process of density λ. There is a single server. The service times are identically distributed, independent random variables with distribution function

$$(1) \qquad H(x) = \begin{cases} 1 - e^{-\mu x} & \text{if } x \geqq 0, \\ 0 & \text{if } x < 0. \end{cases}$$

Denote by $\xi(t)$ the queue size at the instant t.

The process $\{\xi(t)\}$ is, like the process treated in the previous section, a homogeneous Markov process. Let $\mathbf{P}\{\xi(t) = k \mid \xi(0) = i\} = P_{ik}(t)$.

THEOREM 1. *We have*

$$(2) \qquad P_{ik}(t) = p_{ik}(t) + \begin{cases} \left(1 - \dfrac{\lambda}{\mu}\right)\left(\dfrac{\lambda}{\mu}\right)^k & \text{if } \lambda < \mu, \\ 0 & \text{if } \lambda \geq \mu, \end{cases}$$

where

$$(3) \quad p_{ik}(t) = \frac{2e^{-(\lambda+\mu)t}\left(\dfrac{\lambda}{\mu}\right)^{(k-i)/2}}{\pi} \int_0^\pi \frac{e^{2\sqrt{\lambda\mu}\,t\cos y}}{\left(1 - 2\sqrt{\dfrac{\lambda}{\mu}}\cos y + \dfrac{\lambda}{\mu}\right)}$$

$$\cdot \left[\sin iy - \left(\frac{\lambda}{\mu}\right)^{\frac12}\sin(i+1)y\right]\left[\sin ky - \left(\frac{\lambda}{\mu}\right)^{\frac12}\sin(k+1)y\right] dy.$$

PROOF. If the size of the waiting room in the queueing process investigated in Section 1 is infinity, then we get the present queueing process. Denote by $\xi_N(t)$ the queue size at time t if the waiting room has size $N - 1$. The sequence $\{\xi_N(t)\}$ is monotone increasing if $N \to \infty$. The limit $\lim_{N\to\infty} \xi_N(t) = \xi(t)$ exists and $\xi(t)$ is the queue size at time t if the size of the waiting room is infinity. Thus, if we let $N \to \infty$ in (3) and (4) of Section 1 we get (2). It is convenient to write $y_j = j\pi/(N+1)$ and $\Delta y_j = y_{j+1} - y_j = \pi/(N+1)$ in the second part of (3) of Section 1, when it will be a Riemann sum approximating the integral (3). If $N \to \infty$ then this approximating sum tends to (3). An alternative expression for $P_{ik}(t)$ is given by

THEOREM 2. *We have*

$$(4) \quad P_{ik}(t) = e^{-(\lambda+\mu)t}\left[\left(\frac{\lambda}{\mu}\right)^{(k-i)/2} I_{k-i}(2\sqrt{\lambda\mu}\,t)\right.$$

$$+ \left(\frac{\lambda}{\mu}\right)^{(k-i+1)/2} I_{k+i+1}(2\sqrt{\lambda\mu}\,t)$$

$$+ \left.\left(1 - \frac{\lambda}{\mu}\right)\left(\frac{\lambda}{\mu}\right)^k \sum_{r=i+k+2}^\infty \left(\frac{\lambda}{\mu}\right)^{-(r/2)} I_r(2\sqrt{\lambda\mu}\,t)\right],$$

where $I_r(x)$ $(r = 0, \pm 1, \pm 2, \ldots)$ is the modified Bessel function of order r. If $r \geqq 0$ then

$$(5) \qquad I_r(x) = \sum_{j=0}^{\infty} \frac{(x/2)^{r+2j}}{j!(j+r)!}$$

and $I_{-r}(x) = I_r(x)$.

PROOF. The integrand of (3) is an even function of y and periodic with period 2π. Hence we can replace the integral $\int_0^\pi$ by $\frac{1}{2}\int_0^{2\pi}$ in (3).

Proceeding so let us put $z = e^{y\sqrt{-1}}$ in (3). Then $\cos y = \frac{1}{2}\left(z + \frac{1}{z}\right)$, $\sin ky = \dfrac{z^k - z^{-k}}{2\sqrt{-1}}$ and $dy = \dfrac{dz}{z\sqrt{-1}}$. Thus we obtain

$$(6) \qquad p_{ik}(t) = \frac{e^{-(\lambda+\mu)t}\left(\dfrac{\lambda}{\mu}\right)^{(k-i)/2}}{4\pi\sqrt{-1}} \oint_{|z|=1} \frac{f(z)}{z}\,dz,$$

where

$$f(z) = \frac{-e^{(z+1/z)\sqrt{\lambda\mu}\,t}}{\left[1 - \left(z + \dfrac{1}{z}\right)\sqrt{\dfrac{\lambda}{\mu}} + \dfrac{\lambda}{\mu}\right]}$$

$$\cdot \left[(z^i - z^{-i}) - \left(\frac{\lambda}{\mu}\right)^{1/2}(z^{i+1} - z^{-i-1})\right]$$

$$\cdot \left[(z^k - z^{-k}) - \left(\frac{\lambda}{\mu}\right)^{1/2}(z^{k+1} - z^{-k-1})\right].$$

The integrand in (6) has two singularities in the unit circle $|z| \leqq 1$, namely, $z = 0$ and $z = \sqrt{\dfrac{\lambda}{\mu}}$ if $\lambda < \mu$ and $z = \sqrt{\dfrac{\mu}{\lambda}}$ if $\mu < \lambda$. If $\lambda = \mu$ then $z = 0$ is the only singularity. By using the theorem of residues we obtain that

$$p_{ik}(t) = \frac{e^{-(\lambda+\mu)t}\left(\dfrac{\lambda}{\mu}\right)^{(k-i)/2}}{2} f_0 \pm \frac{1}{2}\left(1 - \frac{\lambda}{\mu}\right)\left(\frac{\lambda}{\mu}\right)^k,$$

where in the case $\lambda > \mu$, the plus sign is to be taken and in the case $\lambda < \mu$ the minus sign. If $\lambda = \mu$ then the last term is zero. Here f_0 is the constant term in the Laurent expansion of $f(z)$ at $z = 0$. Hence by (2) we obtain that

$$(7) \qquad P_{ik}(t) = \frac{e^{-(\lambda+\mu)t}\left(\dfrac{\lambda}{\mu}\right)^{(k-i)/2}}{2} f_0 + \frac{1}{2}\left(1 - \frac{\lambda}{\mu}\right)\left(\frac{\lambda}{\mu}\right)^k$$

in every case.

By some transformations we can write that

$$f(z) = e^{(z+1/z)\sqrt{\lambda\mu}\,t}\left[z^{i-k} + z^{k-i} + \frac{\sqrt{\mu} - z\sqrt{\lambda}}{\sqrt{\lambda} - z\sqrt{\mu}}z^{i+k+1}\right.$$

$$\left. + \frac{\sqrt{\lambda} - z\sqrt{\mu}}{\sqrt{\mu} - z\sqrt{\lambda}}z^{-i-k-1}\right]$$

$$= e^{(z+1/z)\sqrt{\lambda\mu}\,t}\left[z^{i-k} + z^{k-i} + \sqrt{\frac{\mu}{\lambda}}z^{i+k+1} + \sqrt{\frac{\lambda}{\mu}}z^{-i-k-1}\right.$$

$$- \left(1 - \frac{\lambda}{\mu}\right)\sum_{\nu=1}^{\infty}\left(\frac{\lambda}{\mu}\right)^{(\nu-1)/2}z^{\nu-i-k-1}$$

$$\left. + \left(1 - \frac{\lambda}{\mu}\right)\sum_{\nu=1}^{\infty}\left(\frac{\mu}{\lambda}\right)^{(\nu+1)/2}z^{\nu+i+k+1}\right].$$

Since

$$(8) \qquad e^{(z+1/z)\sqrt{\lambda\mu}\,t} = \sum_{r=-\infty}^{\infty} I_r(2\sqrt{\lambda\mu}\,t)z^r,$$

where $I_r(x)$ is the modified Bessel function defined by (5), we obtain that

$$f_0 = 2I_{k-i}(2\sqrt{\lambda\mu}\,t) + \left(\sqrt{\frac{\mu}{\lambda}} + \sqrt{\frac{\lambda}{\mu}}\right)I_{i+k+1}(2\sqrt{\lambda\mu}\,t)$$

$$- \left(1 - \frac{\lambda}{\mu}\right)\sum_{\nu=1}^{\infty}\left(\frac{\lambda}{\mu}\right)^{(\nu-1)/2}I_{\nu-i-k-1}(2\sqrt{\lambda\mu}\,t)$$

$$+ \left(1 - \frac{\lambda}{\mu}\right)\sum_{\nu=1}^{\infty}\left(\frac{\mu}{\lambda}\right)^{(\nu+1)/2}I_{\nu+i+k+1}(2\sqrt{\lambda\mu}\,t).$$

Using the relation $I_{-r}(x) = I_r(x)$ and (8), having put $z = \sqrt{\lambda/\mu}$ in it, we obtain that

$$f_0 = 2I_{k-i}(2\sqrt{\lambda\mu}\, t) + 2\left(\frac{\lambda}{\mu}\right)^{\frac{1}{2}} I_{i+k+1}(2\sqrt{\lambda\mu}\, t)$$
$$+ 2\left(1 - \frac{\lambda}{\mu}\right)\left(\frac{\lambda}{\mu}\right)^{(k+i)/2}$$

$$(9) \quad \cdot \sum_{r=i+k+2}^{\infty}\left(\frac{\lambda}{\mu}\right)^{-(r/2)} I_r(2\sqrt{\lambda\mu}\, t) - \left(1 - \frac{\lambda}{\mu}\right)\left(\frac{\lambda}{\mu}\right)^{(i+k)/2} e^{(\lambda+\mu)t}.$$

Putting (9) into (7) we get (2) as was to be proved.

THEOREM 3. *If* $\lambda < \mu$ *then the limiting probability distribution* $\lim_{t\to\infty} P_{ik}(t) = P_k^*$ $(k = 0, 1, 2, \ldots)$ *exists and is independent of the initial state. We have*

$$(10) \qquad P_k^* = \left(1 - \frac{\lambda}{\mu}\right)\left(\frac{\lambda}{\mu}\right)^k \qquad (k = 0, 1, 2, \ldots).$$

If $\lambda \geqq \mu$ *then* $\lim_{t\to\infty} P_{ik}(t) = 0$ *for every k and i.*

PROOF. It is easy to see that in every case

$$\lim_{t\to\infty} p_{ik}(t) = 0$$

in (2). Hence (10) follows.

THE STATIONARY PROCESS. If we suppose that $\lambda < \mu$ and that the initial distribution of the queue size is $\{P_k^*\}$ defined by (10) then we obtain that

$$(11) \qquad \mathbf{P}\{\xi(t) = k\} = P_k^* \qquad (k = 0, 1, 2, \ldots)$$

for all $t \geqq 0$. For,

$$\mathbf{P}\{\xi(t) = k\} = \sum_{i=0}^{\infty} P_i^* P_{ik}(t),$$

where $P_{ik}(t) = p_{ik}(t) + P_k^*$. By (3) we have

$$\sum_{i=0}^{\infty}\left(\frac{\lambda}{\mu}\right)^i p_{ik}(t) = 0$$

and hence (11) follows.

THE AVERAGE QUEUE SIZE. By using (2) we can prove that the average queue size given $\xi(0) = i$, that is,

$$\mathbf{E}\{\xi(t)\,|\,\xi(0) = i\} = \sum_{k=0}^{\infty} kP_{ik}(t)$$

can be expressed as follows

$$\mathbf{E}\{\xi(t)\,|\,\xi(0) = i\} = \frac{2e^{-(\lambda+\mu)t}\left(\dfrac{\lambda}{\mu}\right)^{(1-i)/2}}{\pi}\int_0^{\pi}\frac{e^{2\sqrt{\lambda\mu}\,t\cos y}\sin y}{\left(1 - 2\sqrt{\dfrac{\lambda}{\mu}}\cos y + \dfrac{\lambda}{\mu}\right)^2}$$

$$\cdot\left[\sin iy - \left(\frac{\lambda}{\mu}\right)^{\frac{1}{2}}\sin (i+1)y\right]dy + \begin{cases}\dfrac{\lambda}{\mu-\lambda} & \text{if } \lambda < \mu, \\[2mm] 0 & \text{if } \lambda \geqq \mu.\end{cases}$$

In the stationary case, when $\lambda < \mu$, the average queue size is

$$\mathbf{E}\{\xi(t)\} = \sum_{k=0}^{\infty} kP_k^* = \frac{\lambda}{\mu-\lambda}$$

and the variance is

$$\mathbf{D}^2\{\xi(t)\} = \frac{\lambda\mu}{(\mu-\lambda)^2}.$$

Now let us denote by ξ_n the queue size immediately before the arrival of the nth customer, that is, $\xi_n = \xi(\tau_n - 0)$. The sequence of random variables $\{\xi_n\}$ forms a homogeneous Markov chain with transition probabilities

$$\mathbf{P}\{\xi_{n+1} = k\,|\,\xi_n = j\} = p_{jk},$$

where

$$p_{jk} = \begin{cases}\left(\dfrac{\lambda}{\lambda+\mu}\right)\left(\dfrac{\mu}{\lambda+\mu}\right)^{j+1-k} & \text{if } k = 1, 2, \ldots, j+1, \\[3mm] \left(\dfrac{\mu}{\lambda+\mu}\right)^{j+1} & \text{if } k = 0,\end{cases}$$

and $p_{jk} = 0$ otherwise.

We note that we can write that

(12) $$\xi_{n+1} = [\xi_n + 1 - \nu_n]^+,$$

where $[a]^+ = \max(a, 0)$ and $\{\nu_n\}$ is a sequence of identically distributed, independent random variables with distribution

$$(13) \qquad \mathbf{P}\{\nu_n = j\} = \int_0^\infty e^{-\mu x} \frac{(\mu x)^j}{j!} e^{-\lambda x} \lambda \, dx$$

$$= \left(\frac{\lambda}{\lambda + \mu}\right)\left(\frac{\mu}{\lambda + \mu}\right)^j \qquad (j = 0, 1, \ldots).$$

The above statements can easily be verified if we take into consideration that the process of the departures is a Poisson process of density μ as long as there is a queue. If the queue disappears then the process of departures stops.

The higher transition probabilities

$$p_{ik}^{(n)} = \mathbf{P}\{\xi_{m+n} = k \,|\, \xi_m = i\}$$

are determined by the following

THEOREM 4. *If* $|z| \leqq 1$ *and* $|w| < 1$ *then we have*

$$(14) \qquad \sum_{n=0}^\infty \sum_{k=0}^\infty p_{ik}^{(n)} z^k w^n = \frac{g(w)[\mu - (\lambda + \mu)z]z^i}{[z - g(w)][\mu - \lambda zwg(w)]}$$

$$- \frac{(1 - z)[\mu - (\lambda + \mu)g(w)][g(w)]^i}{[1 - g(w)][z - g(w)][\mu - \lambda zwg(w)]}$$

where

$$(15) \qquad g(w) = \frac{(\lambda + \mu) - \sqrt{(\lambda + \mu)^2 - 4\lambda\mu w}}{2\lambda w}.$$

PROOF. Let us introduce the abbreviations

$$p = \frac{\lambda}{\lambda + \mu} \quad \text{and} \quad q = \frac{\mu}{\lambda + \mu};$$

then we can write that

$$(16) \qquad \mathbf{E}\{z^{\xi_{n+1}} \,|\, \xi_n = j\} = p \sum_{k=1}^{j+1} q^{j+1-k} z^k + q^{j+1}$$

$$= \begin{cases} \dfrac{pz^{j+2} - (1 - z)q^{j+2}}{z - q} & \text{if } z \neq q \\[2mm] [1 + (j + 1)p]q^{j+1} & \text{if } z = q. \end{cases}$$

Now for fixed i let us introduce the generating function

$$G_n(z) = \sum_{k=0}^{\infty} p_{ik}^{(n)} z^k,$$

which is convergent if $|z| \leqq 1$. Then by (16) we have

(17) $(z - q)G_{n+1}(z) = pz^2 G_n(z) - (1 - z)q^2 G_n(q)$ $(n = 0, 1, 2, \ldots)$.

If we form for $|w| < 1$ the generating function

$$\sum_{n=0}^{\infty} G_n(z)w^n,$$

then by (17) we have

(18) $$\sum_{n=0}^{\infty} G_n(z)w^n = \frac{(z - q)G_0(z) - w(1 - z)q^2 \sum_{n=0}^{\infty} G_n(q)w^n}{z - q - wpz^2},$$

where $G_0(z) = z^i$. The left side of (18) is a regular function of z if $|z| \leqq 1$ and $|w| < 1$. The denominator of the right-hand side of (18) has two roots with modulus greater than one and less than one respectively. The root which is in the unit circle $|z| < 1$ is

$$g(w) = \frac{(\lambda + \mu) - \sqrt{(\lambda + \mu)^2 - 4\lambda\mu w}}{2\lambda w}.$$

This $g(w)$ must be a root of the numerator too. Consequently

$$\sum_{n=0}^{\infty} G_n(q)w^n = \frac{[g(w) - q][g(w)]^i}{wq^2[1 - g(w)]}$$

and finally by (18)

$$\sum_{n=0}^{\infty} G_n(z)w^n = \frac{[1 - g(w)](q - z)z^i - (1 - z)[q - g(w)][g(w)]^i}{[wpz^2 - z + q][1 - g(w)]}.$$

If we take into consideration that

$$wpz^2 - z + q = [z - g(w)][zwpg(w) - q]/g(w),$$

then we get (14), which was to be proved.

To obtain an explicit formula for $p_{ik}^{(n)}$ we have to use Lagrange's expansion of $[g(w)]^k$ (cf. Appendix):

$$(19) \qquad [g(w)]^k = k \sum_{j=0}^{\infty} \binom{2j+k}{j} \frac{q^{j+k}p^j}{(2j+k)} w^{j+k}.$$

REMARK 1. If the initial queue size $\xi(0) = i$, then the probability that the nth customer does not have to wait is

$$\mathbf{P}\{\xi_n = 0 \,|\, \xi(0) = i\} = \begin{cases} p_{i-1,0}^{(n)} & \text{if } i \geqq 1, \\ p_{0,0}^{(n-1)} & \text{if } i = 0. \end{cases}$$

For if $\xi(0) = i \geqq 1$ then we may suppose, without loss of generality, that a customer arrived at $t = -0$. If $\xi(0) = 0$ then the customer arriving first finds the system empty.

If we put $z = 0$ in (14), we obtain

$$\sum_{n=1}^{\infty} p_{i0}^{(n)} w^n = \frac{[\mu - (\lambda + \mu)g(w)][g(w)]^i}{\mu[1 - g(w)]}.$$

REMARK 2. If specifically $i = 0$ in (14), then we have

$$\sum_{n=0}^{\infty} \sum_{k=0}^{\infty} p_{0k}^{(n)} z^k w^n = \frac{\lambda g(w)}{[1 - g(w)][\mu - \lambda z g(w)]},$$

whence

$$(20) \qquad \sum_{n=0}^{\infty} p_{0k}^{(n)} w^n = \left(\frac{\lambda}{\mu}\right)^k \frac{[g(w)]^k}{[1 - g(w)]},$$

and by (19) we get

$$p_{0k}^{(n)} = \left(\frac{p}{q}\right)^k \sum_{j=k}^{n} \frac{j}{(2n-j)} \binom{2n-j}{n} p^{n-j}q^n.$$

THEOREM 5. *If $\lambda < \mu$ then the limiting distribution* $\lim\limits_{n \to \infty} p_{ik}^{(n)} = P_k(k = 0, 1, 2, \ldots)$ *exists and is independent of the initial state. We have*

$$(21) \qquad P_k = \left(1 - \frac{\lambda}{\mu}\right)\left(\frac{\lambda}{\mu}\right)^k \qquad (k = 0, 1, 2, \ldots).$$

If $\lambda \geqq \mu$ then $\lim\limits_{n \to \infty} p_{ik}^{(n)} = 0$ *for every i and k.*

PROOF. The limit $\lim\limits_{n\to\infty} \mathbf{P}\{\xi_n = k\} = P_k$ $(k = 0, 1, 2, \ldots)$ always exists and is independent of the initial distribution. Either every $P_k > 0$ and $\{P_k\}$ is a probability distribution or every $P_k = 0$. Thus we may suppose that $\xi_1 = 0$. By using Abel's theorem (cf. Appendix), we have

$$P_k = \lim_{w\to 1} (1 - w) \sum_{n=0}^{\infty} p_{0k}^{(n)} w^n$$

and the right-hand side can be calculated by (20). If we use that $g(1) = 1$ and $g'(1) = \mu/(\mu - \lambda)$ when $\lambda \leqq \mu$, then we get (21). Further since $g(1) < 1$ when $\lambda > \mu$ we obtain that in this case $P_k = 0$ for every k.

THE DISTRIBUTION OF THE NUMBER OF SERVICES IN A BUSY PERIOD. If $\xi_n = k$ then we say that the system is in state E_k at the nth step. Denote by $f_{00}^{(n)}$ the probability that starting from state E_0 the system returns to the state E_0 for the first time at the nth step. In other words $f_{00}^{(n)}$ is the probability that a busy period consists of n services.

THEOREM 6. *We have for* $|w| < 1$ *that*

(22)
$$\sum_{n=1}^{\infty} f_{00}^{(n)} w^n = g(w),$$

where $g(w)$ *is defined by* (15). *Hence*

(23)
$$f_{00}^{(n)} = \frac{1}{2n - 1} \binom{2n - 1}{n - 1} \frac{\lambda^{n-1}\mu^n}{(\lambda + \mu)^{2n-1}}.$$

PROOF. By the theorem of total probability we can write that

$$p_{00}^{(n)} = f_{00}^{(n)} + f_{00}^{(n-1)} p_{00}^{(1)} + \cdots + f_{00}^{(1)} p_{00}^{(n-1)} \qquad (n = 1, 2, \ldots).$$

Forming the generating function we get by (20) that

$$\sum_{n=1}^{\infty} f_{00}^{(n)} w^n = \frac{\displaystyle\sum_{n=1}^{\infty} p_{00}^{(n)} w^n}{\displaystyle\sum_{n=0}^{\infty} p_{00}^{(n)} w^n} = g(w),$$

which was to be proved.

If $\lambda \leqq \mu$ then $g(1) = 1$ and $\{f_{00}^{(n)}\}$ is a non-degenerate probability distribution. If $\lambda > \mu$ then $g(1) = \mu/\lambda < 1$, i.e.

$$\sum_{n=1}^{\infty} f_{00}^{(n)} < 1.$$

In this case the number of services in a busy period will be infinite with probability $1 - \dfrac{\mu}{\lambda}$.

The expected number of services in a busy period is

$$\rho = \sum_{n=1}^{\infty} n f_{00}^{(n)} = g'(1) = \frac{\mu}{\mu - \lambda}$$

if $\lambda < \mu$. If $\lambda = \mu$ then $\rho = \infty$.

THE BUSY PERIOD. It is clear that the time of the server is composed of idle periods and busy periods. The durations of the successive idle periods and busy periods are independent random variables. The distribution function of the length of an idle period is clearly $F(x) = 1 - e^{-\lambda x}$ if $x \geqq 0$. If $\xi(0) = 0$ then the process starts with an idle period and the length of every busy period has the same distribution function, say $G(x)$. If $\xi(0) = i$, where $i \geqq 1$, then the process starts with a busy period. It is easy to see that the distribution function of the initial busy period is $G_i(x)$, where $G_i(x)$ is the i-fold convolution of $G(x)$ with itself. The distribution function of the length of the following busy periods is $G(x)$ as before. Now we shall prove that the distribution function of the length of the initial busy period is $G_i(x)$. First of all let us note that from the point of view of the server it is perfectly indifferent whether the customers will be served in the order of their arrival or not. This affects the customers only, but the distribution function of the busy period remains unaltered. If the initial queue size is i then let us consider the following system of service in which the busy period consists of i phases. The first phase consists of the actual service and the serving of the new arrivals as long as they come. When there are no more new arrivals the second phase starts with the serving of one of the remaining $i - 1$ customers and this procedure will be continued through all the i phases. The lengths of the different phases are evidently identically distributed, independent random variables with the same distribution function

$G(x)$. If $i = 0$ then we agree to write $G_0(x) = 1$ if $x \geq 0$ and $G_0(x) = 0$ if $x < 0$.

Now let us determine the distribution function $G(x)$. We shall prove

THEOREM 7. *Let us denote by*

$$(24) \qquad \Gamma(s) = \int_0^\infty e^{-sx}\, dG(x)$$

the Laplace-Stieltjes transform of the distribution function $G(x)$, **which** *is convergent if* $\Re(s) \geqq 0$. *We have*

$$(25) \qquad \Gamma(s) = \frac{(\lambda + \mu + s) - \sqrt{(\lambda + \mu + s)^2 - 4\lambda\mu}}{2\lambda}$$

and by inversion we get

$$(26) \qquad G'(x) = \mu e^{-(\lambda+\mu)x}[I_0(2\sqrt{\lambda\mu}\, x) - I_2(2\sqrt{\lambda\mu}\, x)]$$

if $x \geqq 0$, *where*

$$(27) \qquad I_r(x) = \sum_{j=0}^\infty \frac{(x/2)^{r+2j}}{j!\,(r+j)!}$$

is the modified Bessel function of order r.

If $\lambda \leqq \mu$ *then* $G(\infty) = 1$ *and* $G(x)$ *is a proper distribution function, whereas if* $\lambda > \mu$ *then* $G(\infty) = \mu/\lambda$ *and* $G(x)$ *is an improper distribution function, namely in this case the busy period will be infinite with probability* $1 - \dfrac{\mu}{\lambda}$.

PROOF. To determine $G(x)$ we can write the following relation

$$(28) \qquad G(x) = \int_0^x e^{-(\lambda+\mu)y}\mu\, dy + \int_0^x e^{-(\lambda+\mu)y} G_2(x-y)\lambda\, dy,$$

where

$$G_2(x) = \int_0^x G(x-y)\, dG(y)$$

is the convolution of $G(x)$ with itself. The equation (28) can be proved as follows. Let us suppose that initially the queue size is $\xi(0) = 1$; then evidently $G_1(x) = G(x)$. The initial busy period has the length at most x if either the actual service ends in the time interval $(0, x]$

and during this service no new customers arrive, or if the first customer arrives at time y $(0 < y < x)$, the initial service is still in progress at this time, and the remainder of the busy period has a length at most $x - y$, the probability of which is $G_2(x - y)$. Forming the Laplace-Stieltjes transform of (28) we get

$$\Gamma(s) = \frac{\mu}{\lambda + \mu + s} + \frac{\lambda}{\lambda + \mu + s}[\Gamma(s)]^2.$$

This algebraic equation of order 2 has two roots. One of them has modulus $\leqq 1$ while the other has modulus $\geqq 1$. We must choose the first root because $|\Gamma(s)| \leqq 1$ if $\Re(s) \geqq 0$. So we obtain (25). By inversion we get (26). Since evidently

$$\lim_{x \to \infty} G(x) = \lim_{s \to 0} \Gamma(s),$$

the proof of the theorem is complete.

The expectation of the length of the busy period

$$\tau = \int_0^\infty x \, dG(x)$$

is given by

$$\tau = \begin{cases} \dfrac{1}{\mu - \lambda} & \text{if } \lambda < \mu, \\ \infty & \text{if } \lambda = \mu. \end{cases}$$

This can be obtained by

$$\tau = -\Gamma'(0)$$

if $G(\infty) = \Gamma(0) = 1$. If $G(\infty) < 1$ then we agree to write $\tau = \infty$.

REMARK 3. The average length of the busy period can be determined directly as follows. Let us denote by ρ the expected number of services during a busy period. Then we have $\tau = \rho/\mu$. Now we shall prove the following relation

$$\frac{\rho}{\lambda} = \frac{\rho}{\mu} + \frac{1}{\lambda}.$$

Let us consider the starting points of two consecutive busy periods. The expectation of the distance between them is on the one hand clearly ρ/λ and on the other hand it is equal to the sum of ρ/μ, the expected length of the busy period, and $1/\lambda$, the expected length of the idle period. If $\lambda < \mu$ then $\rho = 1/\left(1 - \dfrac{\lambda}{\mu}\right)$ is finite, and if $\lambda \geqq \mu$ then ρ must be infinite.

THE JOINT DISTRIBUTION OF THE NUMBER OF SERVICES AND THE LENGTH OF A BUSY PERIOD. Let us denote by $\tilde{G}_n(x)$ the probability that the busy period consists in serving n customers and its length is at most x. Write

$$\Gamma_n(s) = \int_0^\infty e^{-sx}\, d\tilde{G}_n(x)$$

if $\Re(s) \geqq 0$. We shall prove

THEOREM 8. *If $\Re(s) \geqq 0$ then*

(29) $\qquad \Gamma_n(s) = \dfrac{1}{(2n-1)}\dbinom{2n-1}{n-1}\dfrac{\lambda^{n-1}\mu^n}{(\lambda+\mu+s)^{2n-1}},$

whence

(30) $\qquad \dfrac{d\tilde{G}_n(x)}{dx} = e^{-(\lambda+\mu)x}\dfrac{\lambda^{n-1}\mu^n x^{2n-2}}{n!(n-1)!}$

when $x \geqq 0$.

PROOF. Now we can write the following relations

$$\tilde{G}_1(x) = \int_0^x e^{-(\lambda+\mu)y}\mu\, dy$$

and

$$\tilde{G}_n(x) = \sum_{j=1}^{n-1}\int_0^x e^{-(\lambda+\mu)y}[\tilde{G}_j(x-y) * \tilde{G}_{n-j}(x-y)]\lambda\, dy$$

$$(n = 2, 3, \ldots).$$

Hence

$$\Gamma_1(s) = \dfrac{\mu}{\lambda+\mu+s}$$

and

$$\Gamma_n(s) = \dfrac{\lambda}{(\lambda+\mu+s)}\sum_{j=1}^{n-1}\Gamma_j(s)\Gamma_{n-j}(s) \qquad (n = 2, 3, \ldots).$$

Let us form the generating function

$$\gamma(s, w) = \sum_{n=1}^{\infty} \Gamma_n(s) w^n$$

for $|w| < 1$. It satisfies the following relation

$$(\lambda + \mu + s)\gamma(s, w) = \lambda[\gamma(s, w)]^2 + \mu w.$$

Since $|\gamma(s, w)| < 1$ if $\Re(s) \geq 0$ and $|w| < 1$, we get

$$\gamma(s, w) = \frac{(\lambda + \mu + s) - \sqrt{(\lambda + \mu + s)^2 - 4\lambda\mu w}}{2\lambda}$$

$$= \sum_{n=1}^{\infty} \frac{1}{2n - 1} \binom{2n - 1}{n - 1} \frac{\lambda^{n-1}\mu^n}{(\lambda + \mu + s)^{2n-1}} w^n,$$

whence

$$\Gamma_n(s) = \frac{1}{(2n - 1)} \binom{2n - 1}{n - 1} \frac{\lambda^{n-1}\mu^n}{(\lambda + \mu + s)^{2n-1}}.$$

By inversion we get (30).

THE PROBABILITY THAT THE SERVER IS IDLE AT TIME t. If the initial queue size $\xi(0) = i$, then clearly $P_{i0}(t)$ is the probability that the server is idle at time t.

THEOREM 9. *We have*

(31)
$$P_{i0}(t) = e^{-(\lambda + \mu)t} \left[\left(\frac{\mu}{\lambda}\right)^{i/2} I_i(2\sqrt{\lambda\mu}\, t) + \left(\frac{\mu}{\lambda}\right)^{(i-1)/2} I_{i+1}(2\sqrt{\lambda\mu}\, t) \right.$$

$$\left. + \left(1 - \frac{\lambda}{\mu}\right) \sum_{r=i+2}^{\infty} \left(\frac{\mu}{\lambda}\right)^{r/2} I_r(2\sqrt{\lambda\mu}\, t) \right]$$

and the Laplace transform of $P_{i0}(t)$ is

(32)
$$\int_0^\infty e^{-st} P_{i0}(t)\, dt = \frac{[\Gamma(s)]^{i+1}}{\mu[1 - \Gamma(s)]},$$

where $\Gamma(s)$ is defined by (25).

PROOF. Putting $k = 0$ in (4) we get (31). Now we shall show that the Laplace transform of $P_{i0}(t)$ is (32), whence (31) can be obtained also by inversion.

Let us denote by $M_0(t)$ the expected number of the transitions $E_0 \rightarrow E_1$ occurring in the time interval $(0, t]$, given that $\xi(0) = i$. Then by the theory of recurrent processes we can write that

$$(33) \qquad M_0(t) = G_i(t) * F(t) + G_i(t) * F(t) * G(t) * F(t) + \cdots.$$

For the transitions $E_0 \rightarrow E_1$ form a recurrent process. The distribution function of the length between the first transition $E_0 \rightarrow E_1$ and the origin is $G_i(t) * F(t)$, whereas the distribution function of the length between successive transitions $E_0 \rightarrow E_1$ is $G(t) * F(t)$. Since

$$\int_0^\infty e^{-st} \, dG_i(t) = [\Gamma(s)]^i,$$

by (33) we have for $\Re(s) > 0$ that

$$(34) \qquad \int_0^\infty e^{-st} \, dM_0(t) = \frac{\dfrac{\lambda}{\lambda + s}[\Gamma(s)]^i}{1 - \dfrac{\lambda}{\lambda + s}\Gamma(s)} = \frac{\lambda[\Gamma(s)]^{i+1}}{\mu[1 - \Gamma(s)]},$$

where we used (25). On the other hand we have

$$(35) \qquad M_0(t) = \lambda \int_0^t P_{i0}(u) \, du,$$

for, if we introduce a new time variable involved only when there is state E_0, then the transitions $E_0 \rightarrow E_1$ form a Poisson process of density λ.

Comparing (34) and (35) we obtain that for $\Re(s) > 0$

$$\int_0^\infty e^{-st} P_{i0}(t) \, dt = \frac{[\Gamma(s)]^{i+1}}{\mu[1 - \Gamma(s)]} = \frac{1}{\mu} \sum_{n=i+1}^\infty [\Gamma(s)]^n.$$

Hence by inversion we obtain the interesting formula

$$(36) \qquad P_{i0}(t) = \frac{1}{\mu} \sum_{n=i+1}^\infty G_n'(t).$$

By inversion from

$$\int_0^\infty e^{-sx}\, dG_n(x) = [\Gamma(s)]^n$$

we get

$$G_n'(x) = n\left(\frac{\mu}{\lambda}\right)^{n/2} e^{-(\lambda+\mu)x} I_n(2\sqrt{\lambda\mu}\, x)/x$$

$$= \mu\left(\frac{\mu}{\lambda}\right)^{(n-1)/2} e^{-(\lambda+\mu)x}[I_{n-1}(2\sqrt{\lambda\mu}\, x) - I_{n+1}(2\sqrt{\lambda\mu}\, x)]$$

using the relation

$$2nI_n(x) = x[I_{n-1}(x) - I_{n+1}(x)].$$

Thus we get (31).

THE WAITING TIME. Denote by $\eta(t)$ the virtual waiting time at the instant t, i.e. $\eta(t)$ is the time that a customer would wait if he joined the queue at the instant t. Suppose that $\xi(0) = i$ is fixed.

THEOREM 10. *If* $\mathbf{P}\{\eta(t) \leqq x\} = W(t, x)$ *then under the condition* $\xi(0) = i$ *we have*

$$(37) \qquad W(t, x) = P_{i0}(t) + \sum_{k=1}^\infty P_{ik}(t) \int_0^x e^{-\mu y} \frac{(\mu y)^{k-1}}{(k-1)!} \mu\, dy.$$

If $\lambda < \mu$ *then the limiting distribution* $\lim_{t\to\infty} W(t, x) = W^*(x)$ *exists and we have*

$$(38) \qquad W^*(x) = \begin{cases} 1 - \dfrac{\lambda}{\mu} e^{(\lambda-\mu)x} & \text{if } x \geqq 0, \\[2mm] 0 & \text{if } x < 0. \end{cases}$$

If $\lambda \geqq \mu$ *then* $\lim_{t\to\infty} W(t, x) = 0$ *for every* x.

PROOF. If $\xi(t) = k$ then the time needed to complete the service of all the k customers present at time t is the sum of k independent random variables each of which has the distribution function $H(x) = 1 - e^{-\mu x}$ $(x \geqq 0)$, i.e.

$$W(t, x) = \sum_{k=0}^\infty P_{ik}(t) H_k(x),$$

where $H_k(x)$ is the kth iterated convolution of $H(x)$ with itself. If $t \to \infty$ then $\lim\limits_{t \to \infty} P_{ik}(t) = P_k^*$ defined by (10) when $\lambda < \mu$ and $\lim\limits_{t \to \infty} P_{ik}(t) = 0$ when $\lambda \geqq \mu$. Thus if $\lambda < \mu$ then

$$\lim_{t \to \infty} W(t, x) = \left(1 - \frac{\lambda}{\mu}\right)[1 + \lambda \int_0^x e^{(\lambda - \mu)y}\, dy],$$

which agrees with (38). If $\lambda \geqq \mu$ then $\lim\limits_{t \to \infty} W(t, x) = 0$ for every x.

STATIONARY PROCESS. If we suppose that $\lambda < \mu$ and $\mathbf{P}\{\xi(0) = k\} = P_k^*$ then the process $\{\eta(t)\}$ will be a stationary process for which

$$\mathbf{P}\{\eta(t) \leqq x\} = W^*(x)$$

for all $t \geqq 0$. In this case $\mathbf{P}\{\xi(t) = k\} = P_k^*$ also holds for all $t \geqq 0$. In the stationary case the average waiting time is

$$\mathbf{E}\{\eta(t)\} = \int_0^\infty x\, dW^*(x) = \frac{\lambda}{\mu(\lambda + \mu)}$$

and its variance is

$$\mathbf{D}^2\{\eta(t)\} = \frac{\lambda^2}{\mu^2(\lambda + \mu)^2}.$$

THE WAITING TIME OF THE nTH CUSTOMER. If we denote by η_n the waiting time of the nth customer then we can write that

(39) $\eta_{n+1} = [\eta_n + \chi_n - \theta_n]^+$ $(n = 1, 2, \ldots)$

where χ_n is the service time of the nth customer and $\theta_n = \tau_{n+1} - \tau_n$ is the inter-arrival time between the nth and $n + 1$st arrival. The $\{\chi_n\}$ and $\{\theta_n\}$ are independent sequences of identically distributed, independent random variables with distribution functions $\mathbf{P}\{\chi_n \leqq x\} = H(x) = 1 - e^{-\mu x}(x \geqq 0)$ and $\mathbf{P}\{\theta_n \leqq x\} = F(x) = 1 - e^{-\lambda x}$ $(x \geqq 0)$. We need the following

LEMMA 1. *Let θ and ξ be non-negative independent random variables for which*

(40) $$\mathbf{P}\{\theta \leqq x\} = \begin{cases} 1 - e^{-\lambda x} & \text{if } x \geqq 0, \\ 0 & \text{if } x < 0. \end{cases}$$

Then we have for $\Re(s) \geqq 0$

$$(41) \qquad \mathbf{E}\{e^{-s[\xi-\theta]^+}\} = \begin{cases} \dfrac{\lambda\mathbf{E}\{e^{-s\xi}\} - s\mathbf{E}\{e^{-\lambda\xi}\}}{\lambda - s} & \text{if } s \neq \lambda, \\[3mm] \lambda\mathbf{E}\{\xi e^{-\lambda\xi}\} + \mathbf{E}\{e^{-\lambda\xi}\} & \text{if } s = \lambda, \end{cases}$$

and

$$(42) \qquad \mathbf{P}\{[\xi - \theta]^+ = 0\} = \mathbf{E}\{e^{-\lambda\xi}\}.$$

PROOF. For non-negative x values we have

$$\mathbf{E}\{e^{-s[\xi-\theta]^+}|\xi = x\} = \begin{cases} \dfrac{\lambda e^{-sx} - se^{-\lambda x}}{\lambda - s} & \text{if } s \neq \lambda, \\[3mm] \lambda x e^{-\lambda x} + e^{-\lambda x} & \text{if } s = \lambda, \end{cases}$$

and

$$\mathbf{P}\{[\xi - \theta]^+ = 0 | \xi = x\} = e^{-\lambda x}$$

and unconditionally we obtain (41) and (42).

THEOREM 11. *The Laplace-Stieltjes transforms*

$$(43) \qquad \Omega_n(s) = \mathbf{E}\{e^{-s\eta_n}\} \qquad (n = 1, 2, \ldots)$$

are given by the following generating function

$$(44) \quad \sum_{n=1}^{\infty} \Omega_n(s)w^n$$
$$= \frac{(\lambda - s)(\mu + s)[1 - g(w)]\Omega_1(s) - \mu s w \Omega_1(\lambda[1 - g(w)])}{[1 - g(w)][(\lambda - s)(\mu + s) - \lambda\mu w]}$$

where

$$(45) \qquad g(w) = \frac{\lambda + \mu - \sqrt{(\lambda + \mu)^2 - 4\lambda\mu w}}{2\lambda w}.$$

PROOF. By using (39) and Lemma 1 we have for $\Re(s) \geqq 0$

$$(46) \qquad (\lambda - s)\Omega_{n+1}(s) = \frac{\lambda\mu}{\mu + s}\Omega_n(s) - s\mathbf{P}\{\eta_{n+1} = 0\},$$

and forming the generating function for $|w| < 1$ we get

$$(47) \quad \sum_{n=1}^{\infty} \Omega_n(s)w^n = \frac{(\lambda - s)(\mu + s)\Omega_1(s) - s\sum_{n=2}^{\infty}\mathbf{P}\{\eta_n = 0\}w^n}{(\lambda - s)(\mu + s) - \lambda\mu w}.$$

The left-hand side of (47) is a regular function of s if $\Re(s) \geqq 0$ and $|w| < 1$. In this domain the denominator of the right-hand side of (47) has exactly one root

$$s = \frac{\lambda - \mu + \sqrt{(\lambda + \mu)^2 - 4\lambda\mu w}}{2},$$

which can be written as

$$s = \lambda[1 - wg(w)],$$

where $g(w)$ is defined by (15). This $s = \lambda[1 - wg(w)]$ must be a root of the numerator of the right-hand side of (47) too. So we obtain

$$(48) \qquad \sum_{n=2}^{\infty} \mathbf{P}\{\eta_n = 0\}w^n = w \frac{\mu\Omega_1(\lambda[1 - wg(w)])}{[1 - g(w)]}.$$

Putting (48) into (47) we get (44) which was to be proved.

THEOREM 12. *If* $\lambda < \mu$ *then the limiting probability distribution* $\lim_{n \to \infty} \mathbf{P}\{\eta_n \leqq x\} = W^*(x)$ *exists and is independent of the initial distribution.* $W^*(x)$ *is defined by* (38). *If* $\lambda \geqq \mu$ *then* $\lim_{n \to \infty} \mathbf{P}\{\eta_n \leqq x\}$ $= 0$ *for all* x.

This theorem is a particular case of the following more general theorem proved by *D. V. Lindley* (1952).

THEOREM 13. *Let* $\xi_1, \xi_2, \ldots, \xi_n, \ldots$ *be identically distributed, independent random variables whose expectation exists, and define the sequence* $\eta_0, \eta_1, \ldots, \eta_n, \ldots$ *as follows:* η_0 *is an arbitrary random variable and*

$$\eta_n = [\eta_{n-1} + \xi_n]^+ \qquad (n = 1, 2, \ldots).$$

If $\mathbf{E}\{\xi_n\} < 0$ *then the limiting distribution* $\lim_{n \to \infty} \mathbf{P}\{\eta_n \leqq x\}$ *exists and is independent of the distribution of* η_0. *If* $\mathbf{E}\{\xi_n\} \geqq 0$ *but* $\xi_n \not\equiv 0$, *then* $\lim_{n \to \infty} \mathbf{P}\{\eta_n \leqq x\} = 0$ *for every* x.

PROOF. It is easy to see that η_n can be written also as follows

$$\eta_n = \max (0, \xi_n, \xi_n + \xi_{n-1}, \ldots, \xi_n + \xi_{n-1} + \cdots$$
$$+ \xi_2, \xi_n + \xi_{n-1} + \cdots + \xi_1 + \eta_0).$$

Since the random variables $\{\xi_n\}$ are identically distributed and independent

$$\bar{\eta}_n = \max (0, \xi_1, \xi_1 + \xi_2, \ldots, \xi_1 + \xi_2 + \cdots$$
$$+ \xi_{n-1}, \xi_1 + \xi_2 + \cdots + \xi_n + \eta_0)$$

has the same distribution as η_n.

First let us suppose that $\eta_0 \equiv 0$ and write $\zeta_0 = 0$ and

$$\zeta_n = \sum_{i=1}^{n} \xi_i \qquad (n = 1, 2, \ldots).$$

Then

$$\bar{\eta}_n = \max_{0 \leq k \leq n} \zeta_k$$

and

$$\lim_{n \to \infty} \mathbf{P}\{\bar{\eta}_n \leq x\} = \mathbf{P}\{\sup_{0 \leq k} \zeta_k \leq x\} = W(x),$$

because the events $\{ \max_{0 \leq k \leq n} \zeta_k \leq x\}$ form a monotone non-increasing sequence whose limit is $\{ \sup_{0 \leq k} \zeta_k \leq x\}$. Evidently $W(x)$ is a non-negative and monotone non-decreasing function of x, $W(x) = 0$ for $x < 0$. Thus $W(x)$ is a distribution function if and only if $W(\infty) = 1$.

By the strong law of large numbers

$$\lim_{n \to \infty} \frac{\zeta_n}{n} = \mathbf{E}\{\xi_n\}$$

with probability 1. This shows at once that $W(x) = 0$ for every x if $\mathbf{E}\{\xi_n\} > 0$ and $W(\infty) = 1$ if $\mathbf{E}\{\xi_n\} < 0$. If $\mathbf{E}\{\xi_n\} = 0$ but $\xi_n \not\equiv 0$, then a theorem of *K. L. Chung* and *W. H. J. Fuchs* [9] shows that $W(x) = 0$ for every x.

It remains only to show that $W(x)$ is independent of the distribution of η_0. Let us suppose that $\eta_0 = y$ is fixed. In this case we have

$$\mathbf{P}\{ \max_{0 \leq k \leq n-1} \zeta_k \leq x\} - \mathbf{P}\{\zeta_n > x - y\} \leq \mathbf{P}\{\bar{\eta}_n \leq x \,|\, \eta_0 = y\}$$
$$\leq \mathbf{P}\{ \max_{0 \leq k \leq n-1} \zeta_k \leq x\}.$$

If $\mathbf{E}\{\xi_n\} < 0$ then $\lim_{n \to \infty} \mathbf{P}\{\zeta_n > x - y\} = 0$ and thus

$$\lim_{n \to \infty} \mathbf{P}\{\bar{\eta}_n \leq x \,|\, \eta_0 = y\} = W(x)$$

irrespective of y. If $\mathbf{E}\{\xi_n\} \geqq 0$ but $\xi_n \not\equiv 0$ then

$$\lim_{n \to \infty} \mathbf{P}\{\bar{\eta}_n \leqq x \mid \eta_0 = y\} = 0$$

for every y.

Since

$$\mathbf{P}\{\bar{\eta}_n \leqq x\} = \int_{-\infty}^{\infty} \mathbf{P}\{\bar{\eta}_n \leqq x \mid \eta_0 = y\} \, d\mathbf{P}\{\eta_0 \leqq y\},$$

we obtain finally that

$$\lim_{n \to \infty} \mathbf{P}\{\bar{\eta}_n \leqq x\} = W(x)$$

irrespective of the distribution of η_0. The distribution of $\bar{\eta}_n$ agrees with that of η_n and thus the theorem is proved.

It remains only to find the explicit form of the limiting distribution. If

$$\lim_{n \to \infty} W_n(x) = W(x)$$

exists then

$$\lim_{n \to \infty} \Omega_n(s) = \Omega(s)$$

also exists and

$$\Omega(s) = \int_0^{\infty} e^{-sx} \, dW(x)$$

whenever $\Re(s) \geqq 0$. This is a consequence of the *Helly-Bray* theorem (cf. Appendix). It remains, therefore, only to find $\Omega(s)$ the Laplace-Stieltjes transform of $W(x)$. We have seen that the limiting distribution is independent of the initial distribution. If we suppose that $\eta_1 \equiv 0$ then by using Abel's theorem (cf. Appendix) it follows from (44) that

$$\Omega(s) = \lim_{w \to 1} (1 - w) \sum_{n=1}^{\infty} \Omega_n(s) w^n = \begin{cases} \dfrac{(\mu - \lambda)(\mu + s)}{(\mu - \lambda + s)\mu} & \text{if } \lambda < \mu, \\[2mm] 0 & \text{if } \lambda \geqq \mu, \end{cases}$$

because $g(1) < 1$ if $\lambda > \mu$, $g'(1) = \mu/(\mu - \lambda)$ if $\lambda < \mu$, and $g(1) = 1$ and $g'(1) = \infty$ if $\lambda = \mu$. Hence

$$W(x) = \begin{cases} 1 - \dfrac{\lambda}{\mu} e^{(\lambda - \mu)x} & \text{if } x \geqq 0, \\[2mm] 0 & \text{if } x < 0, \end{cases}$$

whenever $\lambda < \mu$. If $\lambda \geqq \mu$ then $W(x) = 0$ for every x. That is $W(x) = W^*(x)$ if $\lambda < \mu$.

STATIONARY PROCESS. If we suppose that $\lambda < \mu$ and $\mathbf{P}\{\eta_1 \leqq x\} = W^*(x)$ then we obtain easily that

$$\mathbf{P}\{\eta_2 \leqq x\} = \int_0^\infty (1 - e^{-(\mu-\lambda)(x+y)})e^{-\lambda y}\lambda\, dy = W^*(x)$$

and hence

$$\mathbf{P}\{\eta_n \leqq x\} = W^*(x)$$

for every n.

THE PROCESS OF DEPARTURES. Let us denote by $\tau_1', \tau_2', \ldots, \tau_n', \ldots$ the instants of the successive departures and denote by ζ_n the queue size immediately after the nth departure. Then we have

$$\zeta_{n+1} = [\zeta_n - 1]^+ + \nu_{n+1}^*,$$

where ν_{n+1}^* is the number of customers arriving during the $n + 1$st service, and the inter-departure time is given by

$$(49) \qquad \tau_{n+1}' - \tau_n' = \chi_{n+1} + \begin{cases} \theta_{n+1}^* & \text{if } \zeta_n = 0, \\ 0 & \text{if } \zeta_n \geqq 1, \end{cases}$$

where χ_{n+1} is the service time of the $n + 1$st customer and $\{\theta_n^*\}$ is a sequence of identically distributed, independent random variables with distribution function $\mathbf{P}\{\theta_n^* \leqq x\} = F(x) = 1 - e^{-\lambda x}(x \geqq 0)$ and $\{\theta_n^*\}$ is independent of $\{\chi_n\}$. Evidently we have

$$\mathbf{P}\{\nu_n^* = j \mid \chi_n = x\} = e^{-\lambda x}\frac{(\lambda x)^j}{j!} \qquad (j = 0, 1, 2, \ldots).$$

If we suppose that $\lambda < \mu$ and the distribution of the initial queue size is $\{P_j\}$, where

$$P_j = \left(1 - \frac{\lambda}{\mu}\right)\left(\frac{\lambda}{\mu}\right)^j \qquad (j = 0, 1, 2, \ldots)$$

then we arrive at the stationary process and in this case every ζ_n has the same distribution $\{P_j\}$. In the case of the stationary process the distribution function of the inter-departure times is given by

$$(50) \quad \mathbf{P}\{\tau_{n+1}' - \tau_n' \leqq x\} = F(x) = \begin{cases} 1 - e^{-\lambda x} & \text{if } x \geqq 0, \\ 0 & \text{if } x < 0. \end{cases}$$

For, by (49)

(51) $\mathbf{P}\{\tau'_{n+1} - \tau'_n \leqq x\} = P_0 H(x) * F(x) + (1 - P_0)H(x),$

where

$$H(x) = \begin{cases} 1 - e^{-\mu x} & \text{if } x \geqq 0, \\ 0 & \text{if } x < 0. \end{cases}$$

The Laplace-Stieltjes transform of the distribution function (51) is

$$\left(1 - \frac{\lambda}{\mu}\right)\left(\frac{\mu}{\mu + s}\right)\left(\frac{\lambda}{\lambda + s}\right) + \frac{\lambda}{\mu}\left(\frac{\mu}{\mu + s}\right) = \frac{\lambda}{\lambda + s},$$

which proves (50).

Now we shall prove the following theorem of *P. J. Burke* (1956).

THEOREM 14. *In the case of a stationary process the sequence of departure times forms a Poisson process of density* λ.

PROOF. We have shown that the inter-departure times are identically distributed random variables with distribution function $F(x) = 1 - e^{-\lambda x}$ when $x \geqq 0$. It remains only to prove that they are independent of each other. We shall prove that ζ_{n+1} and $\tau'_{n+1} - \tau'_n$ are independent random variables. By the theorem of total expectation we can write for $\Re(s) \geqq 0$ and $|z| \leqq 1$ that

$$\mathbf{E}\{e^{-s(\tau'_{n+1} - \tau'_n)} z^{\zeta_{n+1}}\} = \sum_{j=0}^{\infty} \mathbf{P}\{\zeta_n = j\}\mathbf{E}\{e^{-s(\tau'_{n+1} - \tau'_n)} z^{\zeta_{n+1}} | \zeta_n = j\}$$

$$= \left(\frac{\lambda}{\lambda + s}\right)\left(\frac{\mu - \lambda}{\mu - \lambda z}\right),$$

since

$$\mathbf{E}\{e^{-s\chi_{n+1}} z^{\zeta_{n+1}} | \zeta_n = j\} = z^{[j-1]^+} \frac{\mu}{\mu + s + \lambda(1 - z)}.$$

Thus

$$\mathbf{E}\{e^{-s(\tau'_{n+1} - \tau'_n)} z^{\zeta_{n+1}}\} = \mathbf{E}\{e^{-s(\tau'_{n+1} - \tau'_n)}\}\mathbf{E}\{z^{\zeta_{n+1}}\},$$

which proves the independence of $(\tau'_{n+1} - \tau'_n)$ and ζ_{n+1}. The independence of $\tau'_{n+1} - \tau'_n$ and all subsequent inter-departure times follows from the fact that the joint distribution of the lengths of these intervals is uniquely determined if ζ_{n+1} is given but ζ_{n+1} is independent of $\tau'_{n+1} - \tau'_n$. Thus the inter-departure times are mutually independent random variables. This completes the proof of the theorem.

Problems for solution

PROBLEM 1. Find the transition probability $P_{ik}(t) = \mathbf{P}\{\xi(t) = k \,|\, \xi(0) = i\}$ by using the following representation of $\xi(t)$. Let $\{\nu_1(t)\}$ and $\{\nu_2(t)\}$ be two independent Poisson processes of density λ and μ respectively. Let $\nu_1(0) = \nu_2(0) = 0$. Define

$$\zeta(t) = \nu_1(t) - \nu_2(t)$$

and

$$\zeta^*(t) = \inf_{0 \leq u \leq t} \zeta(u).$$

Then we can write that

$$\xi(t) = \begin{cases} \xi(0) + \zeta(t) & \text{if } \zeta^*(t) + \xi(0) \geq 0, \\ \zeta(t) - \zeta^*(t) & \text{if } \zeta^*(t) + \xi(0) \leq 0. \end{cases}$$

PROBLEM 2. Find the Laplace transform

$$\pi_{ik}(s) = \int_0^\infty e^{-st} P_{ik}(t)\, dt.$$

PROBLEM 3. Determine the limiting distribution $\lim\limits_{n \to \infty} \mathbf{P}\{\xi_n = k\}$ $(k = 0, 1, \ldots)$.

PROBLEM 4. Find the stationary distribution of the stochastic sequence $\{\eta_n\}$.

3. The time dependence of single server queues with Poisson input and general service times

Let us consider a counter with a single server, at which customers are arriving at the instants $\tau_1, \tau_2, \ldots, \tau_n, \ldots$. Suppose that the interarrival times $\theta_n = \tau_{n+1} - \tau_n$ $(n = 0, 1, \ldots; \tau_0 = 0)$ are identically distributed, independent, positive random variables with distribution function $\mathbf{P}\{\theta_n \leq x\} = F(x)$, where

(1)
$$F(x) = \begin{cases} 1 - e^{-\lambda x} & \text{if } x \geq 0, \\ 0 & \text{if } x < 0, \end{cases}$$

i.e. the input process is a homogeneous Poisson process of density λ.

If a customer arrives at the counter at an instant when the server is idle then his service starts immediately. If he arrives at an instant when the server is busy, then his service starts immediately after the departure of the preceding customer in the queue. Suppose that the durations of the successive service times are identically distributed, independent, positive random variables with distribution function $H(x)$, and further that they are also independent of $\{\tau_n\}$.

Denote by $\eta(t)$ the virtual waiting time at the instant t, i.e. $\eta(t)$ is the time that a customer would wait if he joined the queue at the instant t.

Denote by $\xi(t)$ the queue size at the instant t, i.e. the number of customers waiting or being served at the instant t. We say that the system is in state E_k at the instant t if $\xi(t) = k$.

Let us denote by $\tau'_1, \tau'_2, \ldots, \tau'_n, \ldots$ the instants of the successive departures.

Further define $\eta_n = \eta(\tau_n - 0)$, i.e. η_n is the waiting time of the nth customer and let $\xi_n = \xi(\tau'_n + 0)$, i.e. ξ_n is the queue size immediately after the nth departure.

In the following we shall determine the transient behavior of the stochastic processes $\{\eta(t)\}$ and $\{\xi(t)\}$ and that of the stochastic sequences $\{\eta_n\}$ and $\{\xi_n\}$. Further we shall determine the asymptotic behavior of these processes and the stochastic law of the busy period.

Throughout this section we use

LEMMA 1. *If $\Re(s) \geqq 0$ and $|w| \leqq 1$ then $z = \gamma(s, w)$, the root of the equation*

$$(2) \qquad\qquad z = w\psi(s + \lambda(1 - z))$$

which has the smallest absolute value, is

$$(3) \qquad \gamma(s, w) = w \sum_{j=1}^{\infty} \frac{(-\lambda w)^{j-1}}{j!} \left(\frac{d^{j-1}[\psi(\lambda + s)]^j}{ds^{j-1}} \right),$$

or equivalently

$$(4) \qquad \gamma(s, w) = \sum_{j=1}^{\infty} \frac{\lambda^{j-1} w^j}{j!} \int_0^{\infty} e^{-(\lambda+s)x} x^{j-1} \, dH_j(x),$$

where $H_j(x)$ denotes the jth iterated convolution of $H(x)$ with itself. This is a continuous function of s and w if $\Re(s) \geqq 0$ and $|w| \leqq 1$ and further $z = \gamma(s, w)$ is the only root of (2) in the unit circle $|z| < 1$ if

$\Re(s) \geqq 0$ *and* $|w| < 1$ *or* $\Re(s) > 0$ *and* $|w| \leqq 1$ *or* $\Re(s) \geqq 0$, $|w| \leqq 1$
and $\lambda\alpha > 1$. *Specifically,* $\omega = \gamma(0, 1)$ *is the smallest positive real root
of the equation*

$$(5) \qquad\qquad \omega = \psi(\lambda(1 - \omega)).$$

If $\lambda\alpha > 1$ *then* $\omega < 1$ *and if* $\lambda\alpha \leqq 1$ *then* $\omega = 1$.

PROOF. If $\Re(s) \geqq 0$ and $|w| < 1$ or $\Re(s) > 0$ and $|w| \leqq 1$
then by Rouché's theorem (cf. Appendix) it follows that (2) has one
and only one root in the circle $|z| < 1 - \epsilon$ where $\epsilon > 0$ is small
enough. For, in this case $|w\psi(s + \lambda(1 - z))| < 1 - \epsilon$ if $|z| = 1 - \epsilon$
and ϵ is a sufficiently small positive number. Similarly if $\Re(s) \geqq 0$,
$|w| \leqq 1$ and $\lambda\alpha > 1$, then by Rouché's theorem it follows that (2)
has exactly one root in the circle $|z| < 1 - \epsilon$, where ϵ is a sufficiently
small positive number. For, in this case $|w\psi(s + \lambda(1 - z))| \leqq \psi(\epsilon) <
1 - \epsilon$ if $|z| = 1 - \epsilon$ and $\epsilon > 0$ is small enough. Let us denote this
root by $z = \gamma(s, w)$. This can be obtained in the form of an infinite
series by Lagrange's theorem (cf. *E. T. Whittaker* and *G. N. Watson*
[65], p. 132 or Appendix).

Clearly, $z = \gamma(s, w)$ is that root of (2) which has the smallest
absolute value and is a continuous function of s and w in this domain.

On the other hand if $z = \gamma(s, w)$ is that root of (2) which has the
smallest absolute value, then $\gamma(s, w)$ is defined uniquely for $\Re(s) \geqq 0$
and $|w| \leqq 1$ as an inverse function of $s = \psi^{-1}(z/w) - \lambda(1 - z)$ for
fixed w, or as an inverse function of $w = z/\psi(s + \lambda(1 - z))$ for fixed s.
It can be shown that the function $z = \gamma(s, w)$ is a continuous function
of s and w if $\Re(s) \geqq 0$ and $|w| \leqq 1$. Since this function agrees with (3)
in the domain $\Re(s) \geqq 0$, $|w| < 1$ or $\Re(s) < 0$, $|w| \leqq 1$ or $\Re(s) \geqq 0$,
$|w| \leqq 1$ if $\lambda\alpha > 1$, it also agrees with (3) in the domain $\Re(s) \geqq 0$,
$|w| \leqq 1$, which follows from the continuity of (3).

We have always $|\gamma(s, w)| \leqq 1$ if $\Re(s) \geqq 0$ and $|w| \leqq 1$. Note also
that (2) has at most one root (possibly double) on the unit circle
$|z| = 1$, namely $z = 1$ is a root if $w\psi(s) = 1$.

It remains only to prove the second half of the lemma. Clearly,
for real x the function $\psi(x)$ is monotone decreasing if $0 \leqq x < \infty$ and
$\psi'(+0) = -\alpha$. Consequently if $\lambda\alpha > 1$ then (5) has only one real
root in the interval $(0, 1)$, and if $\lambda\alpha \leqq 1$ then $\omega = 1$ is the only real
root of (5). Furthermore the equation $z = \psi(\lambda(1 - z))$ has only one
root in the unit circle $|z| < 1$ if $\lambda\alpha > 1$ and has no root if $\lambda\alpha \leqq 1$.

For, if $\lambda\alpha \leq 1$ and $|z| \leq 1$, but $z \neq 1$, then we have $|\psi'(\lambda(1 - z))|$ < 1, whence $|\psi(\lambda(1 - z)) - 1| < |z - 1|$.

We introduce the following notation: $\gamma(s) = \gamma(s, 1)$ and $g(w) = \gamma(0, w)$. Clearly, $\omega = \gamma(0) = g(1)$.

Let us note that if $\omega = 1$, then by using (2) we get that

$$
(6) \qquad \gamma'(0) = \begin{cases} -1/(1 - \lambda\alpha) & \text{if } \lambda\alpha < 1, \\ \infty & \text{if } \lambda\alpha = 1, \end{cases}
$$

and

$$
(7) \qquad g'(1) = \begin{cases} 1/(1 - \lambda\alpha) & \text{if } \lambda\alpha < 1, \\ \infty & \text{if } \lambda\alpha = 1. \end{cases}
$$

Finally we remark, that by using Lagrange's expansion of $[\gamma(s, w)]^k$ $(k = 1, 2, \ldots)$ we get

$$
[\gamma(s, w)]^k = k \sum_{n=k}^{\infty} \frac{w^n \lambda^{n-k}}{n(n - k)!} \int_0^{\infty} e^{-(\lambda+s)x} x^{n-k}\, dH_n(x),
$$

where $H_n(x)$ denotes the nth iterated convolution of $H(x)$ with itself.

REMARK 1. The function

$$
\zeta(s, w) = s + \lambda[1 - \gamma(s, w)]
$$

satisfies in ζ the equation

$$
\zeta = \lambda + s - \lambda w \psi(\zeta)
$$

if $\Re(s) \geq 0$ and $|w| \leq 1$. Conversely if $\Re(s) > 0$ and $|w| \leq 1$ or $\Re(s) \geq 0$ and $|w| < 1$ or $\Re(s) \geq 0$, $|w| \leq 1$ and $\lambda\alpha > 1$, then by Rouché's theorem it follows that this equation has only one root $\zeta = \zeta(s, w)$ in the domain $\Re(\zeta) \geq 0$. For,

$$
|\psi(\zeta)| < \left| \frac{\lambda + s - \zeta}{\lambda w} \right|
$$

if $\Re(\zeta) = \epsilon$ and $\epsilon > 0$ is small enough or $\Re(\zeta) \geq \epsilon$, where ϵ is a sufficiently small positive number, and $|\zeta|$ is large enough.

THE DISTRIBUTION OF THE VIRTUAL WAITING TIME. The stochastic behavior of the process $\{\eta(t), 0 \leq t < \infty\}$ can be described as follows: $\eta(0)$ is the initial occupation time of the server. If $\eta(0) = 0$ then the server is idle at time $t = 0$. If $\eta(0) \neq 0$ then $\eta(0)$ gives the instant when the server ceases to be busy for the first time if no new customer joins the queue. In the instants τ_n $(n = 1, 2, 3, \ldots)$ the value of $\eta(t)$ has a jump of magnitude χ_n. The value of $\eta(t)$ decreases linearly with slope -1 until it jumps or reaches 0. If at the instant t the $\eta(t)$ reaches 0, then it remains 0 until a customer arrives at the counter. (Cf. Figure 1.)

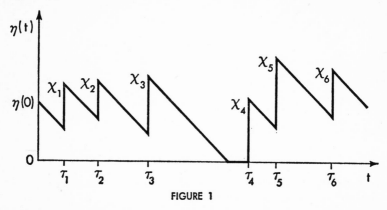

FIGURE 1

The process described by the family of random variables $\{\eta(t), 0 \leq t < \infty\}$ is a so-called continuous parameter Markov process of the mixed type. The change of state may happen continuously or by jumps. Processes of this type have been investigated by *A. N. Kolmogorov* [39] and *W. Feller* [20].

REMARK 2. Let us introduce a new process $\{\bar{\eta}(t), 0 \leq t < \infty\}$ as follows: $\bar{\eta}(0) = 0$, $\bar{\eta}(t)$ has a jump of magnitude χ_n at time $t = \tau_n$ $(n = 1, 2, \ldots)$, otherwise $\bar{\eta}(t)$ decreases linearly with slope -1. (Cf. Figure 2.)

If $\eta(0) = 0$ then we have

$$\eta(t) = \bar{\eta}(t) - \inf_{0 \leq u \leq t} \bar{\eta}(u),$$

that is,

$$\eta(t) = \sup_{0 \leq u \leq t} [\bar{\eta}(t) - \bar{\eta}(u)].$$

The process $\{\bar{\eta}(t), 0 \leq t < \infty\}$ is homogeneous and has independent increments; consequently $\eta(t)$ has the same distribution as

$$\sup_{0 \leq u \leq t} \bar{\eta}(u).$$

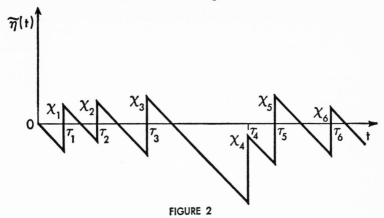

FIGURE 2

Thus it follows that the limit

$$\lim_{t \to \infty} \mathbf{P}\{\eta(t) \leq x\} = \mathbf{P}\{\sup_{0 \leq u < \infty} \bar{\eta}(u) \leq x\}$$

exists. Possibly this is not a distribution function in x.

If $\eta(0)$ is arbitrary then we can write that

$$\eta(t) = \begin{cases} \bar{\eta}(t) - \inf_{0 \leq u \leq t} \bar{\eta}(u) & \text{if } \inf_{0 \leq u \leq t} \bar{\eta}(u) \leq -\eta(0), \\ \bar{\eta}(t) + \eta(0) & \text{if } \inf_{0 \leq u \leq t} \bar{\eta}(u) \geq -\eta(0). \end{cases}$$

In this case we can prove also that

$$\lim_{t \to \infty} \mathbf{P}\{\eta(t) \leq x\} = \mathbf{P}\{\sup_{0 \leq u < \infty} \bar{\eta}(u) \leq x\}$$

irrespective of the distribution of $\eta(0)$.

Let $\mathbf{P}\{\eta(t) \leq x\} = W(t, x)$ be the distribution function of the virtual waiting time $\eta(t)$ and write $\hat{W}(x) = W(0, x)$. Further let

$$\Omega(t, s) = \mathbf{E}\{e^{-s\eta(t)}\} = \int_0^\infty e^{-sx}\, d_x W(t, x)$$

and $\hat{\Omega}(s) = \Omega(0, s)$.

THEOREM 1. *The Laplace-Stieltjes transform of the distribution function of the virtual waiting time is given by*

$$(8) \quad \Omega(t, s) = e^{st - [1 - \psi(s)]\lambda t}\{\hat{\Omega}(s) - s\int_0^t e^{-su + [1 - \psi(s)]\lambda u} P_0(u)\, du\},$$

where $P_0(t) = \mathbf{P}\{\eta(t) = 0\}$ can be obtained by the Laplace transform

(9)
$$\int_0^\infty e^{-st} P_0(t)\, dt = \frac{\hat{\Omega}[s + \lambda(1 - \gamma(s))]}{s + \lambda - \lambda\gamma(s)}$$

if $\Re(s) > 0$ and $z = \gamma(s)$ is the root with smallest absolute value of the equation

(10)
$$z = \psi(s + \lambda(1 - z))$$

in the unit circle $|z| < 1$.

PROOF. Denote by $\delta_{\Delta t}$ the number of customers arriving at the counter during the time interval $(t, t + \Delta t]$. By assumption

$$\mathbf{P}\{\delta_{\Delta t} = j\} = e^{-\lambda\Delta t}\frac{(\lambda\Delta t)^j}{j!} \qquad (j = 0, 1, 2, \ldots).$$

Using the theorem of total probability we can write that

$$\Omega(t + \Delta t, s) = \mathbf{E}\{e^{-s\eta(t+\Delta t)}\} = \sum_{j=0}^\infty \mathbf{P}\{\delta_{\Delta t} = j\}\mathbf{E}\{e^{-s\eta(t+\Delta t)}\,|\,\delta_{\Delta t} = j\}.$$

Since $\mathbf{P}\{\delta_{\Delta t} = 0\} = 1 - \lambda\,\Delta t + o(\Delta t)$, $\mathbf{P}\{\delta_{\Delta t} = 1\} = \lambda\,\Delta t + o(\Delta t)$ and $\mathbf{P}\{\delta_{\Delta t} > 1\} = o(\Delta t)$, we have

(11) $\quad \Omega(t + \Delta t, s) = (1 - \lambda\Delta t)\mathbf{E}\{e^{-s\eta(t+\Delta t)}\,|\,\delta_{\Delta t} = 0\}$

$$+ \lambda\,\Delta t\,\mathbf{E}\{e^{-s\eta(t+\Delta t)}\,|\,\delta_{\Delta t} = 1\} + o(\Delta t).$$

Under the condition $\delta_{\Delta t} = 0$ we have

$$\eta(t + \Delta t) = \begin{cases} \eta(t) - \Delta t & \text{if } \eta(t) > \Delta t, \\ 0 & \text{if } \eta(t) \leq \Delta t, \end{cases}$$

whence

$$\mathbf{E}\{e^{-s\eta(t+\Delta t)}\,|\,\delta_{\Delta t} = 0\} = W(t, \Delta t) + e^{s\Delta t}\int_{\Delta t}^\infty e^{-sx}\, d_x W(t, x).$$

Since $W(t, x)$ is right-continuous in x

$$W(t, \Delta t) = W(t, 0) + O(\Delta t),$$

whence

$$0 \leq \int_0^{\Delta t} x\, d_x W(t, x) \leq \Delta t[W(t, \Delta t) - W(t, 0)] = o(\Delta t).$$

Thus

(12) $\mathbf{E}\{e^{-s\eta(t+\Delta t)} \,|\, \delta_{\Delta t} = 0\} = (1 + s\,\Delta t)\,\Omega(t, s) - s\,\Delta t\,P_0(t) + o(\Delta t),$

because $W(t, 0) = P_0(t)$.

On the other hand if $y > \Delta t$, then

$$\mathbf{E}\{e^{-s\eta(t+\Delta t)} \,|\, \delta_{\Delta t} = 1, \eta(t) = y\} = \psi(s)e^{-s(y-\Delta t)}$$

and if $y \le \Delta t$, then

$$\mathbf{E}\{e^{-s\eta(t+\Delta t)} \,|\, \delta_{\Delta t} = 1, \eta(t) = y\} = \psi(s)e^{-s\epsilon_t \Delta t},$$

where $0 \le \epsilon_t \le 1$. Thus

$$\mathbf{E}\{e^{-s\eta(t+\Delta t)} \,|\, \delta_{\Delta t} = 1, \eta(t) = y\} = \psi(s)e^{-sy} + O(\Delta t)$$

for every y, and dropping the condition $\eta(t) = y$ we get

(13) $\mathbf{E}\{e^{-s\eta(t+\Delta t)} \,|\, \delta_{\Delta t} = 1\} = \Omega(t, s)\psi(s) + O(\Delta t).$

By (11), (12), and (13),

$$\Omega(t + \Delta t, s) = \Omega(t, s) + s\,\Delta t\,[\Omega(t, s) - P_0(t)]$$

$$- \lambda\,\Delta t\,\Omega(t, s)[1 - \psi(s)] + o(\Delta t),$$

and forming the limit

$$\lim_{\Delta t \to 0} \frac{\Omega(t + \Delta t, s) - \Omega(t, s)}{\Delta t} = \frac{\partial \Omega(t, s)}{\partial t},$$

we get

(14) $\dfrac{\partial \Omega(t, s)}{\partial t} = [s - \lambda(1 - \psi(s))]\Omega(t, s) - sP_0(t).$

The solution of this differential equation is (8).

It remains only to determine $P_0(t)$. This can be done by a probabilistic method (cf. Theorem 7) or by the theory of functions of a complex variable.

Let us write $s = \zeta$ in (8) and form the Laplace transform of $\Omega(t, \zeta)$ with respect to t, then we have

(15) $\displaystyle\int_0^\infty e^{-st}\Omega(t, \zeta)\,dt = \dfrac{\hat{\Omega}(\zeta) - \zeta \displaystyle\int_0^\infty e^{-st}P_0(t)\,dt}{s - \zeta + \lambda[1 - \psi(\zeta)]}.$

If $\Re(s) > 0$ and $\Re(\zeta) > 0$, then (15) is a regular function of ζ. By Rouché's theorem it follows that the denominator of the right-hand side of (15) has one and only one root $\zeta = \zeta(s)$ in this domain. By Lemma 1 we have

(16) $$\zeta(s) = s + \lambda[1 - \gamma(s)],$$

where $z = \gamma(s)$ is the root of the equation

$$z = \psi(s + \lambda(1 - z)),$$

which has the smallest absolute value. Accordingly $\zeta = \zeta(s)$ must be a root of the numerator of the right-hand side of (15). Hence

(17) $$\int_0^\infty e^{-st} P_0(t) \, dt = \frac{\hat{\Omega}(\zeta(s))}{\zeta(s)}.$$

Putting (16) into (17) we obtain (9).

REMARK 3. The distribution function $W(t, x)$ satisfies the integro-differential equation

(18) $$\frac{\partial W(t, x)}{\partial t} = \frac{\partial W(t, x)}{\partial x} - \lambda[W(t, x) - \int_0^x H(x - y) \, d_y W(t, y)]$$

for almost all $x \geq 0$ and $t \geq 0$.

By the theorem of total probability we can write that

(19) $$W(t + \Delta t, x) = (1 - \lambda \, \Delta t) W(t, x + \Delta t)$$
$$+ \lambda \, \Delta t \int_0^x H(x - y) \, d_y W(t, y) + o(\Delta t).$$

For, the event $\eta(t + \Delta t) \leq x$ may happen in several mutually exclusive ways:

(1) In the time interval $(t, t + \Delta t]$ no customer arrives at the counter and $\eta(t) \leq x + \Delta t$, the probability of which is

$$(1 - \lambda \, \Delta t) W(t, x + \Delta t) + o(\Delta t).$$

(2) In the time interval $(t, t + \Delta t]$ one customer arrives at the counter and his service time is less than $x - \eta(t) + \Delta t$ when $\eta(t) > \Delta t$ or less than $x - \eta(t) + \theta_t \, \Delta t$, where $0 \leq \theta_t \leq 1$, when $\eta(t) \leq \Delta t$, the

probability of which is

$$\lambda\, \Delta t \int_0^x H(x - y)\, d_y W(t, y) + o(\Delta t).$$

(3) In the time interval $(t, t + \Delta t]$ more than one customer arrives at the counter, the probability of which is $o(\Delta t)$.

Since

$$W(t, x + \Delta t) = W(t, x) + \frac{\partial W(t, x)}{\partial x}\, \Delta t + o(\Delta t)$$

for almost all $x \geqq 0$, by (19) we obtain (18), if we form the limit

$$\lim_{\Delta t \to 0} \frac{W(t + \Delta t, x) - W(t, x)}{\Delta t}.$$

THE AVERAGE WAITING TIME. Let us denote by $a(t)$ the average waiting time at the instant t, that is, $a(t) = \mathbf{E}\{\eta(t)\}$. We have

$$(20) \qquad a(t) = a(0) + \int_0^t P_0(u)\, du - (1 - \lambda\alpha)t.$$

Denote by $\nu(t)$ the number of customers joining the queue in the time interval $(0, t]$ and define $\zeta(t) = 1$ if the server is busy at the instant t and $\zeta(t) = 0$ if the server is idle at the instant t. We can write that

$$\eta(t) = \eta(0) + \sum_{0 \leqq \tau_n \leqq t} \chi_n - \int_0^t \zeta(u)\, du.$$

Now

$$\mathbf{E}\{\sum_{0 \leqq \tau_n \leqq t} \chi_n\} = \alpha\mathbf{E}\{\nu(t)\} = \alpha\lambda t$$

and

$$\mathbf{E}\left\{\int_0^t \zeta(u)\, du\right\} = \int_0^t \mathbf{E}\{\zeta(u)\}\, du = \int_0^t [1 - P_0(u)]\, du,$$

whence (20) follows.

EXAMPLE. If we suppose that $\eta(0) = y$ (constant) then by (9) we have

$$\int_0^\infty e^{-st} P_0(t)\, dt = \frac{e^{-y\{s + \lambda[1 - \gamma(s)]\}}}{s + \lambda[1 - \gamma(s)]},$$

and the Lagrange expansion (cf. Appendix) of this function is given by

$$\int_0^\infty e^{-st} P_0(t)\, dt = \frac{e^{-(\lambda+s)y}}{\lambda + s}$$

$$+ \lambda \sum_{n=1}^\infty \frac{(-\lambda)^{n-1}}{n!} \frac{d^{n-1}}{ds^{n-1}} \left\{ \frac{e^{-(\lambda+s)y}[1 + (\lambda + s)y][\psi(\lambda + s)]^n}{(\lambda + s)^2} \right\}.$$

Hence by inversion we get

$$P_0(t) = \sum_{n=0}^\infty e^{-\lambda t} \frac{(\lambda t)^n}{n!} \int_0^{t-y} \left(1 - \frac{u}{t}\right) dH_n(u)$$

if $t \geq y$ and $P_0(t) = 0$ if $t < y$. Here $H_n(u)$ denotes the nth iterated convolution of $H(u)$ with itself; $H_0(u) = 1$ if $u \geq 0$ and $H_0(u) = 0$ if $u < 0$.

If $\eta(0) = y$ then by (8) we obtain

$$W(t, x) = K(t, t + x - y) - \frac{\partial}{\partial x} \int_0^t K(t - u, t - u + x) P_0(u)\, du,$$

where

$$K(t, x) = \sum_{n=0}^\infty e^{-\lambda t} \frac{(\lambda t)^n}{n!} H_n(x).$$

THE DISTRIBUTION FUNCTION OF THE WAITING TIME OF THE nTH CUSTOMER. The random variable η_n gives the waiting time of the nth customer. We can write that

$$(21) \qquad \eta_{n+1} = [\eta_n + \chi_n - \theta_n]^+,$$

where χ_n is the service time of the nth customer and $\theta_n = \tau_{n+1} - \tau_n$. The $\{\chi_n\}$ and $\{\theta_n\}$ are independent sequences of identically distributed, independent random variables with distribution functions $\mathbf{P}\{\chi_n \leq x\} = H(x)$ and $\mathbf{P}\{\theta_n \leq x\} = F(x) = 1 - e^{-\lambda x}$ if $x \geq 0$.

THEOREM 2. *The Laplace-Stieltjes transforms*

$$(22) \qquad \Omega_n(s) = \mathbf{E}\{e^{-s\eta_n}\} \qquad (n = 1, 2, \ldots)$$

are given by the following generating function

(23)

$$\sum_{n=1}^{\infty} \Omega_n(s)w^n = w \frac{[1 - g(w)](\lambda - s)\Omega_1(s) - sg(w)\Omega_1(\lambda[1 - g(w)])}{[1 - g(w)][\lambda - s - w\lambda\psi(s)]},$$

where $z = g(w)$ is the root with smallest absolute value of the equation

(24) $$z = w\psi(\lambda(1 - z)).$$

PROOF. By using (21) and Lemma 1 of Section 2, we have

(25) $$(\lambda - s)\,\Omega_{n+1}(s) = \lambda\,\Omega_n(s)\psi(s) - sP\{\eta_{n+1} = 0\},$$

and forming the generating function for $|w| < 1$, we get

(26) $$\sum_{n=1}^{\infty} \Omega_n(s)w^n = \frac{(\lambda - s)w\Omega_1(s) - s\sum_{n=2}^{\infty} P\{\eta_n = 0\}w^n}{\lambda - s - w\lambda\psi(s)}.$$

The left-hand side of (26) is a regular function of s if $\Re(s) > 0$ and $|w| < 1$. In this domain the denominator of the right-hand side of (26) has exactly one root

$$s = \lambda[1 - g(w)],$$

where $z = g(w)$ is the root with the smallest absolute value of the equation (24). This $s = \lambda[1 - g(w)]$ must be a root of the numerator of the right-hand side of (26) too. So we obtain

(27) $$\sum_{n=2}^{\infty} P\{\eta_n^* = 0\}w^n = \frac{wg(w)\Omega_1(\lambda[1 - g(w)])}{[1 - g(w)]}.$$

Putting (27) into (26) we get (23), which was to be proved.

THE STOCHASTIC LAW OF THE BUSY PERIOD. It is clear that the time of the server is composed of alternating idle and busy periods. The durations of the successive idle periods and busy periods are independent random variables. The distribution function of the length of an idle period is clearly $F(x) = 1 - e^{-\lambda x}$ if $x \geqq 0$. If $\eta(0) = 0$ then the process starts with an idle period and the length of every busy period has the same distribution function, say $G(x)$. If $\eta(0) \neq 0$ then the process starts with a busy period. In this case let us denote by $\hat{G}(x)$ the distribution function of the length of the initial busy period.

The distribution function of the lengths of the other busy periods is $G(x)$. If $\eta(0) = 0$ then we agree to write $\hat{G}(x) = 1$ if $x \geq 0$ and $\hat{G}(x) = 0$ if $x < 0$.

Let us introduce the following Laplace-Stieltjes transforms

$$(28) \qquad \Gamma(s) = \int_0^\infty e^{-sx}\, dG(x)$$

and

$$(29) \qquad \hat{\Gamma}(s) = \int_0^\infty e^{-sx}\, d\hat{G}(x)$$

for $\Re(s) \geq 0$. Now we shall prove

THEOREM 3. *We have* $\Gamma(s) = \gamma(s)$ *for* $\Re(s) \geq 0$, *where* $\gamma(s)$ *equals the root with smallest absolute value in* z *of the equation*

$$(30) \qquad z = \psi(s + \lambda(1 - z)),$$

and

$$(31) \qquad \lim_{x \to \infty} G(x) = \omega,$$

where ω *is the root with smallest absolute value in* z *of the equation*

$$(32) \qquad z = \psi(\lambda(1 - z)).$$

If $\lambda\alpha \leq 1$ *then* $\omega = 1$ *and* $G(x)$ *is a proper distribution function. If* $\lambda\alpha > 1$ *then* $\omega < 1$ *and* $G(x)$ *is an improper distribution function, namely, in this case the busy period will be infinite with probability* $1 - \omega$.

The Laplace-Stieltjes transform $\hat{\Gamma}(s)$ *can be obtained as follows:*

$$(33) \qquad \hat{\Gamma}(s) = \hat{\Omega}(s + \lambda - \lambda\Gamma(s)).$$

If $\lambda\alpha \leq 1$ *then* $\hat{G}(\infty) = 1$ *and if* $\lambda\alpha > 1$ *and* $\eta(0) \neq 0$ *then* $\hat{G}(\infty) < 1$.

The distribution function $G(x)$ *can be expressed in the following explicit form*

$$(34) \qquad G(x) = \sum_{j=1}^\infty \int_0^x e^{-\lambda u} \frac{(\lambda u)^{j-1}}{j!}\, dH_j(u),$$

where $H_j(x)$ *denotes the* j*th iterated convolution of* $H(x)$ *with itself. If* *we suppose that $\eta(0) = y$ (constant) then we have*

(35)

$$\hat{G}(x) = \begin{cases} \lambda y \sum_{j=0}^{\infty} \int_0^{x-y} e^{-\lambda(y+u)} \dfrac{[\lambda(y+u)]^{j-1}}{j!} \, dH_j(u) & \text{if } x \geqq y, \\ 0 & \text{if } x < y. \end{cases}$$

PROOF. Let us denote by $M_0(t)$ the expected number of transitions $E_0 \rightarrow E_1$ occurring in the time interval $(0, t]$. By the theory of recurrent processes (cf. Appendix) we can write that

$$M_0(t) = \hat{G}(t) * F(t) + \hat{G}(t) * F(t) * G(t) * F(t) + \cdots,$$

whence

$$\int_0^{\infty} e^{-st} \, dM_0(t) = \frac{\lambda \hat{\Gamma}(s)}{s + \lambda[1 - \Gamma(s)]}.$$

On the other hand

$$M_0(t) = \lambda \int_0^t P_0(u) \, du.$$

For, if we introduce a new time variable involved only when the server is idle, then the transitions $E_0 \rightarrow E_1$ form a Poisson process of density λ. Hence by using (9) we obtain

$$\int_0^{\infty} e^{-st} \, dM_0(t) = \lambda \int_0^{\infty} e^{-st} P_0(t) \, dt = \frac{\lambda \hat{\Omega}(s + \lambda[1 - \gamma(s)])}{s + \lambda[1 - \gamma(s)]}.$$

Comparing the above formulas we get for $\Re(s) > 0$

$$\frac{\hat{\Gamma}(s)}{s + \lambda[1 - \Gamma(s)]} = \frac{\hat{\Omega}(s + \lambda[1 - \gamma(s)])}{s + \lambda[1 - \gamma(s)]}.$$

If, in particular, $\eta(0) = 0$ then $\hat{\Gamma}(s) \equiv \Omega(s) \equiv 1$ and consequently

$$\Gamma(s) = \gamma(s),$$

and using this equation again we also get

$$\hat{\Gamma}(s) = \Omega(s + \lambda[1 - \gamma(s)]),$$

which was to be proved. Clearly $G(\infty) = \gamma(0) = \omega$ where ω is given by Lemma 1.

By (4) we have

$$\Gamma(s) = \sum_{j=1}^{\infty} \int_0^{\infty} e^{-(\lambda+s)x} \frac{(\lambda x)^{j-1}}{j!} \, dH_j(x),$$

whence (34) follows by inversion.

If $\eta(0) = y$ (constant) then by (33)

$$\hat{\Gamma}(s) = e^{-y[s+\lambda(1-\Gamma(s))]}.$$

Now take into consideration that $\Gamma(s)$ satisfies (30) in z and form the Lagrange's expansion of $\hat{\Gamma}(s)$ (cf. Appendix); then we get

$$\hat{\Gamma}(s) = e^{-(\lambda+s)y} + \lambda y \sum_{j=1}^{\infty} \int_0^{\infty} e^{-(\lambda+s)(y+u)} \frac{[\lambda(y+u)]^{j-1}}{j!} \, dH_j(u),$$

whence (35) follows by inversion. This completes the proof of Theorem 3.

Now we shall give another proof of Theorem 3. This proof has the advantage that it can be generalized so that we can determine the joint distribution of the length of the busy period and the number of customers served during the busy period.

In order to determine $G(x)$ let us consider a customer who arrives at the counter when the server is idle. Denote by χ the duration of his service time. We have $\mathbf{P}\{\chi \leqq x\} = H(x)$. Further denote by ν the number of new customers joining the queue during the service time of this customer. Clearly we have

$$\mathbf{P}\{\nu = j \,|\, \chi = y\} = e^{-\lambda y} \frac{(\lambda y)^j}{j!},$$

whence

(36) $$\mathbf{P}\{\nu = j\} = \int_0^{\infty} e^{-\lambda y} \frac{(\lambda y)^j}{j!} \, dH(y).$$

THEOREM 4. *Define $\{\Theta_n\}$ as a sequence of identically distributed, independent random variables having the distribution function $G(x)$ and suppose that $\{\Theta_n\}$ is independent of ν and χ. We have*

(37) $$G(x) = \mathbf{P}\{\chi + \Theta_1 + \Theta_2 + \cdots + \Theta_\nu \leqq x\},$$

where the empty sum is 0 when $\nu = 0$.

PROOF. First of all let us note that from the point of view of the server it is perfectly indifferent whether the customers are served in the order of their arrival or not. This affects the customers only. The distribution function of the waiting time of a customer is changed by this fact, but the distribution function of the busy period remains unaltered. We shall consider a special system of service in which the busy period is composed of the serving of the first customer, the length of which is χ, and if during the service time of the first customer ν customers join the queue, then it contains ν further phases, the lengths of which are denoted by $\Theta_1, \Theta_2, \ldots, \Theta_\nu$. Let us suppose that the first phase starts with the serving of one of the above mentioned ν customers and continues with the serving of the new arrivals as long as they come. When there are no more new arrivals the second phase starts with the serving of one of the remaining $\nu - 1$ customers and this procedure is continued through all the ν phases. Thus the duration of the busy period is $\chi + \Theta_1 + \cdots + \Theta_\nu$ where clearly $\Theta_1, \Theta_2, \ldots, \Theta_n, \ldots$ are independent random variables with distribution function $\mathbf{P}\{\theta_n \leqq x\} = G(x)$ and the sequence $\{\Theta_n\}$ is independent of χ and ν. This completes the proof of (37).

Let us denote by $G_j(x)$ the distribution function of the random variable $\Theta_1 + \Theta_2 + \cdots + \Theta_j$ $(j = 0, 1, 2, \ldots)$, i.e. $G_j(x)$ is the jth iterated convolution of $G(x)$ with itself. By (37) we have

$$\mathbf{P}\{\chi + \Theta_1 + \cdots + \Theta_\nu \leqq x \,|\, \chi = y\}$$

$$= \mathbf{P}\{\Theta_1 + \cdots + \Theta_\nu \leqq x - y \,|\, \chi = y\}$$

$$= \sum_{j=0}^{\infty} e^{-\lambda y} \frac{(\lambda y)^j}{j!} G_j(x - y),$$

being $\Theta_1 + \cdots + \Theta_\nu$ a sum of a random number of random variables. Unconditionally we have

$$(38) \qquad G(x) = \int_0^\infty \sum_{j=0}^{\infty} e^{-\lambda y} \frac{(\lambda y)^j}{j!} G_j(x - y) \, dH(y).$$

Passing from equation (38) to the Laplace-Stieltjes transform we obtain for $\Re(s) \geqq 0$ that

$$\Gamma(s) = \sum_{j=0}^{\infty} [\Gamma(s)]^j \int_0^\infty e^{-(s+\lambda)y} \frac{(\lambda y)^j}{j!} \, dH(y)$$

$$= \int_0^\infty e^{-[s+\lambda-\lambda\Gamma(s)]y} \, dH(y) = \psi(s + \lambda - \lambda\Gamma(s)),$$

that is, $z = \Gamma(s)$ satisfies (30). If $\Re(s) > 0$ then $|\Gamma(s)| < 1$ and (30) has exactly one root in this domain. Consequently if $\Re(s) > 0$ then $z = \Gamma(s) = \gamma(s)$ is the root with smallest absolute value of the equation (30). The required result for $\Re(s) \geq 0$ can be obtained by using the continuity of $\Gamma(s)$. Clearly $G(\infty) = \gamma(0) = \omega$ where ω is given by Lemma 1.

If $\mathbf{P}\{\eta(0) \leq x\} = \hat{W}(x)$ then the distribution function of the length of the initial busy period is

$$(39) \qquad \hat{G}(x) = \int_0^x \sum_{j=0}^{\infty} e^{-\lambda x} \frac{(\lambda x)^j}{j!} G_j(x - y) \, d\hat{W}(y).$$

For, to obtain $G(x)$ we can apply word for word the proof of (38), only χ is to be replaced by the initial occupation time $\eta(0)$ and ν is to be defined as the number of customers joining the queue in the time interval $(0, \eta(0)]$. Similarly to (38) we now get (39). Forming the Laplace-Stieltjes transform of (39) we obtain (33). Since

$$\lim_{x \to \infty} \hat{G}(x) = \lim_{s \to 0} \hat{\Gamma}(s) = \hat{\Omega}(\lambda(1 - \omega)),$$

we obtain that $\hat{G}(\infty) = 1$ if $\lambda\alpha \leq 1$ and $\hat{G}(\infty) < 1$ if $\lambda\alpha > 1$ and $\eta(0) \not\equiv 0$.

Now let us denote by $\tilde{G}_n(x)$ the probability that the busy period consists in serving n customers and its length is at most x. Write

$$(40) \qquad \Gamma_n(s) = \int_0^{\infty} e^{-sx} \, d\tilde{G}_n(x)$$

if $\Re(s) \geq 0$. We shall prove

THEOREM 5. *If $\Re(s) \geq 0$ and $|w| \leq 1$ then*

$$(41) \qquad \sum_{n=1}^{\infty} \Gamma_n(s)w^n = \gamma(s, w),$$

where $z = \gamma(s, w)$ is the root with smallest absolute value in z of the equation $z = w\psi(s + \lambda(1 - z))$.

We have

$$(42) \qquad \Gamma_n(s) = \int_0^{\infty} e^{-(\lambda+s)x} \frac{(\lambda x)^{n-1}}{n!} \, dH_n(x),$$

whence by inversion

$$(43) \qquad \tilde{G}_n(x) = \int_0^x e^{-\lambda y} \frac{(\lambda y)^{n-1}}{n!} \, dH_n(y),$$

where $H_n(x)$ denotes the nth iterated convolution of $H(x)$ with itself.

PROOF. A reasoning similar to the proof of (37) shows that

$$(44) \quad \tilde{G}_n(x) = \mathbf{P}\{\chi + \Theta_1 + \cdots + \Theta_\nu \leqq x; \delta_1 + \cdots + \delta_\nu = n - 1\},$$

where $\delta_1, \delta_2, \ldots, \delta_\nu$ denotes the numbers of customers joining the queue during the 1st, 2nd, $\ldots$, νth phase of the busy period respectively. By (44) we have

$$\tilde{G}_n(x) = \sum_{j+n_1+\cdots+n_j=n-1} \int_0^x e^{-\lambda y} \frac{(\lambda y)^j}{j!}$$
$$\cdot \tilde{G}_{n_1}(x - y) * \cdots * \tilde{G}_{n_j}(x - y) \, dH(y),$$

whence

$$\Gamma_n(s) = \sum_{j+n_1+\cdots+n_j=n-1} \Gamma_{n_1}(s) \ldots \Gamma_{n_j}(s) \int_0^\infty e^{-(\lambda+s)y} \frac{(\lambda y)^j}{j!} \, dH(y).$$

Multiplying both sides of this equation by w^n and summing over $n = 1, 2, \ldots$ we get that

$$\gamma(s, w) = \sum_{n=1}^\infty \Gamma_n(s) w^n$$

satisfies in z the following equation

$$(45) \qquad z = w\psi(s + \lambda(1 - z)).$$

Clearly $\gamma(s, w)$ is a continuous function of s and w and $|\gamma(s, w)| \leqq 1$ whenever $\Re(s) \geqq 0$ and $|w| \leqq 1$. If $\Re(s) > 0$ then (45) has one and only one root in the unit circle and hence this is the required $\gamma(s, w)$. By using the continuity of $\gamma(s, w)$ we see that the theorem is also valid in the case $\Re(s) \geqq 0$. The formula (42) follows from (4).

REMARK 4. Let us denote by $\hat{G}_n(x)$ $(n = 0, 1, 2, \ldots)$ the probability that the length of the initial busy period is $\leqq x$ and during this period n newcomers join the queue. Write

$$\hat{\Gamma}_n(s) = \int_0^\infty e^{-sx}\, d\hat{G}_n(x)$$

and

$$\hat{\gamma}(s, w) = \sum_{n=0}^\infty \hat{\Gamma}_n(s) w^n.$$

A reasoning similar to the proof of (33) shows that

$$\hat{\gamma}(s, w) = \hat{\Omega}(s + \lambda - \lambda\gamma(s, w))$$

where $\gamma(s, w)$ is defined by (41). If we suppose in particular that $\eta(0) = y$ (constant), then

$$\hat{\gamma}(s, w) = e^{-y[s+\lambda-\lambda\gamma(s,w)]}.$$

Now take into consideration that $\gamma(s, w)$ satisfies (45) in z and form Lagrange's expansion of $\hat{\gamma}(s, w)$ (cf. Appendix); then we get

$$\hat{\gamma}(s, w) = e^{-(\lambda+s)y} + \lambda y \sum_{j=1}^\infty w^j \int_0^\infty e^{-(\lambda+s)(y+u)} \frac{[\lambda(y + u)]^{j-1}}{j!}\, dH_j(u),$$

whence

$$\hat{\Gamma}_n(s) = \lambda y \int_0^\infty e^{-(\lambda+s)(y+u)} \frac{[\lambda(y + u)]^{n-1}}{n!}\, dH_n(u),$$

and by inversion we get

$$(46)\quad \hat{G}_n(x) = \begin{cases} \lambda y \displaystyle\int_0^{x-y} e^{-\lambda(y+u)} \dfrac{[\lambda(y + u)]^{n-1}}{n!}\, dH_n(u) & \text{if } x \geqq y \\ 0 & \text{if } x < y. \end{cases}$$

THE AVERAGE LENGTH OF THE BUSY PERIOD. This can be obtained by the following

THEOREM 6. *Denote by* τ *the expectation of the length of the busy period. We have*

$$(47)\qquad \tau = \frac{\alpha}{1 - \lambda\alpha}$$

if $\lambda\alpha < 1$ *and* $\tau = \infty$ *if* $\lambda\alpha \geqq 1$.

PROOF. Now

$$\tau = \int_0^\infty x \, dG(x)$$

and by (37) we have

$$\tau = \mathbf{E}\{\chi + \theta_1 + \cdots + \theta_\nu\}.$$

Since $\mathbf{E}\{\chi\} = \alpha$ and $\mathbf{E}\{\nu\} = \lambda\alpha$ therefore

$$\tau = \alpha + \lambda\alpha\tau.$$

There are two possibilities, $\tau < \infty$ or $\tau = \infty$. If $\lambda\alpha < 1$ then $\tau = \alpha/(1 - \lambda\alpha)$ is finite and if $\lambda\alpha \geq 1$ then $\tau = \infty$ must hold.

We remark that if

$$\hat{\tau} = \int_0^\infty x \, d\hat{G}(x)$$

then by (39)

$$\hat{\tau} = a(0)(1 + \lambda\tau) = \frac{a(0)}{\alpha} \tau.$$

THE PROBABILITY THAT THE SERVER IS IDLE. In what follows we shall give another proof of (9).

THEOREM 7. *The probability $P_0(t)$ that the server is idle at time t satisfies the following integral equation*

$$(48) \qquad P_0(t) = \hat{G}(t) - \lambda \int_0^t [1 - G(t - u)]P_0(u) \, du.$$

The Laplace-Stieltjes transform of $P_0(t)$ is

$$(49) \qquad \int_0^\infty e^{-st} P_0(t) \, dt = \frac{\hat{\Gamma}(s)}{s + \lambda - \lambda\Gamma(s)} = \frac{\hat{\Omega}(s + \lambda - \lambda\gamma(s))}{s + \lambda - \lambda\gamma(s)},$$

where $\gamma(s)$ is that root in z of the equation

$$(50) \qquad z = \psi(s + \lambda(1 - z)),$$

which has the smallest absolute value.

PROOF. Let us denote by $M_0(t)$ the expected number of transitions $E_0 \to E_1$ occurring in the time interval $(0, t]$. Then we can write

$$(51) \qquad P_0(t) = \hat{G}(t) - \int_0^t [1 - G(t - u)] \, dM_0(u),$$

which follows from

$$(52) \quad 1 - P_0(t)$$
$$= 1 - \hat{G}(t) + \sum_{n=1}^{\infty} \int_0^t [1 - G(t - u)] \, d\mathbf{P}\{\tau_n \leqq u, \eta_n = 0\}.$$

In (52) the left side is the probability that the server is busy at the instant t. This event can occur in the following mutually exclusive ways: the length of the initial busy period is greater than t, or the last customer arriving in the time interval $(0, t]$ who finds the server idle is the nth one $(n = 1, 2, \ldots)$ and he arrives at the instant u, where $0 < u < t$ and the length of the busy period starting at time u is greater than $t - u$. Since evidently

$$M_0(t) = \sum_{n=1}^{\infty} \mathbf{P}\{\tau_n \leqq t, \eta_n = 0\}$$

we get (51). On the other hand we have

$$(53) \qquad\qquad M_0(t) = \lambda \int_0^t P_0(u) \, du.$$

For, if we introduce a new time variable involved only when the server is idle, then the successive transitions $E_0 \rightarrow E_1$ form a Poisson process of density λ. Putting (53) into (51) we get (48). Forming the Laplace transform of (48) we get (49).

Now we shall find the limiting law.

THEOREM 8. *The limit* $\lim\limits_{t \to \infty} P_0(t) = P_0^*$ *always exists and is independent of the distribution of* $\eta(0)$. *We have*

$$(54) \qquad\qquad P_0^* = 1 - \lambda\alpha$$

if $\lambda\alpha < 1$ *and* $P_0^* = 0$ *if* $\lambda\alpha \geqq 1$.

PROOF. Let us denote by $N_0(t)$ the expected number of transitions $E_1 \rightarrow E_0$ occurring in the time interval $(0, t]$. Then we can write

$$(55) \qquad\qquad P_0(t) = P_0(0)e^{-\lambda t} + \int_0^t e^{-\lambda(t-u)} \, dN_0(u),$$

which can be seen as follows. At time $t = 0$ there is state E_0 and no customer arrives in the time interval $(0, t]$, or the last transition $E_1 \to E_0$ in $(0, t]$ occurs at time u and in the time interval $(u, t]$ no customer arrives. Now the transitions $E_1 \to E_0$ form a recurrent process, that is, the distances between successive transitions $E_1 \to E_0$ are independent random variables with identical distribution function $F(t) * G(t)$. Clearly we have

$$N_0(t) = \hat{G}(t) + \hat{G}(t) * F(t) * G(t) + \cdots.$$

The distribution function $F(t) * G(t)$ is not a lattice distribution and its mean is evidently $\tau + 1/\lambda$, where τ is defined by Theorem 6. Thus by using *D. Blackwell*'s theorem (cf. Appendix) we obtain for all $h > 0$

$$(56) \qquad \lim_{t \to \infty} \frac{N_0(t + h) - N_0(t)}{h} = \lim_{t \to \infty} \frac{N_0(t)}{t} = \frac{\hat{G}(\infty)}{\tau + \dfrac{1}{\lambda}}.$$

If $\tau < \infty$ then $\hat{G}(\infty) = 1$ and if $\tau = \infty$ then (56) is taken to be zero. Now Theorem 8 follows from (55) and (56) by using the fundamental theorem of the recurrent processes (cf. Appendix).

REMARK 5. If $\lim_{t \to \infty} P_0(t) = P_0^*$ exists then obviously

$$\lim_{t \to \infty} \frac{1}{t} \int_0^t P_0(u)\, du = P_0^*$$

also holds. By a well-known Abelian theorem (cf. Appendix) we can conclude that

$$\lim_{s \to 0} s \int_0^\infty e^{-st} P_0(t)\, dt = P_0^*.$$

Thus by (49)

$$P_0^* = \lim_{s \to 0} \frac{s}{s + \lambda[1 - \gamma(s)]}.$$

We have seen that $P_0^* > 0$ if $\lambda\alpha < 1$. Consequently in this case $\gamma(0) = 1$ must hold. This proves that $\omega = 1$ if $\lambda\alpha < 1$.

THE LIMITING DISTRIBUTION OF THE WAITING TIME. The limiting behavior of the distribution of the waiting time is given by

THEOREM 9. *If* $\lambda\alpha < 1$ *then the limiting probability distribution* $\lim_{t\to\infty} W(t, x) = W^*(x)$ *exists and is independent of the distribution of* $\eta(0)$. *The Laplace-Stieltjes transform of* $W^*(x)$ *is given by*

(57)
$$\Omega^*(s) = \frac{(1 - \lambda\alpha)}{1 - \lambda\dfrac{[1 - \psi(s)]}{s}}.$$

If $\lambda\alpha \geqq 1$ *then* $\lim_{t\to\infty} W(t, x) = 0$ *for all* x.

PROOF. If $\lambda\alpha < 1$ and we restrict ourselves to imaginary s then by (8) and (54) it can be proved that $\lim_{t\to\infty} \Omega(t, s) = \Omega^*(s)$ exists if $|s| < a$, where a is a sufficiently small positive number and further that $\Omega^*(s)$ is continuous at $s = 0$. Hence it follows by a theorem of *A. Zygmund* [66] that the limiting distribution $\lim_{t\to\infty} W(t, x) = W^*(x)$ exists and further that the Laplace-Stieltjes transform of $W^*(x)$ is $\lim_{t\to\infty} \Omega(t, s) = \Omega^*(s)$ defined for $\Re(s) \geqq 0$. Thus by (14) we can conclude that $\Omega^*(s)$ has to satisfy the equation

$$[s - \lambda(1 - \psi(s))]\Omega^*(s) = sP_0^*,$$

where P_0^* is defined by (54). This proves (57). If $\lambda\alpha \geqq 1$ then $P_0^* = 0$ and $\lim_{t\to\infty} \Omega(t, s) = 0$ for $\Re(s) \geqq 0$ and therefore $\lim_{t\to\infty} W(t, x) = 0$ for all x. This completes the proof of the theorem.

THE STATIONARY PROCESS. If we suppose that $\lambda\alpha < 1$ and $\hat{W}(x) = W^*(x)$, then we obtain a stationary process $\{\eta(t)\}$ for which

$$W(t, x) = W^*(x)$$

and

$$P_0(t) = P_0^*$$

for all $t \geqq 0$. Conversely it is easy to see that the process $\{\eta(t)\}$ is stationary if and only if $\lambda\alpha < 1$ and the initial distribution of $\eta(0)$ is $W^*(x)$.

REMARK 6. Since we have proved that $\lim_{t\to\infty} \mathbf{P}\{\eta(t) \leqq x\}$ exists and is independent of the initial distribution, therefore it follows that a unique stationary distribution exists if and only if $\lim_{t\to\infty} \mathbf{P}\{\eta(t) \leqq x\}$ is a distribution function.

THEOREM 10. *If $\lambda\alpha < 1$ then the limiting probability distribution* $\lim_{n\to\infty} \mathbf{P}\{\eta_n \leqq x\} = W^*(x)$ *exists and is independent of the distribution of η_1. The Laplace-Stieltjes transform of $W^*(x)$ is given by* (57). *If $\lambda\alpha \geqq 1$ then* $\lim_{n\to\infty} \mathbf{P}\{\eta_n \leqq x\} = 0$ *for all x.*

PROOF. The statement concerning the existence of the limiting distribution is a consequence of a theorem of *D. V. Lindley* [41]. By using Theorem 13 of Section 2 we obtain that $\lim_{n\to\infty} \mathbf{P}\{\eta_n \leqq x\} = W^*(x)$ always exists and is independent of the initial distribution. There are two possibilities, either $W^*(x)$ is a proper distribution function or $W^*(x) \equiv 0$. If we suppose that $\eta_1 \equiv 0$ then by using Abel's theorem it follows from (23) that

$$\Omega^*(s) = \lim_{w\to 1}(1 - w) \sum_{n=1}^{\infty} \Omega_n(s)w^n = \begin{cases} \dfrac{s(1 - \lambda\alpha)}{s - \lambda[1 - \psi(s)]} & \text{if } \lambda\alpha < 1, \\ 0 & \text{if } \lambda\alpha \geqq 1, \end{cases}$$

because $g'(1) = 1/(1 - \lambda\alpha)$ if $\lambda\alpha < 1$. If $\lambda\alpha \geqq 1$ then $\Omega^*(s) = 0$ because $g(1) = 1$.

REMARK 7. If $\lambda\alpha < 1$ then by Lindley's theorem $W^*(x) \not\equiv 0$ and hence $\Omega^*(s) \not\equiv 0$. Thus it is impossible that $|g(1)| < 1$. This proves that $\omega = g(1) = 1$ must hold if $\lambda\alpha < 1$.

THE DISTRIBUTION OF THE QUEUE SIZE. At this point let us suppose that there is a departure at time $t = -0$ and write $\xi_0 = \xi(0)$. It is easy to see that the sequence of random variables $\{\xi_n\}$ forms a homogeneous Markov chain. The transition probabilities

$$p_{ik} = \mathbf{P}\{\xi_{n+1} = k \,|\, \xi_n = i\} \qquad (n = 0, 1, 2, \ldots)$$

are given by

$$p_{ik} = \begin{cases} p_{k-i+1} & \text{if } k \geqq i - 1 \quad \text{and} \quad i = 1, 2, \ldots, \\ p_k & \text{if } k \geqq 0 \qquad \text{and} \quad i = 0, \\ 0 & \text{if } k < i - 1 \quad \text{and} \quad i = 2, 3, \ldots, \end{cases}$$

where

(58) $$p_j = \int_0^\infty e^{-\lambda x} \frac{(\lambda x)^j}{j!} \, dH(x) \qquad (j = 0, 1, 2, \ldots)$$

is the probability that during a service exactly j customers join the queue. Now the matrix of transition probabilities has the following form

$$\pi = \left\| \begin{array}{cccc} p_0 & p_1 & p_2 & \cdots \\ p_0 & p_1 & p_2 & \cdots \\ 0 & p_0 & p_1 & \cdots \\ \cdot & \cdot & \cdot & \cdots \\ \cdot & \cdot & \cdot & \cdots \end{array} \right\|.$$

THEOREM 11. *The higher transition probabilities*

$$p_{ik}^{(n)} = \mathbf{P}\{\xi_n = k \,|\, \xi_0 = i\}$$

are given by the generating function

(59) $$\sum_{n=0}^\infty \sum_{k=0}^\infty p_{ik}^{(n)} w^n z^k$$
$$= \frac{z^{i+1}[1 - g(w)] - (1 - z)w\psi(\lambda(1 - z))[g(w)]^i}{[1 - g(w)][z - w\psi(\lambda(1 - z))]},$$

where $z = g(w)$ is the root with the smallest absolute value of the equation $z = w\psi(\lambda(1 - z))$.

If $|w| \leqq 1$ and $j = 1, 2, \ldots$ then we have

(60) $$[g(w)]^j = j \sum_{n=j}^\infty \frac{w^n \lambda^{n-j}}{n(n - j)!} \int_0^\infty e^{-\lambda x} x^{n-j} \, dH_n(x),$$

where $H_n(x)$ denotes the nth iterated convolution of $H(x)$ with itself.

PROOF. Now we can write that

(61) $$\xi_{n+1} = [\xi_n - 1]^+ + \nu_{n+1},$$

where ν_n denotes the number of customers arriving during the nth service. $\{\nu_n\}$ is a sequence of independent random variables with distribution $\mathbf{P}\{\nu_n = j\} = p_j \ (j = 0, 1, 2, \ldots)$ defined by (58). Now let us suppose that $\xi_0 = i$ is fixed and write

$$U_n(z) = \mathbf{E}\{z^{\xi_n}\};$$

then by (61) we have

$$(62) \quad U_{n+1}(z) = \psi(\lambda(1 - z)) \left[\frac{U_n(z) - \mathbf{P}\{\xi_n = 0\}}{z} + \mathbf{P}\{\xi_n = 0\} \right].$$

Taking into consideration that $U_0(z) = z^i$ and $\mathbf{P}\{\xi_n = 0\} = p_{i0}^{(n)}$ and forming the generating function of (62), we obtain

$$(63) \quad \sum_{n=0}^{\infty} U_n(z)w^n = \frac{z^{i+1} - w(1 - z)\psi(\lambda(1 - z)) \sum_{n=0}^{\infty} p_{i0}^{(n)} w^n}{z - w\psi(\lambda(1 - z))}.$$

The left side of (63) is a regular function of z if $|z| < 1$, and $|w| < 1$. The denominator of the right-hand side has exactly one root $z = g(w)$ in the unit circle $|z| < 1$. This must be a root of the numerator too. So we have

$$(64) \quad \sum_{n=0}^{\infty} p_{i0}^{(n)} w^n = \frac{[g(w)]^i}{[1 - g(w)]}.$$

Putting (64) into (63) we get (59), which was to be proved. By using (60) the probabilities $p_{ik}^{(n)}$ can be determined explicitly.

REMARK 8. If we suppose that $\xi(0) = 0$ and the distribution function of the waiting time of the nth customer joining the queue is denoted by $W_n^*(x)$, then we can write the following obvious relation

$$(65) \quad \mathbf{P}\{\xi_n = k\} = \int_0^{\infty} e^{-\lambda x} \frac{(\lambda x)^k}{k!} \, d[W_n^*(x) * H(x)],$$

whence

$$(66) \quad \mathbf{E}\{z^{\xi_n}\} = \Omega_n^*(\lambda(1 - z))\psi(\lambda(1 - z)).$$

If the initial queue size is arbitrary then $\mathbf{E}\{z^{\xi_n}\}$ can be obtained similarly. Now using (23) we can prove (59) in this way too.

The Markov chain $\{\xi_n\}$ is irreducible and aperiodic and we have

THEOREM 12. *If $\lambda\alpha < 1$ then the Markov chain $\{\xi_n\}$ is ergodic and the limiting probability distribution* $\lim_{n\to\infty} \mathbf{P}\{\xi_n = k\} = P_k$ *$(k = 0, 1, 2, \ldots)$ exists and is independent of the initial distribution.*

We have

(67') $$U(z) = \sum_{k=0}^{\infty} P_k z^k = \frac{(1 - \lambda\alpha)(1 - z)\psi(\lambda(1 - z))}{\psi(\lambda(1 - z)) - z}.$$

If $\lambda\alpha \geqq 1$ then $\lim_{n\to\infty} \mathbf{P}\{\xi_n = k\} = 0$ *for every* k.

PROOF. The limit $\lim_{n\to\infty} \mathbf{P}\{\xi_n = k\} = P_k$ always exists and is independent of the initial distribution. Either every $P_k > 0$ and $\{P_k\}$ is a probability distribution, or every $P_k = 0$. By using Abel's theorem (cf. Appendix), we have

$$\sum_{k=0}^{\infty} P_k z^k = \lim_{w\to 1} (1 - w) \sum_{n=0}^{\infty} \sum_{k=0}^{\infty} p_{ik}^{(n)} z^k w^n$$

and the right-hand side can be calculated by (59). If we use that $g(1) = 1$ and $g'(1) = 1/(1 - \lambda\alpha)$ when $\lambda\alpha \leqq 1$, then we get (67), and since $g(1) < 1$ when $\lambda\alpha > 1$ we obtain that $P_k = 0$ for every k whenever $\lambda\alpha > 1$.

Now we shall investigate the distribution of $\xi(t)$ for finite t. Let us suppose that there is a departure at time $t = -0$. We need the joint distribution of ξ_n and τ'_n for every n. Here $\xi_0 = \xi(0)$ and $\tau'_0 = 0$.

THEOREM 13. *Let us define*

(68) $$U_n(s, z) = \mathbf{E}\{e^{-s\tau'_n} z^{\xi_n}\} \qquad (n = 0, 1, 2, \ldots)$$

for $\Re(s) \geqq 0$ and $|z| \leqq 1$. We have for $|w| < 1$ that

(69) $$\sum_{n=0}^{\infty} U_n(s, z) w^n$$

$$= \frac{zU_0(s, z) - \dfrac{w\psi(s + \lambda(1 - z))[s + \lambda(1 - z)]U_0(s, \gamma(s, w))}{s + \lambda[1 - \gamma(s, w)]}}{z - w\psi(s + \lambda(1 - z))},$$

where $\gamma(s, w)$ is the root with smallest absolute value in z of the equation

(70) $$z = w\psi(s + \lambda(1 - z)).$$

PROOF. Now we can write that

(71) $$\xi_{n+1} = [\xi_n - 1]^+ + \nu_{n+1}$$

and

$$(72) \qquad \tau'_{n+1} = \tau'_n + \chi_{n+1} + \begin{cases} 0 & \text{if } \xi_n \geq 1, \\ \theta^*_n & \text{if } \xi_n = 0, \end{cases}$$

where $\theta^*_n = \tau_{n+1} - \tau'_n$, χ_{n+1} is the service time of the $n + 1$st customer and ν_{n+1} is the number of customers arriving during the $n + 1$st service. $\{\chi_n\}$ and $\{\theta^*_n\}$ are independent sequences of identically distributed, independent random variables with distribution functions $\mathbf{P}\{\chi_n \leq x\} = H(x)$ and $\mathbf{P}\{\theta^*_n \leq x\} = F(x) = 1 - e^{-\lambda x}$ $(x \geq 0)$ respectively. Further we have

$$(73) \qquad \mathbf{P}\{\nu_n = j \,|\, \chi_n = x\} = e^{-\lambda x} \frac{(\lambda x)^j}{j!} \qquad (j = 0, 1, 2, \ldots)$$

for every n.

Since

$$\mathbf{E}\{e^{-s\chi_n z^{\nu_n}}\} = \psi(s + \lambda(1 - z))$$

we get by (71) and (72) that

$$U_{n+1}(s, z) = \psi(s + \lambda(1 - z)) \left[\frac{U_n(s, z) - U_n(s, 0)}{z} + U_n(s, 0) \frac{\lambda}{(\lambda + s)} \right].$$

Hence

$$(74) \quad \sum_{n=0}^{\infty} U_n(s, z) w^n$$

$$= \frac{z U_0(s, z) - w\psi(s\lambda(1 - z)) \dfrac{[s + \lambda(1 - z)]}{(\lambda + s)} \displaystyle\sum_{n=0}^{\infty} U_n(s, 0) w^n}{z - w\psi(s + \lambda(1 - z))}.$$

The left-hand side of (74) is a regular function of z if $|z| < 1$, $\Re(s) \geq 0$ and $|w| < 1$. In this domain the denominator of the right-hand side of (74) has exactly one root $z = \gamma(s, w)$. This must also be a root of the numerator. Thus we have

$$(75) \qquad \sum_{n=0}^{\infty} U_n(s, 0) w^n = \frac{U_0(s, \gamma(s, w))}{1 - \dfrac{\lambda}{(\lambda + s)} \gamma(s, w)}.$$

Putting (75) into (74) we get (69) which was to be proved.

In what follows we always suppose that $t = -0$ is a departure point and write

$$P_{ik}(t) = \mathbf{P}\{\xi(t) = k \,|\, \xi(0) = i\}.$$

THEOREM 14. *Let*

(76)
$$\Pi_{ik}(s) = \int_0^\infty e^{-st} P_{ik}(t)\, dt$$

for $\Re(s) > 0$. *We have for* $\Re(s) > 0$ *and* $|z| \leq 1$

(77)
$$\sum_{k=0}^\infty \Pi_{ik}(s) z^k = \frac{z^{i+1}[1 - \psi(s + \lambda(1 - z))]}{[s + \lambda(1 - z)][z - \psi(s + \lambda(1 - z))]}$$
$$+ \frac{[\gamma(s)]^i}{s + \lambda[1 - \gamma(s)]} \left\{ 1 - z \frac{[1 - \psi(s + \lambda(1 - z))]}{[z - \psi(s + \lambda(1 - z))]} \right\}$$

where $\gamma(s)$ *is the root with smallest absolute value in* z *of the equation*

$$z = \psi(s + \lambda(1 - z)).$$

PROOF. Under the assumption $\xi(0) = i$ let us denote by $M_j(t)$ $(j = 0, 1, 2, \ldots)$ the expectation of the number of transitions $E_j \to E_{j+1}$ occurring in the time interval $(0, t]$ and denote by $N_j(t)$ $(j = 0, 1, 2, \ldots)$ the expectation of the number of transitions $E_{j+1} \to E_j$ occurring in the time interval $(0, t]$. We have evidently

(78)
$$M_0(t) = \lambda \int_0^t P_{i0}(u)\, du$$

and by (9)

(79)
$$\int_0^\infty e^{-st}\, dM_0(t) = \frac{\lambda[\gamma(s)]^i}{s + \lambda[1 - \gamma(s)]}.$$

Since clearly

$$N_j(t) = \sum_{n=1}^\infty \mathbf{P}\{\tau_n' \leq t, \xi_n = j\}$$

we obtain by (69) that

(80)
$$\sum_{j=0}^\infty z^j \int_0^\infty e^{-st}\, dN_j(t) = \sum_{n=1}^\infty U_n(s, z)$$
$$= \psi(s + \lambda(1 - z)) \frac{z^i - \dfrac{[s + \lambda(1 - z)][\gamma(s)]^i}{s + \lambda[1 - \gamma(s)]}}{z - \psi(s + \lambda(1 - z))}.$$

By knowing $M_0(t)$ and $N_j(t)$ $(j = 0, 1, 2, \ldots)$ for all $t \geqq 0$, the probabilities $P_{ik}(t)$ can be obtained as follows. If $k = 1, 2, \ldots$, then

$$(81) \quad P_{ik}(t) = \delta_{ik}^*[1 - H(t)]e^{-\lambda t} \frac{(\lambda t)^{k-i}}{(k - i)!}$$

$$+ \sum_{j=1}^{k} \int_0^t [1 - H(t - u)]e^{-\lambda(t-u)} \frac{[\lambda(t - u)]^{k-j}}{(k - j)!} \, dN_j(u)$$

$$+ \int_0^t [1 - H(t - u)]e^{-\lambda(t-u)} \frac{[\lambda(t - u)]^{k-1}}{(k - 1)!} \, dM_0(u)$$

and

$$(82) \quad P_{i0}(t) = \delta_{i0}^* e^{-\lambda t} + \int_0^t e^{-\lambda(t-u)} \, dN_0(u),$$

where $\delta_{00}^* = 1$, $\delta_{ik}^* = 1$ if $i = 1, 2, \ldots, k$ and $\delta_{ik}^* = 0$ otherwise.

In proving (81) we take into consideration that the event $\xi(t) = k$ $(k = 1, 2, \ldots)$ can occur in the following mutually exclusive ways: At the instant u (where $0 \leq u < t$) there occurs a transition $E_{j+1} \to E_j$ $(j = 1, 2, \ldots, k)$ or a transition $E_0 \to E_1$, the service starting at this instant u does not terminate in the time interval $(u, t]$, and during $(u, t]$ $k - j$ or $k - 1$ customers join the queue. Finally we get (81) if we also take into consideration that the transition $E_{j+1} \to E_j$ may be the 1st, 2nd, $\ldots$, nth, $\ldots$ departure and similarly the transition $E_0 \to E_1$ may be 1st, 2nd, $\ldots$, nth, $\ldots$ arrival. In proving (82) we take into consideration that the event $\xi(t) = 0$ can occur in such a way that at the instant u (where $0 \leq u < t$) there occurs a transition $E_1 \to E_0$ and during $(u, t]$ no customer joins the queue.

Let us form the Laplace transforms of (81) and (82) and write down the generating function of $\Pi_{ik}(s)$; then we get

$$(83) \quad \sum_{k=0}^{\infty} \Pi_{ik}(s)z^k = \frac{[1 - \psi(s + \lambda(1 - z))]}{s + \lambda(1 - z)} \left\{ \sum_{j=1}^{\infty} z^j \int_0^{\infty} e^{-st} \, dN_j(t) \right.$$

$$\left. + z \int_0^{\infty} e^{-st} \, dM_0(t) \right\} + \frac{1}{(\lambda + s)} \int_0^{\infty} e^{-st} \, dN_0(t)$$

$$+ \begin{cases} \dfrac{1}{(\lambda + s)} & i = 0, \\[3mm] z^i \dfrac{1 - \psi(s + \lambda(1 - z))}{s + \lambda(1 - z)} & i > 0. \end{cases}$$

By (78) and (82) we have

$$(84) \quad \int_0^\infty e^{-st}\, dM_0(t) = \delta_{i0}^* \frac{\lambda}{(\lambda + s)} + \frac{\lambda}{(\lambda + s)} \int_0^\infty e^{-st}\, dN_0(t)$$

and hence by (79), (80), (83), and (84) we get (77).

THEOREM 15. *If* $\lambda\alpha < 1$ *then the limiting distribution* $\lim_{t\to\infty} \mathbf{P}\{\xi(t) = k\} = P_k^*$ $(k = 0, 1, 2, \ldots)$ *exists and is independent of the initial distribution. We have* $P_k^* = P_k$ $(k = 0, 1, 2, \ldots)$ *where* $\{P_k\}$ *is defined by* (67). *If* $\lambda\alpha > 1$ *then* $\lim_{t\to\infty} \mathbf{P}\{\xi(t) = k\} = 0$ *for every* k.

PROOF. The transitions $E_{j+1} \to E_j$ $(j = 0, 1, 2, \ldots)$ and similarly the transitions $E_0 \to E_1$ form a recurrent process. The distances between successive transitions are identically distributed, independent random variables having a non-lattice distribution. Therefore by *Blackwell's* theorem (cf. Appendix) it follows that the following limits exist for every $h > 0$ and agree with the corresponding right-hand sides:

$$(85) \quad \lim_{t\to\infty} \frac{N_j(t + h) - N_j(t)}{h} = \lim_{t\to\infty} \frac{N_j(t)}{t} \qquad (j = 0, 1, 2, \ldots)$$

and

$$(86) \quad \lim_{t\to\infty} \frac{M_0(t + h) - M_0(t)}{h} = \lim_{t\to\infty} \frac{M_0(t)}{t}.$$

Furthermore it is easy to see that these limits are independent of the initial state. By using the fundamental theorem of the recurrent processes (cf. Appendix) we obtain from (81), (82), (85), and (86) that the limits

$$\lim_{t\to\infty} P_k(t) = P_k^* \qquad (k = 0, 1, 2, \ldots)$$

always exist and are independent of the initial state. Specifically we have

$$P_0^* = \frac{N_0}{\lambda}$$

and for $k = 1, 2, \ldots$

$$P_k^* = \sum_{j=1}^{k} N_j \int_0^\infty [1 - H(x)]e^{-\lambda x} \frac{(\lambda x)^{k-j}}{(k-j)!}\, dx$$

$$+ M_0 \int_0^\infty [1 - H(x)]e^{-\lambda x} \frac{(\lambda x)^{k-1}}{(k-1)!}\, dx,$$

where

$$N_j = \lim_{t \to \infty} \frac{N_j(t)}{t} \quad \text{and} \quad M_0 = \lim_{t \to \infty} \frac{M_0(t)}{t}.$$

Now the difference of the numbers of transitions $E_k \to E_{k+1}$ and $E_{k+1} \to E_k$ occurring in the time interval $(0, t]$ is at most 1. Hence

(87) $$|M_k(t) - N_k(t)| \leq 1$$

for every k and $t \geq 0$. On the other hand obviously

$$M_k(t) = \lambda \int_0^t P_k(u)\, du \qquad (k = 0, 1, 2, \ldots).$$

Having proved that $\lim\limits_{t \to \infty} P_k(t) = P_k^*$ $(k = 0, 1, 2, \ldots)$ always exists, we can conclude that

(88) $$\lim_{t \to \infty} \frac{M_k(t)}{t} = \lambda P_k^*.$$

By the theory of Markov chains it follows that

(89) $$\lim_{t \to \infty} \frac{N_k(t)}{N(t)} = P_k,$$

where $N(t)$ denotes the expectation of the number of the departing customers in the time interval $(0, t]$, i.e.,

$$N(t) = \sum_{k=0}^{\infty} N_k(t).$$

We have proved that if $\lambda \alpha < 1$ then $P_k > 0$ for every k and $\{P_k\}$ is a probability distribution, whereas if $\lambda \alpha \geq 1$ then $P_k = 0$ for every k. Now by (87)

$$\lim_{t \to \infty} \frac{M_k(t)}{t} = \lim_{t \to \infty} \frac{N_k(t)}{t},$$

and thus by virtue of (88) and (89) we get

$$(90) \qquad P_k^* = \frac{P_k}{\lambda} \lim_{t \to \infty} \frac{N(t)}{t} \qquad (k = 0, 1, 2, \ldots).$$

If we suppose that $\lambda\alpha < 1$ then by (54) and (67) we obtain

$$P_0^* = P_0,$$

and hence if we write $k = 0$ in (90) we get

$$\lim_{t \to \infty} \frac{N(t)}{t} = \lambda$$

and again by (90)

$$P_k^* = P_k \qquad (k = 1, 2, \ldots).$$

If $\lambda\alpha \geqq 1$ then every $P_k = 0$ and since $\lim\limits_{t \to \infty} N(t)/t$ is evidently finite it follows by (90) that $P_k^* = 0$ for every k. This completes the proof of the theorem.

THE PROCESS OF DEPARTURES. Let us suppose that there is a departure at $t = -0$ and denote by $\tau_1', \tau_2', \ldots, \tau_n', \ldots$ the sequence of the instants of the successive departures. Further denote by $N(t)$ the expected number of the departures occurring in the time interval $(0, t]$.

THEOREM 16. *If* $\Re(s) > 0$ *then*

$$(91) \qquad \int_0^\infty e^{-st} \, dN(t) = \frac{\psi(s)}{1 - \psi(s)} \left\{ 1 - \frac{sU_0(\gamma(s))}{s + \lambda[1 - \gamma(s)]} \right\},$$

where $\gamma(s)$ *is the root with smallest absolute value in z of the equation*

$$(92) \qquad z = \psi(s + \lambda(1 - z))$$

and

$$(93) \qquad U_0(z) = \mathbf{E}\{z^{\xi(0)}\}$$

is the generating function of the initial queue size.

PROOF. If we put $z = 1$ in (69) we get

(94) $$\sum_{n=1}^{\infty} \mathbf{E}\{e^{-s\tau'_n}\}w^n = \frac{1 - \dfrac{sw\psi(s)U_0[\gamma(s, w)]}{s + \lambda[1 - \gamma(s, w)]}}{1 - w\psi(s)} - 1.$$

Since

(95) $$N(t) = \sum_{n=1}^{\infty} \mathbf{P}\{\tau'_n \leqq t\}$$

we obtain (91) from (94) letting $w \to 1$.

Now let us suppose that $\lambda\alpha < 1$ and the initial distribution of the queue size agrees with the stationary distribution defined by (67). In this case

$$U_0(z) = \frac{(1 - \lambda\alpha)(1 - z)\psi(\lambda(1 - z))}{\psi(\lambda(1 - z)) - z}$$

and by (91)

(96) $$\int_0^{\infty} e^{-st} \, dN(t)$$

$$= \frac{\psi(s)}{1 - \psi(s)} \left\{ 1 - \frac{(1 - \lambda\alpha)s[1 - \gamma(s)]\psi(\lambda(1 - \gamma(s)))}{\{s + \lambda[1 - \gamma(s)]\}[\psi(\lambda(1 - \gamma(s))) - \gamma(s)]} \right\}.$$

If we suppose in particular that $H(x) = 1 - e^{-\mu x}$ $(x \geqq 0)$, when $\psi(s) = \mu/(\mu + s)$ and $\alpha = 1/\mu$, then by (96) we obtain

$$\int_0^{\infty} e^{-st} \, dN(t) = \frac{\lambda}{s},$$

whence

$$N(t) = \lambda t.$$

The latter equation is in agreement with the fact that in this case the departures follow a Poisson process of density λ. In the general case the output process $\{\tau'_n\}$ cannot be characterized in a similar simple way.

The inter-departure times can always be expressed as follows

(97) $$\tau'_{n+1} - \tau'_n = \begin{cases} \chi_{n+1} & \text{if } \xi_n \geqq 1 \\ \chi_{n+1} + \theta^*_{n+1} & \text{if } \xi_n = 0 \end{cases}$$

where ξ_n is the queue size immediately after the nth departure, χ_{n+1} is the service time of the $n + 1$st customer, $\theta_{n+1}^* = [\tau_{n+1} - \tau_n']^+$. The $\{\chi_n\}$ and $\{\theta_n^*\}$ are independent sequences of identically distributed, independent random variables with distribution functions $\mathbf{P}\{\chi_n \leq x\} = H(x)$ and $\mathbf{P}\{\theta_n^* \leq x\} = F(x) = 1 - e^{-\lambda x}$ if $x \geq 0$. Then we have $\mathbf{P}\{\tau_{n+1}' - \tau_n' \leq x\} = [1 - \mathbf{P}\{\xi_n = 0\}]H(x) + \mathbf{P}\{\xi_n = 0\}H(x) * F(x)$. If $\lambda\alpha < 1$ then

$$\lim_{n \to \infty} \mathbf{P}\{\xi_n = 0\} = 1 - \lambda\alpha,$$

whence

(98) $$\lim_{n \to \infty} \mathbf{P}\{\tau_{n+1}' - \tau_n' \leq x\} = \lambda\alpha H(x) + (1 - \lambda\alpha)H(x) * F(x)$$

and

$$\lim_{n \to \infty} \mathbf{E}\{\tau_{n+1}' - \tau_n'\} = \frac{1}{\lambda}.$$

The Laplace-Stieltjes transform of the limiting distribution (98) is

$$\psi(s) \frac{\lambda(1 + \alpha s)}{(\lambda + s)}.$$

The distribution function (98) is an exponential distribution if and only if

$$H(x) = 1 - e^{-x/\alpha}$$

if $x \geq 0$.

Problems for solution

PROBLEM 5. Find the limiting distribution $\lim_{n \to \infty} \mathbf{P}\{\xi_n = k\}$ $(k = 0, 1, \ldots)$. Consider the particular cases $\chi_n \equiv \alpha$ and $\mathbf{P}\{\chi_n \leq x\} = 1 - e^{-x/\alpha}$ if $x \geq 0$.

PROBLEM 6. Find the stationary distribution of the stochastic sequence $\{\eta_n\}$. Consider the particular cases $\chi_n \equiv \alpha$ and $\mathbf{P}\{\chi_n \leq x\} = H(x) = 1 - e^{-x/\alpha}$ if $x \geq 0$.

PROBLEM 7. Find $\tilde{G}_n(x)$ the probability that the busy period consists in serving n customers and its length is at most x. Consider the particular case $\chi_n \equiv \alpha$.

4. The time dependence of single server queues with Poisson input and general service times in the case of batch service

Let us suppose that customers arrive at a counter at the instants $\tau_1, \tau_2, \ldots, \tau_n, \ldots$ where the inter-arrival times $\tau_n - \tau_{n-1}$ $(n = 1, 2, \ldots; \tau_0 = 0)$ are identically distributed, independent random variables with distribution function

$$(1) \qquad F(x) = \begin{cases} 1 - e^{-\lambda x} & \text{if } x \geqq 0, \\ 0 & \text{if } x < 0, \end{cases}$$

i.e. $\{\tau_n\}$ is a Poisson process. The customers will be served by a single server in batches of size m in the order of their arrival. The server is idle if and only if fewer than m customers are present. Denote by χ_n the service time of the nth batch. The service times χ_n $(n = 1, 2, \ldots)$ are identically distributed, independent, positive random variables with distribution function

$$(2) \qquad \mathbf{P}\{\chi_n \leqq x\} = H(x)$$

and independent of $\{\tau_n\}$.

Denote by $\eta(t)$ the occupation time of the server at the instant t, that is, $\eta(t)$ is the time which elapses from t until the server becomes idle for the first time if no customers join the queue after time t. $\eta(0)$ is the initial occupation time of the server.

Denote by $\xi(t)$ the queue size at the instant t, i.e. $\xi(t)$ is the number of customers waiting or being served at the instant t. We say that the system is in state E_k at the instant t if $\xi(t) = k$. $\xi(0)$ is the initial queue size.

Let us denote by $\tau_1', \tau_2', \ldots, \tau_n', \ldots$ the instants of the successive departures and define $\xi_n = \xi(\tau_n' + 0)$ $(n = 1, 2, \ldots)$, i.e. ξ_n is the queue size immediately after the nth departure. If there is a departure at $t = 0$ then we write $\tau_0' = 0$ and $\xi_0 = \xi(+0)$.

Denote by η_n $(n = 1, 2, \ldots)$ the waiting time of the customer arriving last among those who are served in the nth batch.

Finally, denote by $\tilde{G}_n(x)$ the probability that the busy period consists of n services and its length is at most x.

The Laplace-Stieltjes transform of the distribution function of the service time is denoted by

$$\psi(s) = \int_0^\infty e^{-sx} \, dH(x)$$

which is convergent if $\Re(s) \geqq 0$. The average service time is

$$\alpha = \int_0^\infty x \, dH(x).$$

In the following we shall determine the stochastic behavior of the waiting time, the queue size, and the busy period.

LEMMA 1. *If* (a) $\Re(s) \geqq 0$, $|w| < 1$ *or* (b) $\Re(s) > 0$, $|w| \leqq 1$ *or* (c) $\lambda\alpha > m$ *and* $\Re(s) \geqq 0$, $|w| \leqq 1$ *then the equation*

(1) $$z^m = w\psi(s + \lambda(1 - z))$$

has exactly m roots $z = \gamma_r(s, w)$ $(r = 1, 2, \ldots, m)$ in the unit circle $|z| < 1$. We have

(2) $$\gamma_r(s, w) = \sum_{j=1}^\infty \frac{(-\lambda)^{j-1}(\epsilon_r w^{1/m})^j}{j!} \left(\frac{d^{j-1}[\psi(\lambda + s)]^{j/m}}{ds^{j-1}} \right)$$

where $\epsilon_r = e^{2\pi i r/m}$ $(r = 1, 2, \ldots, m)$ are the mth roots of unity.

If $\gamma_r(s, w)$ is defined by (2) *for $\Re(s) \geqq 0$ and $|w| \leqq 1$, then in this domain $\gamma_r(s, w)$ is a continuous function of s and w, $|\gamma(s, w)| \leqq 1$ and $z = \gamma_r(s, w)$ satisfies the equation*

(3) $$z = \epsilon_r[w\psi(s + \lambda(1 - z))]^{1/m}.$$

The roots $\gamma_r(s, w)$ $(r = 1, 2, \ldots, m)$ are distinct if $w \neq 0$.

PROOF. In cases (a) and (b) we have $|w\psi(s + \lambda(1 - z))| < (1 - \epsilon)^m$ if $|z| = 1 - \epsilon$ and ϵ is a sufficiently small positive number. In case (c) we have $\psi(\lambda\epsilon) < (1 - \epsilon)^m$ if ϵ is a sufficiently small positive number. For, if $0 \leqq \epsilon \leqq 1$ then $\psi(\lambda\epsilon)$ and $(1 - \epsilon)^m$ are monotone decreasing functions of ϵ, they agree at $\epsilon = 0$, and their right-hand derivatives at $\epsilon = 0$ are $-\lambda\alpha$ and $-m$ respectively. Hence $|w\psi(s + \lambda(1 - z))| \leqq \psi(\lambda\epsilon) < (1 - \epsilon)^m$ if $|z| = 1 - \epsilon$ and ϵ is small enough. That is, in each of the three cases $|w\psi(s + \lambda(1 - z))| < (1 - \epsilon)^m$ if $|z| = 1 - \epsilon$ and $\epsilon > 0$ is small enough. Thus it follows by Rouché's theorem (cf. Appendix) that (1) has exactly m roots

$z = \gamma_r(s, w)$ $(r = 1, 2, \ldots, m)$ in the circle $|z| < 1 - \epsilon$ or

$$z = \epsilon_r[w\psi(s + \lambda(1 - z))]^{1/m} \qquad (r = 1, 2, \ldots, m)$$

has exactly one root $z = \gamma_r(s, w)$ in the circle $|z| < 1 - \epsilon$. The explicit form (2) of $\gamma_r(s, w)$ can be obtained by Lagrange's expansion (cf. Appendix). Accordingly, each $\gamma_r(s, w)$ $(r = 1, 2, \ldots, m)$ is the only root in z of the equation (3) in the unit circle. Note that the roots $\gamma_r(s, w)$ $(r = 1, 2, \ldots, m)$ are continuous functions of s and w and they can be defined also in case $\lambda\alpha \leqq m$ for $\Re(s) \geqq 0$ and $|w| \leqq 1$ without changing (2). We have always $|\gamma_r(s, w)| \leqq 1$ $(r = 1, 2, \ldots, m)$ if $\Re(s) \geqq 0$ and $|w| \leqq 1$. The equation (1) has at most one root (possibly multiple) on the unit circle $|z| = 1$, namely $z = 1$ is a root if $w\psi(s) = 1$. Note also that $\gamma_r(s, w) = 0$ if and only if $w = 0$. If $w \neq 0$ then the roots $\gamma_r(s, w)$ $(r = 1, 2, \ldots, m)$ are distinct. This completes the proof.

Let us introduce the following abbreviations. Let $\gamma_r(s) = \gamma_r(s, 1)$, $g_r(w) = \gamma_r(0, w)$ and $\omega_r = \gamma_r(0, 1)$ $(r = 1, 2, \ldots, m)$. They satisfy the equations $z^m = \psi(s + \lambda(1 - z))$, $z^m = w\psi(\lambda(1 - z))$ and $z^m = \psi(\lambda(1 - z))$ respectively.

LEMMA 2. *Let* $\omega_r = \gamma_r(0, 1)$ *where* $\gamma_r(s, w)$ *is defined by* (2). *If* $\lambda\alpha > m$ *then* $\omega_1, \omega_2, \ldots, \omega_m$ *are the* m *roots in* z *of the equation*

$$(4) \qquad\qquad z^m = \psi(\lambda(1 - z))$$

in the unit circle $|z| < 1$. *If* $\lambda\alpha \leqq m$ *then* $\omega_1, \omega_2, \ldots, \omega_{m-1}$ *are the* $m - 1$ *roots in* z *of* (4) *in the unit circle* $|z| < 1$ *while* $\omega_m = 1$.

PROOF. If $\lambda\alpha > m$ then by Lemma 1 we have $|\omega_r| < 1$ $(r = 1, 2, \ldots, m)$. If $\lambda\alpha \leqq m$ then it follows from (3) that $|\omega_r| < 1$ if $r = 1, 2, \ldots, m - 1$ and a probabilistic argument shows that $\omega_m = 1$ (cf. Remark 3 and Remark 4).

If $\omega_m = 1$ then using (1) we get

$$(5) \qquad \gamma'_m(0) = \begin{cases} \alpha/(\lambda\alpha - m) & \text{if } \lambda\alpha < m, \\ \infty & \text{if } \lambda\alpha = m, \end{cases}$$

and

$$(6) \qquad g'_m(1) = \begin{cases} 1/(m - \lambda\alpha) & \text{if } \lambda\alpha < m, \\ \infty & \text{if } \lambda\alpha = m. \end{cases}$$

REMARK 1. The functions

(7) $\zeta_r(s, w) = s + \lambda[1 - \gamma_r(s, w)]$ $(r = 1, 2, \ldots, m)$

satisfy in ζ the equation

(8) $$\left(\frac{\lambda + s - \zeta}{\lambda}\right)^m = w\psi(\zeta)$$

if $\Re(s) \geqq 0$ and $|w| \leqq 1$. Conversely in cases (a), (b), and (c) it follows by Rouché's theorem that (8) has exactly m roots in the domain $\Re(\zeta) > 0$ or

$$\zeta = (\lambda + s) - \epsilon_r\lambda[w\psi(\zeta)]^{1/m} \qquad (r = 1, 2, \ldots, m)$$

has exactly one root $\zeta = \zeta_r(s, w)$ in the domain $\Re(s) > 0$. For,

$$|w\psi(\zeta)| < \left|\left(\frac{\lambda + s - \zeta}{\lambda}\right)^m\right|$$

if $\Re(\zeta) = \epsilon > 0$ and ϵ is small enough or $\Re(\zeta) \geqq \epsilon$ where ϵ is a sufficiently small positive number and $|\zeta|$ is large enough.

Let us write $\zeta_r(s) = \zeta_r(s, 1) = s + \lambda[1 - \gamma_r(s)]$. Clearly $\zeta_r(0) = \lambda(1 - \omega_r)$.

Finally, we remark that by forming the Lagrange expansion of $[\gamma_r(s, w)]^n$ $(r = 1, 2, \ldots, m)$ we can prove the following formula

(9) $$\sum_{r=1}^m [\gamma_r(s, w)]^n = n \sum_{j \geqq n/m} \frac{w^j \lambda^{mj-n}}{j(mj - n)!} \int_0^\infty e^{-(\lambda+s)x} x^{mj-n} \, dH_j(x),$$

where $H_j(x)$ denotes the jth iterated convolution of $H(x)$ with itself. By using this formula we can obtain explicit formulas for the probabilities considered in this section.

THE TRANSIENT BEHAVIOR OF THE PROCESS $\{\eta(t)\}$. The process $\{\eta(t)\}$ can be described as follows. The $\eta(0)$ is the initial occupation time of the server and $\eta(t)$ decreases linearly with slope -1 until it jumps or reaches 0. The jumps occur at the arrivals of every mth customer and their magnitude is the service time of the corresponding batch. If $\eta(t)$ reaches 0 then it remains 0 until the queue size increases to m. The process $\{\eta(t)\}$ in itself is not a Markov process, but if we introduce in addition another random variable defining the queue size modulo m, then the process will be a Markovian one. Accordingly we shall define the random variables $\nu(t)$ $(0 \leq t < \infty)$ as follows: $\nu(t)$ assumes only the values $1, 2, \ldots, m$ and $\xi(t) \equiv \nu(t) - 1$ (mod. m). Then the vector process $\{\eta(t), \nu(t)\}$ will be a Markov process, for which we can apply standard methods.

Let us introduce the following notation. The distribution function of the occupation time is denoted by

$$W(t, x) = \mathbf{P}\{\eta(t) \leq x\},$$

and its Laplace-Stieltjes transform by

$$\Omega(t, s) = \mathbf{E}\{e^{-s\eta(t)}\} = \int_0^\infty e^{-sx} d_x W(t, x)$$

for $\Re(s) \geq 0$. Furthermore let

$$W_j(t, x) = \mathbf{P}\{\eta(t) \leq x, \nu(t) = j\} \qquad (j = 1, 2, \ldots, m)$$

and

$$\Omega_j(t, s) = \int_0^\infty e^{-sx} d_x W_j(t, x) \qquad (j = 1, 2, \ldots, m).$$

Thus

$$W(t, x) = \sum_{j=1}^m W_j(t, x)$$

and

$$\Omega(t, s) = \sum_{j=1}^m \Omega_j(t, s).$$

Write $\hat{\Omega}(s) = \Omega(0, s)$ and $\hat{\Omega}_j(s) = \Omega_j(0, s)$ $(j = 1, 2, \ldots, m)$ and introduce the generating function

$$R(s, z) = \sum_{j=1}^m \hat{\Omega}_j(s) z^j,$$

which is determined by the initial condition. The probability distribution of the queue size is denoted by

$$P_j(t) = \mathbf{P}\{\xi(t) = j\} \qquad (j = 0, 1, 2, \ldots)$$

and its Laplace transform by

$$\Pi_j(s) = \int_0^\infty e^{-st} P_j(t) \, dt$$

for $\Re(s) > 0$. Obviously

$$W_j(t, 0) = P_{j-1}(t) \qquad (j = 1, 2, \ldots, m)$$

because $\mathbf{P}\{\eta(t) = 0, \nu(t) = j\} = \mathbf{P}\{\xi(t) = j - 1\}$ if $j = 1, 2, \ldots, m$.
Finally, for $|z| \leq 1$ let us introduce the generating functions

(10) $$P(t, z) = \sum_{j=0}^{m-1} P_j(t)z^j$$

and

(11) $$\Pi(s, z) = \sum_{j=0}^{m-1} \Pi_j(s)z^j.$$

We shall prove

THEOREM 1. *The Laplace-Stieltjes transform of the distribution function of the occupation time,*

(12) $$\Omega(t, \varsigma) = \mathbf{E}\{e^{-\varsigma\eta(t)}\} = \int_0^\infty e^{-\varsigma x}\, d_x W(t, x),$$

is given by

(13) $$\Omega(t, \varsigma) = \frac{[1 - \psi(\varsigma)]}{m\psi(\varsigma)} \sum_{j=1}^m \frac{\epsilon_j[\psi(\varsigma)]^{1/m}}{1 - \epsilon_j[\psi(\varsigma)]^{1/m}}$$

$$\cdot \, [e^{s_j t}R(\varsigma, \epsilon_j[\psi(\varsigma)]^{1/m}) - \varsigma\int_0^t e^{s_j(t-u)}P(u, \epsilon_j[\psi(\varsigma)]^{1/m})\, du],$$

where

(14) $$s_j = \varsigma - \lambda + \lambda\epsilon_j[\psi(\varsigma)]^{1/m}$$

and $\epsilon_j = e^{2\pi ij/m}$ $(j = 1, 2, \ldots, m)$. If $\Re(s) > 0$ and $|z| \leq 1$ then the Laplace transform of $P(t, z)$ is

(15) $$\Pi(s, z) = \int_0^\infty e^{-st}P(t, z)\, dt$$

$$= \sum_{j=1}^m \frac{R(s + \lambda[1 - \gamma_j(s)], \gamma_j(s))}{s + \lambda[1 - \gamma_j(s)]} \prod_{r \neq j} \left(\frac{z - \gamma_r(s)}{\gamma_j(s) - \gamma_r(s)}\right)$$

where $z = \gamma_r(s)$ $(r = 1, 2, \ldots, m)$ are the m roots in z of the equation

(16) $$z^m = \psi(s + \lambda(1 - z))$$

in the unit circle $|z| < 1$.

PROOF. A simple argument shows that

$$W_1(t + \Delta t, x) \,|$$
$$= (1 - \lambda \, \Delta t) W_1(t, x + \Delta t) + \lambda \, \Delta t \int_0^x H(x - y) \, d_y W_m(t, y) + o(\Delta t)$$

and for $j = 2, 3, \ldots, m$

$$W_j(t + \Delta t, x) = (1 - \lambda \, \Delta t) W_j(t, x + \Delta t) + \lambda \, \Delta t \, W_{j-1}(t, x) + o(\Delta t).$$

For almost all t and x we have

$$W_j(t + \Delta t, x) = W_j(t, x) + \frac{\partial W_j(t, x)}{\partial t} \Delta t + o(\Delta t)$$

and

$$W_j(t, x + \Delta t) = W_j(t, x) + \frac{\partial W_j(t, x)}{\partial x} \Delta t + o(\Delta t),$$

and hence we get

(17) $$\frac{\partial W_1(t, x)}{\partial t} = \frac{\partial W_1(t, x)}{\partial x} - \lambda W_1(t, x) + \lambda \int_0^x H(x - y) \, d_y W_m(t, y)$$

and for $j = 2, 3, \ldots, m$

(18) $$\frac{\partial W_j(t, x)}{\partial t} = \frac{\partial W_j(t, x)}{\partial x} - \lambda W_j(t, x) + \lambda W_{j-1}(t, x).$$

These equations hold for almost all t and x. Forming the Laplace-Stieltjes transforms of (17) and (18) we get for $\Re(\zeta) > 0$ that

(19) $$\frac{\partial \Omega_1(t, \zeta)}{\partial t} = (\zeta - \lambda)\Omega_1(t, \zeta) + \lambda\psi(\zeta)\Omega_m(t, \zeta) - \zeta P_0(t)$$

and for $j = 2, 3, \ldots, m$

(20) $$\frac{\partial \Omega_j(t, \zeta)}{\partial t} = (\zeta - \lambda)\Omega_j(t, \zeta) + \lambda\Omega_{j-1}(t, \zeta) - \zeta P_{j-1}(t).$$

Now let us introduce the following matrix notation

$$
\mathbf{A} = \left\|
\begin{array}{ccccc}
(\zeta - \lambda) & 0 & \cdots & 0 & \lambda\psi(\zeta) \\
\lambda & (\zeta - \lambda) & \cdots & 0 & 0 \\
\cdot & \cdot & \cdots & \cdot & \cdot \\
0 & 0 & \cdots & \lambda & (\zeta - \lambda)
\end{array}
\right\|
$$

and

$$
\Omega(t, \zeta) = \left\|
\begin{array}{c}
\Omega_1(t, \zeta) \\
\Omega_2(t, \zeta) \\
\cdot \\
\cdot \\
\cdot \\
\Omega_m(t, \zeta)
\end{array}
\right\|, \qquad
\mathbf{P}(t) = \left\|
\begin{array}{c}
P_0(t) \\
P_1(t) \\
\cdot \\
\cdot \\
\cdot \\
P_{m-1}(t)
\end{array}
\right\|.
$$

Combining (19) and (20) we get the following matrix differential equation

$$
(21) \qquad \frac{\partial\Omega(t, \zeta)}{\partial\zeta} = \mathbf{A}\Omega(t, \zeta) - \zeta\mathbf{P}(t),
$$

the solution of which is

$$
(22) \qquad \Omega(t, \zeta) = e^{\mathbf{A}t}\hat{\Omega}(\zeta) - \zeta\int_0^t e^{\mathbf{A}(t-u)}\mathbf{P}(u)\, du,
$$

where

$$
\hat{\Omega}(\zeta) = \Omega(0, \zeta)
$$

is determined by the initial condition and $\mathbf{P}(t)$ is yet to be determined.

$\mathbf{P}(t)$ can be obtained by the requirement that

$$
\int_0^\infty e^{-st}\Omega(t, \zeta)\, dt
$$

is a regular vector function of ζ if $\Re(\zeta) > 0$ and $\Re(s) > 0$. Forming the Laplace transform of (22) we obtain

$$
(23) \qquad \int_0^\infty e^{-st}\Omega(t, \zeta)\, dt = [\mathbf{A} - s\mathbf{I}]^{-1}\left[\hat{\Omega}(\zeta) - \zeta\int_0^\infty e^{-st}\mathbf{P}(t)\, dt\right],
$$

where $\mathbf{I}$ is the $(m \times m)$ unit matrix. To determine the components of (23), express $\mathbf{A}$ in canonical form. The characteristic equation of $\mathbf{A}$ is

$$
|\mathbf{A} - s\mathbf{I}| = (\zeta - \lambda - s)^m - (-1)^m\lambda^m\psi(\zeta) = 0,
$$

and hence the proper values of $\mathbf{A}$ are

$$s_j = s_j(\zeta) = \zeta - \lambda + \lambda \epsilon_j [\psi(\zeta)]^{1/m} \qquad (j = 1, 2, \ldots, m)$$

where $\epsilon_j = e^{2\pi i j/m}$ $(j = 1, 2, \ldots, m)$ are the mth roots of unity. A simple calculation shows that

(24) $$\mathbf{A} = \| \alpha_{ij} \| \Lambda \| \beta_{jk} \|,$$

where Λ is the diagonal matrix $[s_1, s_2, \ldots, s_m]$ and $\| \alpha_{ij} \|$ and $\| \beta_{jk} \|$ are inverse matrices for which

$$\alpha_{ij} = \left(\frac{\lambda}{\lambda + s_j - \zeta} \right)^i$$

and

$$\beta_{jk} = \frac{1}{m} \left(\frac{\lambda + s_j - \zeta}{\lambda} \right)^k.$$

Thus

$$[\mathbf{A} - s\mathbf{I}]^{-1} = \| \alpha_{ij} \| [\Lambda - s\mathbf{I}]^{-1} \| \beta_{jk} \| = \| \gamma_{ij} \|,$$

where

$$\gamma_{ik} = \sum_{j=1}^{m} \frac{\alpha_{ij} \beta_{jk}}{s_j - s} = \frac{1}{m} \sum_{j=1}^{m} \left(\frac{\lambda + s_j - \zeta}{\lambda} \right)^{k-i} \frac{1}{(s_j - s)}.$$

Finally by (23) we get for $i = 1, 2, \ldots, m$

(25) $$\int_0^\infty e^{-st} \Omega_i(t, \zeta) \, dt = \sum_{k=1}^{m} \gamma_{ik} [\hat{\Omega}_k(\zeta) - \zeta \Pi_{k-1}(s)]$$

$$= \frac{1}{m} \sum_{k=1}^{m} \sum_{j=1}^{m} \left(\frac{\lambda + s_j - \zeta}{\lambda} \right)^{k-i} \frac{[\hat{\Omega}_k(\zeta) - \zeta \Pi_{k-1}(s)]}{(s_j - s)}$$

$$= \frac{1}{m} \sum_{j=1}^{m} \left(\frac{\lambda + s_j - \zeta}{\lambda} \right)^{i-1}$$

$$\cdot \frac{\left[R \left(\zeta, \frac{\lambda + s_j - \zeta}{\lambda} \right) - \zeta \Pi \left(s, \frac{\lambda + s_j - \zeta}{\lambda} \right) \right]}{(s_j - s)}.$$

The Laplace-Stieltjes transform (25) is a regular function of ζ if $\Re(\zeta) > 0$ and $\Re(s) > 0$. If $\zeta = \zeta_j(s)$ $(j = 1, 2, \ldots, m)$ is that root in ζ of the equation

$$\left(\frac{\lambda + s - \zeta}{\lambda}\right)^m = \psi(\zeta),$$

for which

$$\lambda + s - \zeta_j(s) = \lambda\epsilon_j[\psi(\zeta_j(s))]^{1/m};$$

then by (14) $s_j(\zeta_j(s)) = s$ and $s_r(\zeta_j(s)) \neq s$ if $r \neq j$. Therefore the co-efficient of $1/(s_j - s)$ on the right-hand side of (25) must vanish if $\zeta = \zeta_j(s) = s + \lambda[1 - \gamma_j(s)]$, that is,

$$(26) \quad s + \lambda[1 - \gamma_j(s)]\Pi(s, \gamma_j(s)) = R(s + \lambda[1 - \gamma_j(s)], \gamma_j(s))$$

when $j = 1, 2, \ldots, m$. The function $\Pi(s, z)$ in z is a polynomial of degree $m - 1$ and by using the Lagrange interpolation formula we obtain from (26) that

$$(27) \quad \Pi(s, z) = \sum_{j=1}^{m} \frac{R(s + \lambda[1 - \gamma_j(s)], \gamma_j(s))}{s + \lambda[1 - \gamma_j(s)]} \prod_{r \neq j} \left(\frac{z - \gamma_r(s)}{\gamma_j(s) - \gamma_r(s)}\right).$$

This proves (15). Using the representation (24) we obtain from (22) that

$$(28) \quad \Omega_i(t, \zeta) = \frac{1}{m} \sum_{i=1}^{m} \sum_{k=1}^{m} \left(\frac{\lambda + s_j - \zeta}{\lambda}\right)^{k-i}$$

$$\cdot [e^{s_j t}\hat{\Omega}_k(\zeta) - \zeta \int_0^t e^{s_j(t-u)} P_{k-1}(u) \, du],$$

and finally (13) can be obtained by $\Omega(t, s) = \sum_{j=1}^{m} \Omega_j(t, s)$. This completes the proof of the theorem.

By (25) it follows also that

$$\int_0^\infty e^{-st}\Omega(t, \zeta) \, dt = \frac{\lambda[1 - \psi(\zeta)]}{m\psi(\zeta)} \sum_{j=1}^{m} \frac{\epsilon_j[\psi(\zeta)]^{1/m}}{(\zeta - s_j)(s - s_j)}$$

$$\cdot [R(\zeta, \epsilon_j[\psi(\zeta)]^{1/m}) - \zeta\Pi(s, \epsilon_j[\psi(\zeta)]^{1/m})],$$

where s_j is defined by (14) and $\Pi(s, z)$ is given by (15).

REMARK 2. If we suppose that $\xi(0) = 0$ then $\eta(0) = 0$ and $R(s, z) = 1$. In this case

$$(29) \quad \Pi(s, z) = \frac{1}{s + \lambda(1 - z)} \left\{ 1 - \prod_{j=1}^{m} \left(\frac{\lambda[z - \gamma_j(s)]}{s + \lambda[1 - \gamma_j(s)]} \right) \right\}.$$

This follows immediately from (26). Now we have

$$[s + \lambda(1 - z)]\Pi(s, z) - 1 = C(s) \prod_{j=1}^{m} [z - \gamma_j(s)],$$

because the left-hand side vanishes if $z = \gamma_j(s)$ $(j = 1, 2, \ldots, m)$. The constant $C(s)$ can be obtained by the substitution $z = (\lambda + s)/\lambda$.

If specifically there is a departure at $t = 0$ and $\xi(+0) = m$ then $\mathbf{P}\{\eta(0) \leq x\} = H(x)$ and $R(s, z) = \psi(s)$. In this case

$$(30) \quad \Pi(s, z) = \frac{1}{s + \lambda(1 - z)} \left[z^m - \prod_{j=1}^{m} \left[\frac{z - \gamma_j(s)}{1 - \dfrac{\lambda}{\lambda + s} \gamma_j(s)} \right] \right].$$

THE PROBABILITY THAT THE SERVER IS IDLE. First of all we shall prove the following auxiliary theorem which we shall need in the sequel.

LEMMA 3. *The limit* $\lim_{t \to \infty} P_j(t) = P_j^*$ $(j = 0, 1, 2, \ldots)$ *always exists and is independent of the initial state.*

PROOF. Denote by $M_j(t)$ $(j = 0, 1, \ldots)$ the expectation of the number of transitions $E_j \to E_{j+1}$ occurring in the time interval $(0, t]$ and denote by $N_j(t)$ $(j = 0, 1, \ldots)$ the expectation of the number of transitions $E_{j+m} \to E_j$ occurring in the time interval $(0, t]$. By the theorem of total probability we can write for $k = 0, 1, \ldots, m - 1$ that

$$(31) \quad P_k(t) = P_k(0)e^{-\lambda t}$$
$$+ \int_0^t e^{-\lambda(t-u)} \, dN_k(u) + \int_0^t e^{-\lambda(t-u)} \, dM_{k-1}(u),$$

where the last term on the right-hand side is zero if $k = 0$, and for $k = m + 1, m + 2, \ldots$ that

$$(32) \quad P_k(t) = \sum_{j=m}^{k} q_j(t) e^{-\lambda t} \frac{(\lambda t)^{k-j}}{(k - j)!}$$

$$+ \sum_{j=m}^{k} \int_0^t [1 - H(t - u)] e^{-\lambda(t-u)} \frac{[\lambda(t - u)]^{k-j}}{(k - j)!} dN_j(u)$$

$$+ \int_0^t [1 - H(t - u)] e^{-\lambda(t-u)} \frac{[\lambda(t - u)]^{k-m}}{(k - m)!} dM_{m-1}(u),$$

where $q_j(t)$ is the probability that the initial queue size is j and there is no departure in the time interval $(0, t]$.

In proving (31) we take into consideration that the event $\xi(t) = k$ ($k < m$) can occur in the following mutually exclusive ways: the initial state is E_k and there is no arrival in the time interval $(0, t]$, or at the instant u (where $0 \leq u \leq t$) there occurs a transition $E_{k+m} \to E_k$ or $E_{k-1} \to E_k$ (if $k > 0$) and there is no arrival in the time interval $(u, t]$. Finally we get (31) if we keep in mind that the transition $E_{k+m} \to E_k$ and $E_{k-1} \to E_k$ may be the nth ($n = 1, 2, \ldots$) departure or arrival respectively. Similarly in proving (32) we take into consideration that the event $\xi(t) = k$ ($k \geq m$) can occur in the following mutually exclusive ways: the initial state is E_j ($j = m, \ldots, k$) and in the time interval $(0, t]$ there is no departure and $k - j$ customers arrive, or at the instant u (where $0 \leq u \leq t$) there occurs a transition $E_{j+m} \to E_j$ ($j = m, m + 1, \ldots, k$) or a transition $E_{m-1} \to E_m$, and the service starting at this instant u does not end in the time interval $(u, t]$, and during this time interval $(u, t]$ respectively $k - j$ ($j = m, m + 1, \ldots, k$) or $k - m$ customers arrive. Finally we get (32) if we keep in mind that the transition $E_{j+m} \to E_j$ and $E_{m-1} \to E_m$ may be the nth ($n = 1, 2, \ldots$) departure or arrival respectively.

The transitions $E_{m+j} \to E_j$ ($j = 0, 1, 2, \ldots$) and similarly the transitions $E_j \to E_{j+1}$ ($j = 0, 1, \ldots, m - 1$) form a recurrent process. The distances between successive transitions are identically distributed, independent random variables having non-lattice distributions. Therefore by *Blackwell*'s theorem (cf. Appendix) it follows that the following limits exist for every $h > 0$ and agree with the respective right-hand sides

(33) $\displaystyle\lim_{t\to\infty} \frac{N_j(t + h) - N_j(t)}{h} = \lim_{t\to\infty} \frac{N_j(t)}{t}$ $(j = 0, 1, 2, \ldots)$

and

(34) $\displaystyle\lim_{t\to\infty} \frac{M_j(t + h) - M_j(t)}{h} = \lim_{t\to\infty} \frac{M_j(t)}{t}$ $(j = 0, 1, \ldots, m - 1)$.

Furthermore these limits are independent of the initial condition.

By using the fundamental theorem of recurrent processes (cf. Appendix), we obtain from (31), (32), (33), and (34) that the limit $\lim_{t\to\infty} P_j(t) = P_j^*$ $(j = 0, 1, 2, \ldots)$ always exists irrespective of the initial state.

Specifically we have for $k = 0, 1, \ldots, m - 1$

(35) $$P_k^* = \frac{1}{\lambda} (N_k + M_{k-1})$$

and for $k = m, m + 1, \ldots$

(36) $\displaystyle P_k^* = \sum_{j=m}^{k} N_j \int_0^\infty [1 - H(x)]e^{-\lambda x} \frac{(\lambda x)^{k-j}}{(k - j)!} \, dx$

$$+ M_{m-1} \int_0^\infty [1 - H(x)]e^{-\lambda x} \frac{(\lambda x)^{k-m}}{(k - m)!} \, dx,$$

where $M_{-1} = 0$,

$$N_j = \lim_{t\to\infty} \frac{N_j(t)}{t} \quad \text{and} \quad M_j = \lim_{t\to\infty} \frac{M_j(t)}{t}.$$

Now let us denote by $Q(t)$ the probability that the server is idle at the instant t. Clearly

$$Q(t) = \sum_{j=0}^{m-1} P_j(t).$$

Hence for $\Re(s) > 0$

$$\int_0^\infty e^{-st}Q(t) \, dt = \sum_{j=0}^{m-1} \Pi_j(s) = \Pi(s, 1),$$

where $\Pi(s, z)$ is given by (15).

If specifically $\xi(0) = 0$ then by (29)

$$\int_0^\infty e^{-st}Q(t) \, dt = \frac{1}{s} \left\{ 1 - \prod_{j=1}^{m} \left(\frac{\lambda[1 - \gamma_j(s)]}{s + \lambda[1 - \gamma_j(s)]} \right) \right\}.$$

THEOREM 2. *If $\lambda\alpha < m$ then*

(37)
$$\lim_{t\to\infty} Q(t) = 1 - \frac{\lambda\alpha}{m},$$

and if $\lambda\alpha \geqq m$ then

(38)
$$\lim_{t\to\infty} Q(t) = 0$$

irrespective of the initial condition.

PROOF. Referring to Lemma 3 it is sufficient to restrict ourselves to the case when initially the server is idle. Let us denote by ρ the expected number of services in a busy period (possibly $\rho = \infty$). The starting points of the busy periods agree with the transitions $E_{m-1} \to E_m$. It is easy to see that the expectation of the distance between two successive transitions $E_{m-1} \to E_m$ is $m\rho/\lambda$. Hence by *Blackwell*'s theorem it follows that for every $h > 0$

(39)
$$\lim_{t\to\infty} \frac{M_{m-1}(t + h) - M_{m-1}(t)}{h} = \lim_{t\to\infty} \frac{M_{m-1}(t)}{t} = \frac{\lambda}{m\rho}$$

irrespective of the initial state. We note that $\rho < \infty$ when $\lambda\alpha < m$ and $\rho = \infty$ if $\lambda\alpha \geqq m$. This can be seen as follows. If a busy period terminates, not more than m customers may arrive before the beginning of the next one. Consequently we have the inequality

$$\rho\alpha < \rho\frac{m}{\lambda} \leqq \rho\alpha + \frac{m}{\lambda},$$

whence $\rho \leqq 1/(1 - \lambda\alpha/m)$ if $\lambda\alpha < m$ and $\rho = \infty$ if $\lambda\alpha \geqq m$.

If $G(x)$ denotes the distribution function of the length of the busy period, then we can write that

(40)
$$Q(t) = 1 - \int_0^t [1 - G(t - u)]\, dM_{m-1}(u).$$

If $\rho < \infty$ then obviously

(41)
$$\int_0^\infty [1 - G(x)]\, dx = \rho\alpha$$

and using (39) we obtain from (40) that

$$(42) \qquad \lim_{t\to\infty} Q(t) = 1 - \frac{\lambda\alpha}{m},$$

irrespective of ρ.

Since evidently $|M_k(t) - \sum_{j=0}^{k} N_j(t)| \leq 1 \quad (k = 0, 1, \ldots, m-1)$
holds for all $t \geq 0$, we get by (39) that in case $\rho = \infty$

$$\lim_{t\to\infty} \frac{N_k(t)}{t} = \lim_{t\to\infty} \frac{M_k(t)}{t} = 0 \qquad (k = 0, 1, 2, \ldots, m-1)$$

and by (31)

$$\lim_{t\to\infty} P_k(t) = 0 \qquad (k = 0, 1, \ldots, m-1)$$

irrespective of the initial state.   Hence

$$\lim_{t\to\infty} Q(t) = 0$$

whenever $\rho = \infty$. This completes the proof of the theorem.

REMARK 3. We have seen that $\lim_{t\to\infty} Q(t) = Q^*$ always exists
irrespective of the initial state. In this case obviously

$$\lim_{t\to\infty} \frac{1}{t} \int_0^t Q(u)\, du = Q^*$$

also holds. By a well-known Abelian theorem (cf. Appendix), we can
conclude that

$$\lim_{s\to 0} s \int_0^\infty e^{-st} Q(t)\, dt = Q^*.$$

Thus by (15) we get

$$(43) \qquad Q^* = \lim_{s\to 0} s\Pi(s, 1) = 1 - \lim_{s\to 0} \frac{\lambda[1 - \gamma_m(s)]}{s + \lambda[1 - \gamma_m(s)]}$$

because $|\gamma_j(0)| < 1$ if $j = 1, 2, \ldots, m-1$. If now $|\gamma_m(0)| < 1$ then
$Q^* = 0$. If $\gamma_m(0) = 1$ and $\lambda\alpha \leq m$ then by (43) we get

$$Q^* = \frac{1}{1 - \lambda\gamma_m'(0)} = 1 - \frac{\lambda\alpha}{m}.$$

Since we know that $Q^* = 1 - \dfrac{\lambda\alpha}{m}$ if $\lambda\alpha < m$, therefore $\gamma_m(0) = 1$ must hold if $\lambda\alpha < m$.

Finally we prove

THEOREM 3. *If* $\lambda\alpha \geqq m$ *then* $P_k^* = 0$ $(k = 0, 1, \ldots, m - 1)$, *and if* $\lambda\alpha < m$ *then*

$$(44) \qquad \Pi^*(z) = \sum_{k=0}^{m-1} P_k^* z^k = \left(1 - \frac{\lambda\alpha}{m}\right) \prod_{j=1}^{m-1} \left(\frac{z - \omega_j}{1 - \omega_j}\right).$$

PROOF. If $\lambda\alpha \geqq m$ then $\rho = \infty$ and by the preceding $P_k^* = 0$ $(k = 0, 1, \ldots, m - 1)$. If $\lambda\alpha < m$ then, P_k^* being independent of the initial state, we get by (15) that

$$\sum_{k=0}^{m-1} P_k^* z^k = \lim_{s \to 0} s\Pi(s, z) = \left(1 - \frac{\lambda\alpha}{m}\right) \prod_{j=1}^{m-1} \left(\frac{z - \omega_j}{1 - \omega_j}\right),$$

which proves (44).

THE ASYMPTOTIC BEHAVIOR OF THE PROCESS $\{\eta(t)\}$. If $t \to \infty$ then the stochastic behavior of the process $\{\eta(t)\}$ is given by

THEOREM 4. *If* $\lambda\alpha < m$ *then the limiting distribution* $\lim\limits_{t \to \infty} W(t, x) = W^*(x)$ *exists irrespective of the initial distribution. The Laplace-Stieltjes transform of* $W^*(x)$ *is given by*

$$(45) \quad \Omega^*(\zeta) = \int_0^\infty e^{-\zeta x} \, dW^*(x)$$

$$= \left(1 - \frac{\lambda\alpha}{m}\right) \frac{[1 - \psi(\zeta)]}{m\psi(\zeta)} \sum_{j=1}^{m} \frac{\zeta}{\{\zeta - \lambda[1 - \epsilon_j(\psi(\zeta))^{1/m}]\}}$$

$$\cdot \frac{\epsilon_j[\psi(\zeta)]^{1/m}}{\{1 - \epsilon_j[\psi(\zeta)]^{1/m}\}} \cdot \prod_{r=1}^{m-1} \left(\frac{\epsilon_j[\psi(\zeta)]^{1/m} - \omega_r}{1 - \omega_r}\right)$$

$$= \left(1 - \frac{\lambda\alpha}{m}\right) \left\{1 - \frac{\lambda^m[1 - \psi(\zeta)]}{\lambda^m\psi(\zeta) - (\lambda - \zeta)^m}\right.$$

$$\left. \cdot \prod_{r=1}^{m-1} \left(1 - \frac{\zeta}{\lambda(1 - \omega_r)}\right)\right\}$$

where $\omega_1, \omega_2, \ldots, \omega_{m-1}$ are defined in Lemma 2. If $\lambda\alpha \geqq m$ then $\lim_{t\to\infty} W(t, x) = 0$ *for every* x.

PROOF. Let us introduce the notation

$$W_j^*(x) = \lim_{t\to\infty} W_j(t, x) \qquad (j = 1, 2, \ldots, m)$$

and

$$\Omega_j^*(\zeta) = \int_0^\infty e^{-\zeta x} dW_j^*(x);$$

then

$$W^*(x) = \sum_{j=1}^m W_j^*(x)$$

and

$$\Omega^*(\zeta) = \sum_{j=1}^m \Omega_j^*(\zeta).$$

Furthermore we shall use the following vector notation

$$\Omega^*(\zeta) = \begin{Vmatrix} \Omega_1^*(\zeta) \\ \Omega_2^*(\zeta) \\ \cdot \\ \cdot \\ \cdot \\ \Omega_m^*(\zeta) \end{Vmatrix}, \qquad \mathbf{P} = \begin{Vmatrix} P_0^* \\ P_1^* \\ \cdot \\ \cdot \\ \cdot \\ P_{m-1}^* \end{Vmatrix}.$$

Thus we have

$$\lim_{t\to\infty} \Omega(t, \zeta) = \Omega^*(\zeta).$$

First consider the case $\lambda\alpha < m$. Then $\lim_{t\to\infty} P_j(t) = P_j^* > 0$ $(j = 0, 1, \ldots, m - 1)$ exists and is independent of the initial state. If we restrict ourselves to imaginary ζ, then by (13) it can be proved that $\lim_{t\to\infty} \Omega(t, \zeta) = \Omega^*(\zeta)$ exists if $|\zeta| < a$, where a is a sufficiently small positive number, and that $\Omega^*(\zeta)$ is continuous at $\zeta = 0$. Hence it follows by a theorem of A. *Zygmund* [66] that the limit $\lim_{t\to\infty} W_j(t, x) = W_j^*(x)$ exists and further that the Laplace-Stieltjes transform of $W_j^*(x)$ is $\Omega_j^*(\zeta) = \lim_{t\to\infty} \Omega_j(t, \zeta)$ defined for $\Re(\zeta) \geqq 0$. Thus $\lim_{t\to\infty} \Omega(t, \zeta) = \Omega^*(\zeta)$ also exists and by (21) $\Omega^*(\zeta)$ has to satisfy the equation

$$\mathbf{A}\Omega^*(\zeta) = \zeta\mathbf{P}^*.$$

Since $|\mathbf{A}| \neq 0$ if $\zeta \neq 0$, this equation has one and only one solution if $\zeta \neq 0$. Using the canonical decomposition (24) of $\mathbf{A}$ we get explicitly

$$\Omega_i^*(\zeta) = \frac{\zeta}{m} \sum_{k=1}^{m} \sum_{j=1}^{m} \left(\frac{\lambda + s_j - \zeta}{\lambda}\right)^{k-i} \frac{P_{k-1}^*}{s_j}$$

$$= \frac{\zeta}{m} \sum_{j=1}^{m} \frac{1}{s_j} \left(\frac{\lambda}{\lambda + s_j - \zeta}\right)^{i-1} \Pi^*\left(\frac{\lambda + s_j - \zeta}{\lambda}\right),$$

where s_j is defined by (14) and $\Pi^*(z)$ by (44), whence for $\zeta \neq 0$

$$\Omega^*(\zeta) = \sum_{i=1}^{m} \Omega_i^*(\zeta) = \frac{\zeta[1 - \psi(\zeta)]}{m\psi(\zeta)}$$

$$\cdot \sum_{j=1}^{m} \frac{\epsilon_j[\psi(\zeta)]^{1/m}}{\{1 - \epsilon_j[\psi(\zeta)]^{1/m}\}} \frac{\Pi^*(\epsilon_j[\psi(\zeta)]^{1/m})}{\{\zeta - \lambda[1 - \epsilon_j(\psi(\zeta))^{1/m}]\}}$$

and clearly $\Omega^*(0) = 1$. This proves (45).

If $\lambda\alpha \geq m$ then $P_j^* = 0$ $(j = 0, 1, \ldots, m - 1)$ and $\lim\limits_{t\to\infty} \Omega(t, \zeta) = 0$ for $\Re(\zeta) \geq 0$, whence $\lim\limits_{t\to\infty} W_j(t, x) = 0$ $(j = 1, 2, \ldots, m)$ and $\lim\limits_{t\to\infty} W(t, x) = 0$ for every x. This completes the proof of the theorem.

THE TRANSIENT BEHAVIOR OF THE PROCESS $\{\eta_n\}$. Let us define $\theta_n = \tau_{(n+1)m} - \tau_{nm}$ $(n = 1, 2, \ldots)$; then obviously

(46) $$\eta_{n+1} = [\eta_n + \chi_n - \theta_n]^+,$$

where $[a]^+ = \max (a, 0)$. Here $\{\chi_n\}$ and $\{\theta_n\}$ are independent sequences of identically distributed, independent random variables with distribution functions $\mathbf{P}\{\chi_n \leq x\} = H(x)$ and $\mathbf{P}\{\theta_n \leq x\} = F_m(x)$, where $F_m(x)$ is the mth iterated convolution of $F(x)$ with itself, i.e.

(47) $$F_m(x) = \begin{cases} 1 - \sum_{j=0}^{m-1} e^{-\lambda x} \dfrac{(\lambda x)^j}{j!} & \text{if } x \geq 0, \\ 0 & \text{if } x < 0. \end{cases}$$

We need

LEMMA 4. *Let ξ and θ be non-negative, independent random variables for which* $\mathbf{P}\{\theta \leq x\} = F_m(x)$ *defined by* (47). *Let*

(48) $$\Phi(s) = \mathbf{E}\{e^{-s\xi}\}.$$

If $\Re(s) \geqq 0$ then we have

(49) $\mathbf{E}\{e^{-s[\xi-\theta]^+}\}$

$$
= \begin{cases}
\dfrac{\lambda^m \Phi(s) - \displaystyle\sum_{j=0}^{m-1} \dfrac{(-1)^j \Phi^{(j)}(\lambda)}{j!} [\lambda^m(\lambda - s)^j - \lambda^j(\lambda - s)^m]}{(\lambda - s)^m} & \text{if } s \neq \lambda, \\[4ex]
\displaystyle\sum_{j=0}^{m} \dfrac{(-1)^j \Phi^{(j)}(\lambda)}{j!} & \text{if } s = \lambda.
\end{cases}
$$

PROOF. We have

$$
\mathbf{E}\{e^{-s[\xi-\theta]^+} \mid \xi = x\}
$$

$$
= \sum_{j=0}^{m-1} e^{-\lambda x} \frac{(\lambda x)^j}{j!} + \int_0^x e^{-s(x-y)} e^{-\lambda y} \frac{(\lambda y)^{m-1}}{(m-1)!} \lambda \, dy
$$

$$
= \begin{cases}
\dfrac{\lambda^m e^{-sx} - \displaystyle\sum_{j=0}^{m-1} e^{-\lambda x} \dfrac{x^j}{j!} [\lambda^m(s - \lambda)^j - \lambda^j(s - \lambda)^m]}{(\lambda - s)^m} & \text{if } s \neq \lambda, \\[4ex]
\displaystyle\sum_{j=0}^{m} e^{-\lambda x} \dfrac{(\lambda x)^j}{j!} & \text{if } s = \lambda,
\end{cases}
$$

whence (49) follows.

THEOREM 5. *Let*

(50) $\Omega_n(s) = \mathbf{E}\{e^{-s\eta_n}\}$ $(n = 1, 2, \ldots).$

Then we have for $\Re(s) \geqq 0$ and $|w| < 1$ that

(51) $\displaystyle\sum_{n=1}^{\infty} \Omega_n(s) w^{n-1} = \dfrac{(\lambda - s)^m \Omega_1(s) - s C_{m-1}(s, w)}{(\lambda - s)^m - w\lambda\psi(s)} ,$

where

(52) $C_{m-1}(s, w) = \displaystyle\sum_{r=1}^{m} \dfrac{\Omega_1(\lambda[1 - g_r(w)])[g_r(w)]^m}{[1 - g_r(w)]}$

$$
\cdot \prod_{\nu \neq r} \left\{ \frac{s - \lambda[1 - g_r(w)]}{g_\nu(w) - g_r(w)} \right\}
$$

and $z = g_r(w)$ $(r = 1, 2, \ldots, m)$ *are the m roots in z of the equation*

$$(53) \qquad z^m = w\psi(\lambda(1 - z))$$

in the unit circle $|z| < 1$.

PROOF. By (46) and (49) we have

$$(54) \qquad (\lambda - s)^m \Omega_{n+1}(s) = \lambda^m \psi(s) \Omega_n(s) - sC_{m-1}(s),$$

where $C_{m-1}(s)$ is in s a polynomial of degree $\bar{m} - 1$. Hence

$$(55) \qquad \sum_{n=1}^{\infty} \Omega_n(s)w^{n-1} = \frac{(\lambda - s)^m \Omega_1(s) - sC_{m-1}(s, w)}{(\lambda - s)^m - w\lambda^m \psi(s)},$$

where $C_{m-1}(s, w)$ is in s also a polynomial of degree $m - 1$ with co-efficients depending on w. The left-hand side of (55) is a regular function of s if $\Re(s) > 0$ and $|w| < 1$. In this domain the denominator of the right-hand side of (55) has m roots $s = \lambda[1 - g_r(w)]$ $(r = 1, 2, \ldots, m)$. These must be also roots of the numerator, that is

$$(56) \quad \lambda[1 - g_r(w)]C_{m-1}(\lambda[1 - g_r(w)],w) = \lambda^m[g_r(w)]^m \Omega_1(\lambda[1 - g_r(w)])$$

if $r = 1, 2, \ldots, m$. Therefore the polynomial $C_{m-1}(s, w)$ is determined uniquely. If $w \neq 0$ then these roots are distinct and by the Lagrange interpolation formula we obtain (52). If $w = 0$ then (51) reduces to $\Omega_1(s)$. This proves (51).

If, in particular $\eta_1 \equiv 0$, then $\Omega_1(s) \equiv 1$ and we obtain immediately that

$$(57) \quad C_{m-1}(s, w) = \frac{1}{s}\left\{(\lambda - s)^m - \lambda^m \prod_{r=1}^{m}\left(1 - \frac{s}{\lambda[1 - g_r(w)]}\right)\right\}.$$

THE LIMITING BEHAVIOR OF THE PROCESS $\{\eta_n\}$. Let

$$(58) \qquad \mathbf{P}\{\eta_n \leqq x\} = W_n(x).$$

THEOREM 6. *If* $\lambda\alpha < m$ *then the limiting distribution* $\lim_{n\to\infty} W_n(x) = W(x)$ *exists and is independent of the initial distribution. The Laplace-Stieltjes transform of* $W(x)$ *is*

$$(59) \qquad \Omega(s) = \int_0^{\infty} e^{-sx}\, dW(x) = \left(1 - \frac{\lambda\alpha}{m}\right)\frac{ms\lambda^{m-1}\prod_{r=1}^{m-1}\left(1 - \frac{s}{\lambda(1 - \omega_r)}\right)}{\lambda^m \psi(s) - (\lambda - s)^m}$$

where $\omega_1, \omega_2, \ldots, \omega_{m-1}$ *are the* $m - 1$ *roots in z of the equation*

(60) $$z^m = \psi(\lambda(1 - z))$$

in the unit circle $|z| < 1$. *If* $\lambda\alpha \geqq m$ *then* $\lim\limits_{n\to\infty} W_n(x) = 0$ *for every x.*

PROOF. We have seen that if $\lambda\alpha < m$ then $\lim\limits_{n\to\infty} W_n(x) = W(x)$ exists, independent of the initial distribution, and $W(x)$ is a proper distribution function. If $\lambda\alpha \geqq m$ then $\lim\limits_{n\to\infty} W_n(x) = 0$ for every x. Thus it remains only to find the explicit form of $\Omega(s)$ in the case $\lambda\alpha < m$. Since $\Omega(s)$ is independent of the initial distribution we may suppose that $\eta_1 \equiv 0$. Then from (51) by using Abel's theorem it follows that

$$\Omega(s) = \lim_{w\to 1} (1 - w) \sum_{n=1}^{\infty} \Omega_n(s)w^{n-1}$$

$$= \left(1 - \frac{\lambda\alpha}{m}\right) \frac{ms\lambda^{m-1} \prod_{r=1}^{m-1} \left(1 - \frac{s}{\lambda(1 - \omega_r)}\right)}{\lambda^m\psi(s) - (\lambda - s)^m}$$

because $g'_m(1) = 1/(m - \lambda\alpha)$.

REMARK 4. We have $\omega_m = 1$ for $\lambda\alpha \leqq m$ if $\delta_m = 1$ for $\mu\beta \leqq m$ in Lemma 2 of Section 6. In Theorem 3 of Section 6 $P_0 = 0$ if and only if $\delta_m = 1$. By Lindley's theorem $P_0 = 0$ if $\mu\beta \leqq m$. This proves that $\delta_m = 1$ if $\mu\beta \leqq m$.

THE TRANSIENT BEHAVIOR OF THE QUEUE SIZE. It is easy to see that the sequence of random variables $\{\xi_n\}$ forms a homogeneous Markov chain, namely we have

(61) $$\xi_{n+1} = [\xi_n - m]^+ + \nu_{n+1},$$

where ν_n $(n = 1, 2, \ldots)$ denotes the number of customers arriving during the nth service. The $\{\nu_n\}$ is a sequence of identically distributed, independent random variables for which

$$\mathbf{P}\{\nu_n = j | \chi_n = x\} = e^{-\lambda x} \frac{(\lambda x)^j}{j!}$$

and unconditionally

(62) $$\mathbf{P}\{\nu_n = j\} = \int_0^{\infty} e^{-\lambda x} \frac{(\lambda x)^j}{j!} \, dH(x).$$

Write

$$p_{ik}^{(n)} = \mathbf{P}\{\xi_n = k \mid \xi_0 = i\}.$$

THEOREM 7. *If* $|z| \leqq 1$ *and* $|w| < 1$ *then*

$$(63) \quad \sum_{n=0}^{\infty} \sum_{k=0}^{\infty} p_{0k}^{(n)} w^n z^k = 1 - \frac{w\psi(\lambda(1-z)) \prod_{r=1}^{m} \left(\dfrac{z - g_r(w)}{1 - g_r(w)} \right)}{w\psi(\lambda(1-z)) - z^m}$$

where $z = g_r(w)$ $(r = 1, 2, \ldots, m)$ *are the m roots in z of the equation*

$$(64) \quad\quad\quad z^m = w\psi(\lambda(1-z))$$

in the unit circle $|z| < 1$.

Instead of proving this theorem we shall prove the following more general theorem, from which it can be obtained as a particular case.

THEOREM 8. *Let us define*

$$(65) \quad\quad\quad U_m(s, z) = \mathbf{E}\{e^{-s\tau_n' z^{\xi_n}}\}$$

for $\Re(s) \geqq 0$ *and* $|z| \leqq 1$. *If we suppose that* $\xi(0) = 0$ *then we have for* $\Re(s) \geqq 0$, $|z| \leqq 1$ *and* $|w| < 1$ *that*

$$(66)$$
$$\sum_{n=1}^{\infty} U_n(s, z) w^n = \frac{w\psi(s + \lambda(1-z)) \prod_{r=1}^{m} \left\{ \dfrac{\lambda[z - \gamma_r(s, w)]}{s + \lambda[1 - \gamma_r(s, w)]} \right\}}{z^m - w\psi(s + \lambda(1-z))}$$

where $z = \gamma_r(s, w)$ $(r = 1, 2, \ldots, m)$ *are the m roots in z of the equation*

$$(67) \quad\quad\quad z^m = w\psi(s + \lambda(1-z))$$

in the unit circle $|z| < 1$.

PROOF. First of all it is to be noted that if we know $U_n(s, z)$ then $\mathbf{P}\{\tau_n' \leqq x, \xi_n = j\}$ can be determined for every $x \geqq 0$ and $j = 0, 1, 2, \ldots$. Now we can write that

$$(68) \quad\quad\quad \xi_{n+1} = [\xi_n - m]^+ + \nu_{n+1}$$

and

$$(69) \quad\quad\quad \tau_{n+1}' = \tau_n' + \chi_{n+1} + \sum_{j=1}^{[m-\xi_n]^+} \theta_{n+1}^{(j)},$$

where $\{\chi_n\}$ $(n = 1, 2, \ldots)$ and $\{\theta_n^{(j)}\}$ $(n = 1, 2, \ldots; j = 1, 2, \ldots, m)$ are independent sequences of identically distributed, independent random variables with distribution functions $\mathbf{P}\{\chi_n \leqq x\} = H(x)$ and $\mathbf{P}\{\theta_n^{(j)} \leqq x\} = F(x)$ defined by (1). The random variable ν_n depends only on χ_n and its distribution is given by (62).

Since

$$\mathbf{E}\{e^{-s\chi_n}z^{\nu_n}\} = \psi(s + \lambda(1 - z)),$$

we get by (68) and (69) that

$$U_{n+1}(s, z) = \psi(s + \lambda(1 - z))$$

$$\cdot \left[\frac{U_n(s, z) - \sum_{j=0}^{m-1} C_{nj}(s)z^j}{z^m} + \sum_{j=0}^{m-1} C_{nj}(s) \left(\frac{\lambda}{\lambda + s} \right)^{m-j} \right]$$

where

$$C_{nj}(s) = \mathbf{P}\{\xi_n = j\}\mathbf{E}\{e^{-s\tau_n'} | \xi_n = j\}.$$

Hence

$$(70) \quad \sum_{n=0}^{\infty} U_n(s, z)w^n = \frac{z^m U_0(s, z) - w\psi(s + \lambda(1 - z))C_m(z, s, w)}{z^m - w\psi(s + \lambda(1 - z))},$$

where

$$C_m(z, s, w) = \sum_{n=0}^{\infty} \sum_{j=0}^{m-1} C_{nj}(s)w^n \left[z^j - z^m \left(\frac{\lambda}{\lambda + s} \right)^{m-j} \right]$$

is in z a polynomial of degree m and $C_m(s, z, w)$ vanishes if $z = (\lambda + s)/\lambda$.

The left-hand side of (70) is a regular function of z if $|z| < 1$, $\Re(s) \geqq 0$ and $|w| < 1$. In this domain the denominator of the right-hand side of (70) has exactly m roots $z = \gamma_r(s, w)$ $(r = 1, 2, \ldots, m)$. These must be also roots of the numerator. Thus the polynomial $C_m(z, s, w)$ is determined uniquely. If we exclude the trivial case $w = 0$, then the roots $\gamma_r(s, w)$ are distinct and $C_m(z, s, w)$ can be obtained explicitly by the Lagrange interpolation formula

$$C_m(s, z, w)$$

$$= \sum_{r=1}^{m} \frac{U_0(s, \gamma_r(s, w))[s + \lambda(1 - z)]}{s + \lambda[1 - \gamma_r(s, w)]} \prod_{\nu \neq r} \left(\frac{z - \gamma_r(s, w)}{\gamma_\nu(s, w) - \gamma_r(s, w)} \right).$$

If $\xi(0) = 0$ then $U_n(s, z)$ $(n = 1, 2, \ldots)$ obviously agrees with the $U_n(s, z)$ calculated by the assumption $U_0(s, z) = \left(\dfrac{\lambda}{\lambda + s}\right)^m z^m$. In this case we obtain immediately that

$$C_m(s, z, w) = \left(\frac{\lambda z}{\lambda + s}\right)^m - \prod_{r=1}^{m} \left(\frac{\lambda[z - \gamma_r(s, w)]}{s + \lambda[1 - \gamma_r(s, w)]}\right).$$

This proves the theorem. If we write $s = 0$ in (66), then we get (63) for $i = 0$.

We remark that if, in particular, $\tau_0' = 0$ and $\xi_0 = m$, then $U_0(s, z) = z^m$ and we obtain immediately that

$$C_m(s, z, w) = z^m - \prod_{r=1}^{m} \left(\frac{z - \gamma_r(s, w)}{1 - \dfrac{\lambda}{\lambda + s}\gamma_r(s, w)}\right).$$

REMARK 5.   We have the obvious relation

$$\mathbf{P}\{\xi_n = j\} = \int_0^\infty e^{-\lambda x} \frac{(\lambda x)^j}{j!}\, d[W_n(x) * H(x)],$$

whence

$$\mathbf{E}\{z^{\xi_n}\} = \Omega_n(\lambda(1 - z))\psi(\lambda(1 - z)).$$

Now using (51) we can prove (63) in this way also.

THEOREM 9. *Let*

(71)
$$\Pi_k(s) = \int_0^\infty e^{-st} P_k(t)\, dt$$

for $\Re(s) > 0$. If we suppose that $\xi(0) = 0$ then we have for $\Re(s) > 0$ and $|z| \leq 1$ that

(72)
$$\sum_{k=0}^{\infty} \Pi_k(s) z^k = \frac{1}{s + \lambda(1 - z)}$$

$$\cdot \left\{1 + \frac{(1 - z^m)\psi(s + \lambda(1 - z))}{z^m - \psi(s + \lambda(1 - z))} \prod_{r=1}^{m} \left(\frac{\lambda[z - \gamma_r(s)]}{s + \lambda[1 - \gamma_r(s)]}\right)\right\},$$

where $z = \gamma_r(s)$ $(r = 1, 2, \ldots, m)$ are the m roots in z of the equation

(73) $$z^m = \psi(s + \lambda(1 - z))$$

in the unit circle $|z| < 1$.

PROOF. Let us form the Laplace transforms of (31) and (32) in the special case when the initial queue size is 0; then we get easily that

(74) $$\sum_{k=0}^{m-1} \Pi_k(s) z^k$$

$$= \frac{1}{\lambda + s} \left\{ 1 + \sum_{j=0}^{m-1} z^j \int_0^\infty e^{-st} \, dN_j(t) + z \sum_{j=0}^{m-2} z^j \int_0^\infty e^{-st} \, dM_j(t) \right\}$$

and

(75) $$\sum_{k=m}^{\infty} \Pi_k(s) z^k = \frac{[1 - \psi(s + \lambda(1 - z))]}{s + \lambda(1 - z)}$$

$$\cdot \left\{ \sum_{j=m}^{\infty} z^j \int_0^\infty e^{-st} \, dN_j(t) + z^m \int_0^\infty e^{-st} \, dM_{m-1}(t) \right\}.$$

Since clearly

$$N_j(t) = \sum_{n=1}^{\infty} \mathbf{P}\{\tau_n' \leqq t, \xi_n = j\}$$

we obtain by (66) that

(76) $$\sum_{j=0}^{\infty} z^j \int_0^\infty e^{-st} \, dN_j(t) = \sum_{n=1}^{\infty} U_n(s, z)$$

$$= \frac{\psi(s + \lambda(1 - z)) \prod_{r=1}^{m} \left(\frac{\lambda[z - \gamma_r(s)]}{s + \lambda[1 - \gamma_r(s)]} \right)}{z^m - \psi(s + \lambda(1 - z))}.$$

Further since

$$M_j(t) = \lambda \int_0^t P_j(u) \, du \qquad (j = 0, 1, 2, \ldots)$$

we get by (15) that

(77) $$\sum_{j=0}^{m-1} z^j \int_0^\infty e^{-st} \, dM_j(t) = \lambda \Pi(s, z)$$

$$= \frac{\lambda}{s + \lambda(1 - z)} \left\{ 1 - \prod_{r=1}^{m} \frac{\lambda[z - \gamma_r(s)]}{s + \lambda[1 - \gamma_r(s)]} \right\}.$$

From (77) we get

$$\int_0^\infty e^{-st} \, dM_{m-1}(t) = \prod_{r=1}^m \left(\frac{\lambda}{s + \lambda[1 - \gamma_r(s)]} \right)$$

and from (74) and (77)

$$\sum_{j=0}^{m-1} z^j \int_0^\infty e^{-st} \, dN_j(t)$$

$$= \prod_{r=1}^m \left(\frac{\lambda z}{s + \lambda[1 - \gamma_r(s)]} \right) - \prod_{r=1}^m \left(\frac{\lambda[z - \gamma_r(s)]}{s + \lambda[1 - \gamma_r(s)]} \right).$$

Comparing the above formulas we obtain (72), which was to be proved.

THE LIMITING DISTRIBUTION OF THE QUEUE SIZE. If $n \to \infty$ then the limiting behavior of the sequence $\{\xi_n\}$ is given by

THEOREM 10. *If* $\lambda \alpha < m$ *then the limiting distribution* $\lim_{n \to \infty} \mathbf{P}\{\xi_n = k\} = P_k$ $(k = 0, 1, 2, \ldots)$ *exists and is independent of the initial distribution. We have*

$$(78) \quad \sum_{k=0}^\infty P_k z^k = m \left(1 - \frac{\lambda \alpha}{m} \right) \frac{(z - 1)\psi(\lambda(1 - z)) \displaystyle\prod_{r=1}^{m-1} \left(\frac{z - \omega_r}{1 - \omega_r} \right)}{z^m - \psi(\lambda(1 - z))},$$

where $\omega_1, \omega_2, \ldots, \omega_{m-1}$ *are the* $m - 1$ *roots in* z *of the equation*

$$(79) \quad z^m = \psi(\lambda(1 - z))$$

in the unit circle $|z| < 1$. *If* $\lambda \alpha \geqq m$ *then* $\lim_{n \to \infty} \mathbf{P}\{\xi_n = k\} = 0$ *for every* k.

PROOF. The sequence $\{\xi_n\}$ is an irreducible and aperiodic Markov chain. Therefore $\lim_{n \to \infty} \mathbf{P}\{\xi_n = k\} = P_k$ always exists and is independent of the initial distribution. Either every $P_k > 0$ and $\{P_k\}$ is a probability distribution, or every $P_k = 0$.

By using Abel's theorem we have

$$\sum_{k=0}^\infty P_k z^k = \lim_{w \to 1} (1 - w) \sum_{n=0}^\infty \sum_{k=0}^\infty p_{ik}^{(n)} z^k w^n,$$

and the right-hand side can be calculated by (63). This proves (78).

THEOREM 11. *If* $\lambda\alpha < m$ *then the limiting distribution* $\lim_{t\to\infty} \mathbf{P}\{\xi(t) = k\} = P_k^*$ $(k = 0, 1, 2, \ldots)$ *exists and is independent of the initial distribution. We have*

$$
(80) \qquad P_k^* = \begin{cases} \dfrac{1}{m}(P_0 + P_1 + \cdots + P_k) & \text{if } k < m, \\[2mm] \dfrac{1}{m}(P_{k-m} + P_{k-m+1} + \cdots + P_k) & \text{if } k \geqq m, \end{cases}
$$

where the distribution $\{P_j\}$ *is defined by* (78). *If* $\lambda\alpha \geqq m$ *then* $\lim_{t\to\infty} \mathbf{P}\{\xi(t) = k\} = 0$ *for every* k.

PROOF. Obviously

$$
M_k(t) = \lambda \int_0^t P_k(u)\, du.
$$

We have proved that $\lim_{t\to\infty} P_k(t) = P_k^*$ $(k = 0, 1, 2, \ldots)$ always exists and hence

$$
\lim_{t\to\infty} \frac{M_k(t)}{t} = P_k^*.
$$

On the other hand we can see easily that

$$
\Big| M_k(t) - \sum_{j=k-m+1}^{k} N_j(t) \Big| \leqq 1
$$

for all $t \geqq 0$. Here $N_j(t) = 0$ if $j < 0$. Thus

$$
P_k^* = \frac{1}{\lambda} \lim_{t\to\infty} \frac{M_k(t)}{t} = \lim_{t\to\infty} \frac{1}{\lambda t} \sum_{j=k-m+1}^{k} N_j(t).
$$

Now let us denote by $N(t)$ the expected number of departures occurring in the time interval $(0, t]$. By the theory of Markov chains it follows that

$$
\lim_{t\to\infty} \frac{N_j(t)}{N(t)} = P_j \qquad (j = 0, 1, 2, \ldots)
$$

and therefore

$$
(81) \qquad P_k^* = \frac{1}{\lambda}\Big(\sum_{j=k-m+1}^{k} P_j \Big) \lim_{t\to\infty} \frac{N(t)}{t}.
$$

If we suppose that $\lambda \alpha < m$ then by (37) and (78) we obtain that $P_0/P_0^* = m$ and hence if we write $k = 0$ in (81) we get

$$\lim_{t \to \infty} \frac{N(t)}{t} = \frac{\lambda}{m}$$

and thus by (81)

$$P_k^* = \frac{1}{m} \sum_{j=k-m+1}^{k} P_j$$

for every k. Here $P_j = 0$ if $j < 0$. If $\lambda \alpha \geq m$ then every $P_j = 0$ and since $\lim_{t \to \infty} \dfrac{N(t)}{t}$ is evidently finite we get by (81) that $P_k^* = 0$ for every k. This completes the proof of the theorem.

THE STOCHASTIC LAW OF THE BUSY PERIOD. Let us denote by $\tilde{G}_n(x)$ the probability that the busy period consists of n services and its length is at most x.

THEOREM 12. *The Laplace-Stieltjes transform*

(82)
$$\Gamma_n(s) = \int_0^\infty e^{-sx} \, d\tilde{G}_n(x)$$

is given by the generating function

(83)
$$\sum_{n=1}^{\infty} \Gamma_n(s) w^n = 1 - \prod_{r=1}^{m} [1 - \gamma_r(s, w)]$$

for $\Re(s) \geq 0$ and $|w| \leq 1$, where $\gamma_r(s, w)$ $(r = 1, 2, \ldots, m)$ are defined in Lemma 1.

PROOF. Denote by $G_{nk}(x)$ the probability that the busy period consists of at least n services, the total service time of the first n batches is at most x, and at the end of the nth service k customers are present in the queue. Then evidently

$$\tilde{G}_n(x) = \sum_{k=0}^{m-1} G_{nk}(x).$$

If we write

$$\Gamma_{nk}(s) = \int_0^\infty e^{-sx} \, dG_{nk}(x),$$

then

$$\Gamma_n(s) = \sum_{k=0}^{m-1} \Gamma_{nk}(s).$$

Now by the theorem of total probability we can write that

$$G_{1k}(x) = \int_0^x e^{-\lambda y} \frac{(\lambda y)^k}{k!} \, dH(y)$$

and

$$G_{nk}(x) = \sum_{r=m}^{m+k} \int_0^x G_{n-1,r}(x - y) e^{-\lambda y} \frac{(\lambda y)^{k-r+m}}{(k - r + m)!} \, dH(y)$$

$$(n = 2, 3, \ldots).$$

Forming Laplace-Stieltjes transforms we get

$$\Gamma_{1k}(s) = \int_0^\infty e^{-(\lambda+s)y} \frac{(\lambda y)^k}{k!} \, dH(y)$$

and

$$\Gamma_{nk}(s) = \sum_{r=m}^{m+k} \Gamma_{n-1,r}(s) \int_0^\infty e^{-(\lambda+s)y} \frac{(\lambda y)^{k-r+m}}{(k - r + m)!} \, dH(y).$$

If we introduce the generating function

$$C_n(s, z) = \sum_{k=0}^{\infty} \Gamma_{nk}(s) z^k,$$

then we have

$$C_1(s, z) = \psi(s + \lambda(1 - z))$$

and

$$z^m C_n(s, z) = \psi(s + \lambda(1 - z))[C_{n-1}(s, z) - \sum_{r=0}^{m-1} \Gamma_{n-1,r}(s) z^r].$$

Hence

$$(84) \quad \sum_{n=1}^{\infty} C_n(s, z) w^n = w\psi(s + \lambda(1 - z)) \frac{z^m - \sum_{n=1}^{\infty} \sum_{r=0}^{m-1} \Gamma_{nr}(s) z^r w^n}{z^m - w\psi(s + \lambda(1 - z))}.$$

The left-hand side of (84) is a regular function of z if $|z| < 1$, $\Re(s) \geqq 0$ and $|w| < 1$. In this domain the denominator of the right-hand side has exactly m roots $z = \gamma_r(s, w)$ $(r = 1, 2, \ldots, m)$. These must also be roots of the numerator. Thus the numerator, being a polynomial of degree m, is determined uniquely, namely

$$z^m - \sum_{n=1}^{\infty} \sum_{r=0}^{m-1} \Gamma_{nr}(s) z^r w^n = \prod_{r=1}^{m} [z - \gamma_r(s, w)].$$

If $z = 1$ then

$$\sum_{n=1}^{\infty} \Gamma_n(s)w^n = 1 - \prod_{r=1}^{m} [1 - \gamma_r(s, w)]$$

for $|w| < 1$ and this is true for $|w| = 1$ also, which can be shown by using the continuity of $\gamma_r(s, w)$. This completes the proof of the theorem.

THEOREM 13. *If $G(x)$ denotes the distribution function of the length of the busy period, then we have*

$$(85) \qquad \lim_{x \to \infty} G(x) = \begin{cases} 1 & \text{if } \lambda\alpha \leqq m, \\ 1 - \prod_{r=1}^{m} (1 - \omega_r) & \text{if } \lambda\alpha > m, \end{cases}$$

where $\omega_1, \omega_2, \ldots, \omega_m$ are the m roots in z of the equation

$$(86) \qquad z^m = \psi(\lambda(1 - z))$$

in the unit circle $|z| < 1$.

PROOF. Let

$$\Gamma(s) = \int_0^{\infty} e^{-sx} \, dG(x)$$

be the Laplace-Stieltjes transform of the distribution function of the length of the busy period. By (83) we have

$$\Gamma(s) = 1 - \prod_{r=1}^{m} [1 - \gamma_r(s)].$$

Hence

$$\lim_{x \to \infty} G(x) = \lim_{s \to 0} \Gamma(s) = 1 - \prod_{r=1}^{m} (1 - \omega_r),$$

where $\omega_m = 1$ if $\lambda\alpha \leqq m$, as was to be proved.

REMARK 5. Now let us consider the following queueing process. Customers arrive at a counter at the instants $\tau_1^*, \tau_2^*, \ldots,$ $\tau_n^*, \ldots,$ where the inter-arrival times $\tau_{n+1}^* - \tau_n^*$ $(n = 0, 1, 2, \ldots;$ $\tau_0^* = 0)$ are identically distributed, independent random variables with distribution function

$$(87) \qquad F_m(x) = \begin{cases} 1 - \displaystyle\sum_{j=0}^{m-1} e^{-\lambda x} \frac{(\lambda x)^j}{j!} & \text{if } x \geqq 0, \\ 0 & \text{if } x < 0. \end{cases}$$

We say that $\{\tau_n^*\}$ is an *Erlang process*. The customers will be served by a single server in the order of their arrival. Suppose that the server is idle if and only if there is no customer waiting at the counter. Denote by χ_n^* the service time of the nth customer $(n = 1, 2, \ldots)$. It is supposed that $\{\chi_n^*\}$ is a sequence of identically distributed, independent, positive random variables with distribution function

$$(88) \qquad \mathbf{P}\{\chi_n^* \leqq x\} = H(x)$$

and that $\{\chi_n^*\}$ is independent of $\{\tau_n^*\}$.

Denote by $\eta^*(t)$ the virtual waiting time at the instant t, i.e. $\eta^*(t)$ is the time that a customer would wait if he joined the queue at the instant t. Define $\eta_n^* = \eta(\tau_n^* - 0)$, i.e. η_n^* is the waiting time of the nth customer.

Denote by $\xi^*(t)$ the queue size at the instant t, i.e. $\xi^*(t)$ is the number of customers waiting or being served at the instant t. Further let us denote by $\tau_1', \tau_2', \ldots, \tau_n', \ldots$ the instants of the successive departures and define $\xi_n^* = \xi^*(\tau_n' + 0)$, $(n = 1, 2, \ldots)$, i.e. ξ_n^* is the queue size immediately after the nth departure. If there is a departure at $t = 0$ then we write $\tau_0' = 0$ and $\xi_0^* = \xi^*(+0)$.

Finally, denote by $G_n^*(x)$ the probability that a busy period consists of n services and its length is at most x.

We are interested in the investigation of the stochastic behavior of the waiting time, the queue size, and the busy period of this process. We shall show that if we know the stochastic behavior of the process defined in Section 4, then that of the above process can be deduced immediately. If we identify every mth arrival in the first process (Section 4) with an arrival in the second process, i.e. we suppose that $\tau_n^* = \tau_{nm}$ and similarly if we identify the service time of the nth batch in the first process with the service time of the nth customer in the second process, i.e. $\chi_n^* = \chi_n$ $(n = 1, 2, \ldots)$ then the first process reduces to the second one provided that the initial states are in agreement. For, $F_m(x)$ is the mth iterated convolution of $F(x)$ with itself.

Comparing the two processes we see that the waiting time and the busy period follow the same probability laws in both processes, namely $\eta^*(t) = \eta(t)$, $\eta_n^* = \eta_n$ whenever $\xi(0) \equiv 0 \pmod{m}$ and $G_n^*(x) = \tilde{G}_n(x)$. Further, the departures also agree. However, the queue sizes are different, namely

$$\xi^*(t) = \left[\frac{\xi(t)}{m}\right] \quad \text{and} \quad \xi_n^* = \left[\frac{\xi_n}{m}\right].$$

Problems for solution

PROBLEM 8. Find the stationary distribution of $\{\xi_n\}$.
PROBLEM 9. Find the stationary distribution of $\{\eta_n\}$.

5. The time dependence of single server queues with Palm input and exponentially distributed service times

Let us suppose that customers arrive at a counter at the instants $\tau_0, \tau_1, \tau_2, \ldots, \tau_n, \ldots$, where the inter-arrival times $\tau_{n+1} - \tau_n$ $(n = 0, 1, \ldots; \tau_0 = 0)$ are identically distributed, independent, positive random variables with distribution function

(1) $\mathbf{P}\{\tau_{n+1} - \tau_n \leqq x\} = F(x).$

We say that $\{\tau_n\}$ is a *Palm process*. The customers will be served by a single server. Suppose that the server is idle if and only if there is no customer waiting at the counter; otherwise the order of the services is irrelevant. It is supposed that the service times are identically distributed, independent random variables with distribution function

(2) $$H(x) = \begin{cases} 1 - e^{-\mu x} & \text{if } x \geqq 0, \\ 0 & \text{if } x < 0, \end{cases}$$

and independent of $\{\tau_n\}$.

Denote by $\xi(t)$ the queue size at the instant t, i.e. $\xi(t)$ is the number of customers waiting or being served at the instant t. We say that the system is in state E_j at the instant t if $\xi(t) = j$.

Further define $\xi_n = \xi(\tau_n - 0)$ $(n = 0, 1, 2, \ldots)$, i.e. ξ_n is the queue size immediately before the arrival of the nth customer.

We shall introduce the following notation

$$\phi(s) = \int_0^\infty e^{-sx}\, dF(x),$$

which is convergent if $\Re(s) \geqq 0$ and

$$\beta = \int_0^\infty x\, dF(x).$$

We need the following auxiliary theorem which is exactly the same as Lemma 1 in Section 3 but in different notation.

LEMMA 1. *If* $\Re(s) \geqq 0$ *and* $|w| \leqq 1$ *then* $z = \delta(s, w)$, *the root of the equation*

(3)
$$z = w\phi(s + \mu(1 - z)),$$

which has the smallest absolute value, is

(4)
$$\delta(s, w) = w \sum_{j=1}^\infty \frac{(-\mu w)^{j-1}}{j!}\left(\frac{d^{j-1}[\phi(\mu + s)]^j}{ds^{j-1}}\right).$$

This is a continuous function of s and w if $\Re(s) \geqq 0$ *and* $|w| \leqq 1$ *and further* $z = \delta(s, w)$ *is the only root of* (3) *in the unit circle* $|z| < 1$ *if* $\Re(s) \geqq 0$ *and* $|w| < 1$ *or* $\Re(s) > 0$ *and* $|w| \leqq 1$ *or* $\Re(s) \geqq 0$, $|w| \leqq 1$, *and* $\mu\beta > 1$. *Specifically,* $\delta = \delta(0, 1)$ *is the smallest positive real root of the equation*

$$\delta = \phi[\mu(1 - \delta)].$$

If $\mu\beta > 1$ *then* $\delta < 1$ *and if* $\mu\beta \leqq 1$ *then* $\delta = 1$.

Finally, we introduce the following notation: $\delta(s) = \delta(s, 1)$ and $d(w) = \delta(0, w)$. Clearly, $\delta = \delta(0) = d(1)$.

We remark that by forming Lagrange's expansion of $[\delta(s, w)]^j$ $(j = 1, 2, \ldots)$ (cf. Appendix) we get

(5)
$$[\delta(s, w)]^j = j \sum_{n=j}^\infty \frac{w^n \mu^{n-j}}{n(n - j)!} \int_0^\infty e^{-(\mu+s)x} x^{n-j}\, dF_n(x),$$

where $F_n(x)$ denotes the nth iterated convolution of $F(x)$ with itself.

THE TRANSIENT BEHAVIOR OF THE QUEUE SIZE. Let $\{\nu_n\}$ be a sequence of identically distributed, independent random variables with distribution

$$(6) \quad \mathbf{P}\{\nu_n = j\} = p_j = \int_0^\infty e^{-\mu x} \frac{(\mu x)^j}{j!}\, dF(x) \qquad (j = 0, 1, 2, \ldots).$$

It is easy to see that

$$(7) \qquad\qquad \xi_{n+1} = [\xi_n + 1 - \nu_n]^+.$$

Accordingly the sequence of random variables $\{\xi_n\}$ forms a homogeneous Markov chain. We shall say that the system is in state E_j at the nth step if $\xi_n = j$.

By (7) we obtain that the matrix of transition probabilities $\boldsymbol{\pi} = \| p_{ik} \|$ $(i, k = 0, 1, 2, \ldots)$, where $p_{ik} = \mathbf{P}\{\xi_{n+1} = k \,|\, \xi_n = i\}$ $(n = 0, 1, 2, \ldots)$, has the following form

$$\boldsymbol{\pi} = \left\|
\begin{array}{cccccc}
1 - p_0 & p_0 & 0 & 0 & \cdots \\
1 - p_0 - p_1 & p_1 & p_0 & 0 & \cdots \\
1 - p_0 - p_1 - p_2 & p_2 & p_1 & p_0 & \cdots \\
\cdot & & \cdot & \cdot & \cdot & \cdots \\
\cdot & & \cdot & \cdot & \cdot & \cdots
\end{array}
\right\|,$$

i.e.

$$(8) \quad p_{ik} = \begin{cases} 1 - (p_0 + p_1 + \cdots + p_i) & \text{if } k = 0, \\ p_{i+1-k} & \text{if } 0 < k \leq i + 1, \\ 0 & \text{if } k > i + 1. \end{cases}$$

The generating function of the probability distribution $\{p_j\}$ is

$$\sum_{j=0}^\infty p_j z^j = \phi[\mu(1 - z)].$$

To obtain the higher transition probabilities

$$p_{ik}^{(n)} = \mathbf{P}\{\xi_n = k \,|\, \xi_0 = i\} \qquad (n = 0, 1, 2, \ldots),$$

we shall prove

THEOREM 1. *We have for $|z| \leq 1$ and $|w| < 1$ that*

$$(9) \quad \sum_{n=0}^{\infty} \sum_{i=0}^{\infty} p_{ik}^{(n)} z^i w^n$$

$$= \frac{(1-w)(1-z)z^{k+1} + w\{z - \phi[\mu(1-z)]\}[1 - d(w)][d(w)]^k}{(1-w)(1-z)\{z - w\phi[\mu(1-z)]\}},$$

where $z = d(w)$ is that root of the equation

$$(10) \qquad\qquad z = w\phi[\mu(1-z)]$$

which has the smallest absolute value.

PROOF. By the theorem of total probability we can write that

$$(11) \qquad\qquad p_{ik}^{(n+1)} = \sum_{j=0}^{\infty} p_{ij} p_{jk}^{(n)},$$

for, starting from E_i, the system can reach the state E_k by $n + 1$ steps in such a way that the first step leads the system from E_i to some intermediate state E_j ($j = 0, 1, 2, \ldots$) and the next n steps from E_j to E_k. Thus by (8)

(12)

$$p_{ik}^{(n+1)} = p_0 p_{i+1,k}^{(n)} + p_1 p_{ik}^{(n)} + \cdots + p_i p_{ik}^{(n)} + (1 - p_0 - \cdots - p_i) p_{0k}^{(n)}.$$

Now let k be fixed and for $|z| \leq 1$ introduce the generating function

$$U_n(z) = \sum_{i=0}^{\infty} p_{ik}^{(n)} z^i;$$

then by (12) we have

$$(13) \quad z U_{n+1}(z) - \phi[\mu(1-z)] U_n(z)$$

$$= \{z - \phi[\mu(1-z)]\} p_{0k}^{(n)} / (1-z), \qquad (n = 0, 1, 2, \ldots)$$

and clearly $U_0(z) = z^k$. Further if we introduce the generating function

$$G(z, w) = \sum_{n=0}^{\infty} U_n(z) w^n = \sum_{n=0}^{\infty} \sum_{i=0}^{\infty} p_{ik}^{(n)} z^i w^n,$$

which is convergent if $|z| \leqq 1$ and $|w| < 1$, then by (13) we obtain that

(14) $G(z, w)$

$$= \left\{ z^{k+1} + w \frac{z - \phi[\mu(1 - z)]}{1 - z} \sum_{n=0}^{\infty} p_{0k}^{(n)} w^n \right\} / \{z - w\phi[\mu(1 - z)]\}.$$

Here $G(z, w)$ is a regular function of z if $|z| < 1$ and $|w| < 1$. The denominator of (14) has one and only one root $z = d(w)$ in the unit circle $|z| < 1$. Consequently, $z = d(w)$ must be a root of the numerator of (14) too. Hence we obtain that

(15) $$\sum_{n=0}^{\infty} p_{0k}^{(n)} w^n = \{[1 - d(w)][d(w)]^k\}/(1 - w).$$

Finally, we obtain (9) if we put (15) into (14).

The probabilities $p_{ik}^{(n)}$ can be obtained explicitly by using the expansion (5) with $s = 0$.

The Markov chain $\{\xi_n\}$ is clearly irreducible and aperiodic and we shall prove

THEOREM 2. *The states of the Markov chain* $\{\xi_n\}$ *are recurrent non-null states if* $\mu\beta > 1$, *recurrent null states if* $\mu\beta = 1$, *and transient states if* $\mu\beta < 1$.

PROOF. Denote by $f_0^{(n)}$ the probability that starting from state E_0 the system returns to the state E_0 for the first time at the nth step. By the theorem of total probability we can write that

$$p_{00}^{(n)} = f_0^{(n)} + f_0^{(n-1)} p_{00}^{(1)} + \cdots + f_0^{(1)} p_{00}^{(n-1)} \qquad (n = 1, 2, \ldots).$$

Forming the generating function we get by (15) that

(16) $$\sum_{n=1}^{\infty} f_0^{(n)} w^n = \frac{\displaystyle\sum_{n=1}^{\infty} p_{00}^{(n)} w^n}{\displaystyle\sum_{n=0}^{\infty} p_{00}^{(n)} w^n} = \frac{w - d(w)}{1 - d(w)}$$

if $|w| < 1$ and $d(w)$ is defined by Lemma 1.

Define

$$f_0 = \sum_{n=1}^{\infty} f_0^{(n)}.$$

If $f_0 = 1$, then let

$$\mu_0 = \sum_{n=1}^{\infty} n f_0^{(n)}$$

and if $f_0 < 1$ then let $\mu_0 = \infty$. Here f_0 is the probability that the system ever returns to E_0 and μ_0 is the mean recurrence step number. In an irreducible Markov chain all states belong to the same class. Thus if $f_0 = 1$ then the states are recurrent states and if $f_0 < 1$ then they are transient. If $f_0 = 1$ and $\mu_0 < \infty$, then they are recurrent non-null states, and if $f_0 = 1$ and $\mu_0 = \infty$, then they are recurrent null states.

Now by (16)

$$f_0 = \lim_{w \to 1} \frac{[w - d(w)]}{[1 - d(w)]}.$$

Here $d(1) = \delta$ is the smallest positive real root of the equation $\delta = \phi[\mu(1 - \delta)]$. If $\mu\beta > 1$ then $\delta < 1$ and thus $f_0 = 1$. If $\mu\beta \leq 1$ then $f_0 = 1 - 1/d'(1)$. Since $d(w) = \phi[\mu(1 - d(w))]$ therefore $d'(1) = 1 + \mu\beta\, d'(1)$, i.e. $d'(1) = 1/(1 - \mu\beta)$ if $\mu\beta < 1$ and $d'(1) = \infty$ if $\mu\beta = 1$. Hence $f_0 = \mu\beta$ if $\mu\beta \leq 1$. Further

$$\mu_0 = \lim_{w \to 1} \frac{d}{dw} \left(\frac{w - d(w)}{1 - d(w)} \right)$$

and hence $\mu_0 = 1/(1 - \delta)$ if $\mu\beta > 1$ and $\mu_0 = \infty$ if $\mu\beta \leq 1$. This proves Theorem 2.

THEOREM 3. *If $\mu\beta > 1$ then the limiting distribution* $\lim_{n \to \infty} \mathbf{P}\{\xi_n = k\} = P_k$ *($k = 0, 1, 2, \ldots$) exists and is independent of the initial distribution. We have*

(17) $$P_k = (1 - \delta)\delta^k,$$

where $z = \delta$ is that root of the equation

(18) $$z = \phi[\mu(1 - z)]$$

which has the smallest absolute value. If $\mu\beta \leq 1$ then $\lim_{n \to \infty} \mathbf{P}\{\xi_n = k\} = 0$ *for every k.*

PROOF. The $\lim_{n \to \infty} \mathbf{P}\{\xi_n = k\} = P_k$ always exists and is independent of the initial distribution. By using Abel's theorem we have

$$P_k = \lim_{w \to 1} (1 - w) \sum_{n=0}^{\infty} p_{0k}^{(n)} w^n = \lim_{w \to 1} [1 - d(w)][d(w)]^k,$$

where $\lim_{w \to 1} d(w) = \delta$ and $\delta < 1$ if $\mu\beta > 1$ and $\delta = 1$ if $\mu\beta \leq 1$.

Now let us define the transition probabilities as follows

$$P_{ik}(t) = \mathbf{P}\{\xi(t) = k \mid \xi(0) = i\}$$

and write

$$\Pi_{ik}(s) = \int_0^{\infty} e^{-st} P_{ik}(t) \, dt,$$

which is convergent if $\Re(s) > 0$. If $i = 0$ then $P_{0k}(t)$ reflects the unrealistic condition that $\xi(0) = -1$. This can be interpreted as follows: the initial queue size is 0 and the customer arriving first finds the queue empty.

THEOREM 4. *If* $|z| \leq 1$ *then*

$$(19) \quad \sum_{i=0}^{\infty} \Pi_{ik}(s)z^i = \frac{z^{k+1}\{1 - \phi[s + \mu(1 - z)]\}}{[s + \mu(1 - z)]\{z - \phi[s + \mu(1 - z)]\}}$$

$$+ \frac{\{z\phi(s) - z\phi[s + \mu(1 - z)] - (1 - z)\phi(s)\phi[s + \mu(1 - z)]\}}{(1 - z)[1 - \phi(s)]\{s + \mu[1 - \delta(s)]\}\{z - \phi[s + \mu(1 - z)]\}}$$

$$\cdot [1 - \delta(s)]^2[\delta(s)]^{k-1}$$

when $k > 0$, *and*

$$(20) \quad \sum_{i=0}^{\infty} \Pi_{i0}(s)z^i = \frac{\{(\mu + s)z - (\mu + s + sz)\phi[s + \mu(1 - z)]\}}{s[s + \mu(1 - z)]\{z - \phi[s + \mu(1 - z)]\}}$$

$$- \frac{\{z\phi(s) - z\phi[s + \mu(1 - z)] - (1 - z)\phi(s)\phi[s + \mu(1 - z)]\}}{(1 - z)[1 - \phi(s)]\{s + \mu[1 - \delta(s)]\}\{z - \phi[s + \mu(1 - z)]\}}$$

$$\cdot [1 - \delta(s)]$$

where $z = \delta(s)$ is the root of the equation

(21) $$z = \phi[s + \mu(1 - z)]$$

that has the smallest absolute value.

PROOF. By the theorem of total probability we can write that

(22) $$P_{ik}(t) = \sum_{j=0}^{i} \int_0^t e^{-\mu x} \frac{(\mu x)^j}{j!} P_{i-j+1,k}(t - x) \, dF(x)$$

$$+ \sum_{j=i+1}^{\infty} \int_0^t e^{-\mu x} \frac{(\mu x)^j}{j!} P_{1k}(t - x) \, dF(x)$$

$$+ \begin{cases} [1 - F(t)] \sum_{j=i}^{\infty} e^{-\mu t} \dfrac{(\mu t)^j}{j!} & \text{if } k = 0, \\[2ex] [1 - F(t)]e^{-\mu t} \dfrac{(\mu t)^{i-k}}{(i-k)!} & \text{if } 0 < k \leqq i, \\[2ex] 0 & \text{if } k > i. \end{cases}$$

For, if we suppose that $\tau_1 = x$ $(0 \leqq x \leqq t)$ and in the time interval $(0, x]$ exactly j $(j = 0, 1, \ldots, i)$ departures occur, then under this condition the probability of the event $\xi(t) = k$ is equal to $P_{i-j+1,k}(t - x)$; if $x > t$ and in the time interval $(0, t]$ exactly j $(j = 0, 1, 2, \ldots, i)$ departures occur then under this condition the probability of the event $\xi(t) = k$ is equal to 1 if $k = i - j$ and 0 if $k \neq i - j$.

In particular, if $i = 0$ in (22) then we have

(23) $$P_{0k}(t) = \begin{cases} \displaystyle\int_0^t P_{1k}(t - x) \, dF(x) & \text{if } k > 0, \\[2ex] \displaystyle\int_0^t P_{10}(t - x) \, dF(x) + [1 - F(t)] & \text{if } k = 0. \end{cases}$$

Let us form the Laplace transform of (22) and introduce the generating function

$$U_k(s, z) = \sum_{i=0}^{\infty} \pi_{ik}(s) z^i$$

for fixed k; then we obtain that

(24) $\quad zU_k(s, z) = \phi[s + \mu(1 - z)][U_k(s, z) - \pi_{0k}(s)]$

$$+ \pi_{1k}(s) \frac{z\{\phi(s) - \phi[s + \mu(1 - z)]\}}{1 - z}$$

$$+ \begin{cases} z^{k+1} \dfrac{\{1 - \phi[s + \mu(1 - z)]\}}{s + \mu(1 - z)} & \text{if } k > 0, \\[3mm] \dfrac{z}{1 - z} \left\{ \dfrac{1 - \phi(s)}{s} - z \dfrac{1 - \phi[s + \mu(1 - z)]}{s + \mu(1 - z)} \right\} & \\ & \text{if } k = 0, \end{cases}$$

and by (23)

(25) $\quad \pi_{0k}(s) = \begin{cases} \phi(s)\pi_{1k}(s) & \text{if } k > 0, \\[3mm] \phi(s)\pi_{1k}(s) + \dfrac{[1 - \phi(s)]}{s} & \text{if } k = 0. \end{cases}$

Eliminating $\pi_{1k}(s)$ from (24) by (25), we obtain

(26) $\quad \{z - \phi[s + \mu(1 - z)]\} U_k(s, z)$

$$= \pi_{0k}(s) \left\{ \frac{z}{1 - z} \left[1 - \frac{\phi[s + \mu(1 - z)]}{\phi(s)} \right] - \phi[s + \mu(1 - z)] \right\}$$

$$+ \begin{cases} z^{k+1} \dfrac{[1 - \phi(s + \mu(1 - z))]}{s + \mu(1 - z)} & \text{if } k > 0, \\[3mm] \dfrac{z}{1 - z} \left\{ \left(\dfrac{1 - \phi(s)}{s} \right) \dfrac{\phi(s + \mu(1 - z))}{\phi(s)} \right. & \\[3mm] \left. - z \dfrac{[1 - \phi(s + \mu(1 - z))]}{s + \mu(1 - z)} \right\} & \text{if } k = 0. \end{cases}$$

It remains only to determine $\pi_{0k}(s)$. First we remark that $U_k(s, z)$ is a regular function of z if $|z| < 1$ and $\Re(s) > 0$. Furthermore the equation $z = \phi(s + \mu(1 - z))$ has one and only one root $z = \delta(s)$ in the unit circle $|z| < 1$. Thus if $z = \delta(s)$ then the left-hand side of (26) vanishes, and therefore the right-hand side of (26) must also vanish.

Thus we obtain that

$$(27) \quad \pi_{0k}(s) = \begin{cases} \dfrac{\phi(s)[1 - \delta(s)]^2[\delta(s)]^{k-1}}{[1 - \phi(s)]\{s + \mu[1 - \delta(s)]\}} & \text{if } k > 0, \\[4mm] \dfrac{1}{s} - \dfrac{\phi(s)[1 - \delta(s)]}{[1 - \phi(s)]\{s + \mu[1 - \delta(s)]\}} & \text{if } k = 0. \end{cases}$$

Putting (27) into (26) we obtain (19) and (20) as was to be proved.

THE TRANSIENT BEHAVIOR OF THE WAITING TIME. If we suppose, in particular, that the customers will be served in the order of arrival, then the investigation of the stochastic behavior of the process of the waiting time can be reduced immediately to that of the process of the queue size. For, if η_n denotes the waiting time of the nth customer, then we have

$$\eta_n = \sum_{i=1}^{\xi_n} \chi_i,$$

where $\chi_1, \chi_2, \ldots$ are independent random variables with distribution function $H(x)$ defined by (2) and they are also independent of ξ_n. Similarly, if $\eta(t)$ denotes the virtual waiting time at the instant t, i.e. the time that a customer would wait if he joined the queue at the instant t, then we can write that

$$\eta(t) = \sum_{i=1}^{\xi(t)} \chi_i,$$

where $\chi_1, \chi_2, \ldots$ have the same meaning as above.

If specifically $\xi(0) = 0$ then $\mathbf{P}\{\xi_n = k\} = p_{0k}^{(n-1)}$ $(n = 1, 2, \ldots)$ and if $\Omega_n(s) = \mathbf{E}\{e^{-s\eta_n}\}$ then we have

$$\Omega_n(s) = \sum_{k=0}^{\infty} p_{0k}^{(n-1)} \left(\frac{\mu}{\mu + s} \right)^n \qquad (n = 1, 2, \ldots)$$

whence by using (15)

$$(28) \qquad \sum_{n=1}^{\infty} \Omega_n(s) w^n = \frac{w[1 - d(w)]}{(1 - w)[1 - \mu d(w)/(\mu + s)]},$$

where $d(w) = \delta(0, w)$ is defined by Lemma 1.

THE PROBABILITY LAW OF THE BUSY PERIOD. Denote by $\tilde{G}_n(x)$ the probability that a busy period consists of n services and its length is at most x. Write

$$\Gamma_n(s) = \int_0^\infty e^{-sx} \, d\tilde{G}_n(x),$$

if $\Re(s) \geqq 0$. We shall prove

THEOREM 5. *If* $\Re(s) \geqq 0$ *and* $|w| \leqq 1$ *then*

(29)
$$\sum_{n=1}^\infty \Gamma_n(s)w^n = \frac{\mu[w - \delta(s, w)]}{s + \mu[1 - \delta(s, w)]},$$

where $z = \delta(s, w)$ *is that root of the equation*

$$z = w\phi[s + \mu(1 - z)]$$

which has the smallest absolute value.

We have

(30)
$$\tilde{G}_n(x) = \frac{\mu^n}{(n-1)!} \iint_{\substack{u+v \leqq x \\ 0 \leqq u, \, 0 \leqq v}} e^{-\mu(u+v)} v(u+v)^{n-2}[1 - F(v)] \, du \, dF_{n-1}(v).$$

PROOF. Let us suppose that the queue size is j at the arrival of a customer and under this assumption denote by $G_{j,n}(x)$ the joint probability that the server will be idle for the first time after $n + j$ services and that the total time of these $n + j$ services is at most x. Write

$$\Gamma_{jn}(s) = \int_0^\infty e^{-sx} \, dG_{jn}(x),$$

if $\Re(s) \geqq 0$. Clearly, $\tilde{G}_n(x) = G_{0n}(x)$ and $\Gamma_n(s) = \Gamma_{0n}(s)$.

By the theorem of total probability we can write that

$$G_{j1}(x) = \mu \int_0^x e^{-\mu y} \frac{(\mu y)^j}{j!} [1 - F(y)] \, dy,$$

and

$$G_{j,n+1}(x) = \sum_{i=0}^j \int_0^x e^{-\mu y} \frac{(\mu y)^i}{i!} G_{j+1-i,n}(x - y) \, dF(y)$$

$$(n = 1, 2, \ldots).$$

Hence

(31) $$\Gamma_{j,1}(s) = \mu \int_0^\infty e^{-(s+\mu)x} \frac{(\mu x)^j}{j!} [1 - F(y)] \, dy,$$

and

(32) $$\Gamma_{j,n+1}(s) = \sum_{i=0}^{j} \Gamma_{j+1-i,n}(s) \int_0^\infty e^{-(s+\mu)x} \frac{(\mu x)^i}{i!} \, dF(x).$$

Introducing the generating function

$$\Omega_n(s, z) = \sum_{j=0}^{\infty} \Gamma_{jn}(s) z^j,$$

which is convergent if $\Re(s) \geqq 0$ and $|z| \leqq 1$, we obtain by (31) that

(33) $$\Omega_1(s, z) = \mu[1 - \phi(s + \mu(1 - z))]/[s + \mu(1 - z)]$$

and by (32) that

(34) $$z\Omega_{n+1}(s, z) = \phi(s + \mu(1 - z))[\Omega_n(s, z) - \Gamma_n(s)].$$

By (33) and (34) we obtain

(35) $$\sum_{n=1}^{\infty} \Omega_n(s, z) w^n$$

$$= \frac{\dfrac{z\mu w[1 - \phi(s + \mu(1 - z))]}{s + \mu(1 - z)} - w\phi(s + \mu(1 - z)) \sum_{n=1}^{\infty} \Gamma_n(s) w^n}{z - w\phi(s + \mu(1 - z))}.$$

The right-hand side of (35) is a regular function of z if $|z| < 1$, $\Re(s) \geqq 0$ and $|w| < 1$. By Rouché's theorem it follows that the equation

$$z = w\phi(s + \mu(1 - z))$$

has one and only one root in the unit circle $|z| < 1$ if $\Re(s) \geqq 0$ and $|w| < 1$. This root is denoted by $z = \delta(s, w)$. Accordingly $z = \delta(s, w)$ must be a root of the numerator of (35) too. Hence

(36) $$\sum_{n=1}^{\infty} \Gamma_n(s) w^n = \frac{\mu[w - \delta(s, w)]}{s + \mu[1 - \delta(s, w)]}$$

if $\Re(s) \geqq 0$ and $|w| < 1$. If $z = \delta(s, w)$ is defined as the root with smallest absolute value of $z = w\phi(s + \mu(1 - z))$, then (36) is valid for $\Re(s) \geqq 0$ and $|w| \leqq 1$. For, the left-hand side of (36) is a continuous function of w if $\Re(s) \geqq 0$ and $|w| \leqq 1$ and the required result can be obtained by using the continuity of $\delta(s, w)$.

If we use the expansion of $[\delta(s, w)]^j$ then by (29) we get

$$
\Gamma_n(s) = \sum_{j=1}^{n} \left(\frac{\mu}{\mu + s}\right)^j \frac{\mu^{n-j}}{(n-j)!} \left\{ \binom{j-1}{n-1} \int_0^\infty e^{-(\mu+s)x} x^{n-j} \, dF_{n-1}(x) \right.
$$

$$
\left. - \frac{j}{n} \int_0^\infty e^{-(\mu+s)x} x^{n-j} \, dF_n(x) \right\},
$$

whence by inversion

$$
(37) \quad \tilde{G}_n(x) = \frac{\mu^n}{(n-1)!} \iint_{\substack{u+v \leqq x \\ u \geqq 0, v \geqq 0}} e^{-\mu(u+v)} u(u+v)^{n-2} \, dF_{n-1}(v) \, du
$$

$$
- \frac{\mu^n}{(n-1)!} \iint_{\substack{u+v \leqq x \\ u \geqq 0, v \geqq 0}} e^{-\mu(u+v)} u(u+v)^{n-2} \, dF_n(v) \, du
$$

$$
- \frac{\mu^n}{n!} \iint_{\substack{u+v \leqq x \\ u \geqq 0, v \geqq 0}} e^{-\mu(u+v)} v(u+v)^{n-2} \, dF_n(v) \, du,
$$

which is in agreement with (30).

On the other hand the Lagrange expansion of (29) is given by

$$
(38) \quad \frac{\mu[w - \delta(s, w)]}{s + \mu[1 - \delta(s, w)]}
$$

$$
= \frac{\mu w}{s + \mu} - (s + \mu - \mu w) \sum_{n=1}^{\infty} \frac{(-w\mu)^n}{n!} \frac{d^{n-1}}{ds^{n-1}} \left\{ \frac{[\phi(s + \mu)]^n}{(s + \mu)^2} \right\},
$$

whence $\Gamma_n(s)$ and $\tilde{G}_n(x)$ can be obtained in a similiar way.

If $G(x)$ denotes the probability that the length of the busy period is $\leqq x$, then

$$
\Gamma(s) = \int_0^\infty e^{-sx} \, dG(x)
$$

is given by (38) with $w = 1$. Thus by inversion we get

$$
(39) \quad G(x) = \mu \sum_{n=1}^{\infty} e^{-\mu x} \frac{(\mu x)^{n-1}}{n!} \int_0^x [1 - F_n(y)] \, dy.
$$

Problems for solution

PROBLEM 10. Find the stationary distribution of $\{\xi_n\}$.

PROBLEM 11. Find the stationary distribution of $\{\eta_n\}$ given that the serving happens in the order of the arrival of the customers.

6. The time dependence of single server queues with Palm input and exponential service times in the case of batch arrival

Let us suppose that customers arrive at a counter in batches of size m at the instants $\tau_0, \tau_1, \ldots, \tau_n, \ldots$ where the inter-arrival times $\tau_{n+1} - \tau_n$ $(n = 0, 1, \ldots; \tau_0 = 0)$ are identically distributed, independent, positive random variables with distribution function

$$(1) \qquad\qquad \mathbf{P}\{\tau_{n+1} - \tau_n \leqq x\} = F(x).$$

We say that $\{\tau_n\}$ is a *Palm process*. The customers will be served by a single server. The server is idle if and only if there is no customer waiting at the counter; otherwise the order of the services is irrelevant. The service times are identically distributed, independent random variables with distribution function

$$(2) \qquad\qquad H(x) = \begin{cases} 1 - e^{-\mu x} & \text{if } x \geqq 0, \\ 0 & \text{if } x < 0, \end{cases}$$

and independent of $\{\tau_n\}$.

We are interested in the investigation of the stochastic behavior of the queue size and that of the busy period of this process.

Denote by $\xi(t)$ the queue size at the instant t, i.e. $\xi(t)$ is the number of customers waiting or being served at the instant t. We say that the system is in state E_k at the instant t if $\xi(t) = k$. Further define $\xi_n = \xi(\tau_n - 0)$, i.e. ξ_n is the queue size immediately before the arrival of the nth batch $(n = 0, 1, 2, \ldots)$.

Denote by

$$\phi(s) = \int_0^\infty e^{-sx} \, dF(x)$$

the Laplace-Stieltjes transform of $F(x)$ and let

$$\beta = \int_0^\infty x \, dF(x).$$

Throughout this section we use the following auxiliary theorems which agree with Lemmas 1 and 2 in Section 4.

LEMMA 1. *If* (a) $\Re(s) \geqq 0$, $|w| < 1$ *or* (b) $\Re(s) > 0$, $|w| \leqq 1$ *or* (c) $\lambda\beta > m$ *and* $\Re(s) \geqq 0$, $|w| \leqq 1$, *then the equation*

$$(3) \qquad z^m = w\phi(s + \mu(1 - z))$$

has exactly m roots $z = \delta_r(s, w)$ $(r = 1, 2, \ldots, m)$ in the unit circle $|z| < 1$. We have

$$(4) \qquad \delta_r(s, w) = \sum_{j=1}^\infty \frac{(-\mu)^{j-1}(\epsilon_r w^{1/m})^j}{j!} \left(\frac{d^{j-1}[\phi(\mu + s)]^{j/m}}{ds^{j-1}} \right)$$

where $\epsilon_r = e^{2\pi i r/m}$ $(r = 1, 2, \ldots, m)$ are the mth roots of unity.

If $\delta_r(s, w)$ is defined by (4) for $\Re(s) \geqq 0$ and $|w| < 1$, then in this domain $\delta_r(s, w)$ is a continuous function of s and w, $|\delta_r(s, w)| \leqq 1$, and $z = \delta_r(s, w)$ satisfies the equation

$$(5) \qquad z = \epsilon_r[w\phi(s + \mu(1 - z))]^{1/m}.$$

The roots $\delta_r(s, w)$ $(r = 1, 2, \ldots, m)$ are distinct if $w \neq 0$.

Let us introduce the following abbreviations. Let $\delta_r(s) = \delta_r(s, 1)$, $d_r(w) = \delta_r(0, w)$ and $\delta_r = \delta_r(0, 1)$ $(r = 1, 2, \ldots, m)$. They satisfy the equations $z^m = \phi(s + \mu(1 - z))$, $z^m = w\phi(\mu(1 - z))$ and $z^m = \phi(\mu(1 - z))$ respectively.

Further we have

$$\sum_{r=1}^m [\delta_r(s, w)]^n = n \sum_{j \geqq n/m} \frac{w^j \mu^{mj-n}}{j(mj - n)!} \int_0^\infty e^{-(\mu+s)x} x^{mj-n} \, dF_j(x),$$

where $F_j(x)$ denotes the jth iterated convolution of $F(x)$ with itself.

LEMMA 2. *Let $\delta_r = \delta_r(0, 1)$ where $\delta_r(s, w)$ is defined by (4). If $\mu\beta > m$ then $\delta_1, \delta_2, \ldots, \delta_m$ are the m roots in z of the equation*

$$(6) \qquad z^m = \phi(\mu(1 - z))$$

in the unit circle $|z| < 1$. *If* $\mu\beta \leqq m$ *then* $\delta_1, \delta_2, \ldots, \delta_{m-1}$ *are the* $m - 1$
roots in z *of* (6) *in the unit circle* $|z| < 1$ *whereas* $\delta_m = 1$.

THE TRANSIENT BEHAVIOR OF THE QUEUE SIZE. Let $\{\nu_n\}$ be a
sequence of identically distributed, independent random variables
with distribution

$$(7) \qquad \mathbf{P}\{\nu_n = j\} = \int_0^\infty e^{-\mu x} \frac{(\mu x)^j}{j!} \, dF(x) \qquad (j = 0, 1, 2, \ldots).$$

It is easy to see that

$$(8) \qquad \qquad \xi_{n+1} = [\xi_n + m - \nu_n]^+.$$

Accordingly the sequence of random variables $\{\xi_n\}$ forms a homogeneous Markov chain. We shall say that the system is in state E_k at
the nth step if $\xi_n = k$.

The higher transition probabilities

$$p_{ik}^{(n)} = \mathbf{P}\{\xi_n = k \,|\, \xi_0 = i\} \qquad (n = 0, 1, 2, \ldots)$$

can be obtained by the following

THEOREM 1. *If* $|z| \leqq 1$, $|w| < 1$ *and* $|y| < 1$, *then we have*

$$(9) \quad (1 - y)(1 - w) \sum_{i=0}^\infty \sum_{k=0}^\infty \sum_{n=0}^\infty p_{ik}^{(n)} y^i z^k w^n = \prod_{r=1}^m \left(\frac{1 - d_r(w)}{1 - z d_r(w)} \right)$$

$$- \frac{y(1 - z)(1 - w)}{(1 - zy)[y^m - w\phi(\mu(1 - y))]} \prod_{r=1}^m \left(\frac{y - d_r(w)}{1 - z d_r(w)} \right),$$

where $d_r(w)$ $(r = 1, 2, \ldots, m)$ *are the* m *roots in* z *of the equation*

$$(10) \qquad \qquad z^m = w\phi(\mu(1 - z))$$

in the unit circle $|z| < 1$.

Instead of proving this theorem we shall prove the more general
Theorem 2 from which Theorem 1 can be deduced as a particular case.
Theorem 2 determines the joint distribution of τ_n and ξ_n which we
need at the investigation of the stochastic law of the busy period.
Theorem 2 can be proved in exactly the same way as the more special
Theorem 1.

The joint distribution of the random variables τ_n and ξ_n is determined by the probabilities

$$P_{ik}^{(n)}(x) = \mathbf{P}\{\tau_n \leq x, \xi_n = k \,|\, \xi_0 = i\},$$

and these probabilities can be uniquely determined by the Laplace-Stieltjes transforms

$$\pi_{ik}^{(n)}(s) = \int_0^\infty e^{-sx} \, dP_{ik}^{(n)}(x).$$

We have

THEOREM 2. *If* $\Re(s) \geq 0$, $|z| \leq 1$, $|w| < 1$ *and* $|y| < 1$, *then we have*

$$(1 - y)[1 - w\phi(s)] \sum_{i=0}^\infty \sum_{k=0}^\infty \sum_{n=0}^\infty \pi_{ik}^{(n)}(s) y^i z^k w^n = \prod_{r=1}^m \left(\frac{1 - \delta_r(s, w)}{1 - z\delta_r(s, w)} \right)$$

(11)

$$- \frac{y(1 - z)[1 - w\phi(s)]}{(1 - zy)[y^m - w\phi(s + \mu(1 - y))]} \prod_{r=1}^m \left(\frac{y - \delta_r(s, w)}{1 - z\delta_r(s, w)} \right),$$

where $\delta_r(s, w)$ $(r = 1, 2, \ldots, m)$ *are the m roots in z of the equation*

(12) $$z^m = w\phi(s + \mu(1 - z))$$

in the unit circle $|z| < 1$.

PROOF. If $w = 0$ then the theorem is obviously true; therefore we suppose that $w \neq 0$. We shall use only the following theorem of the theory of functions of a complex variable: If $f(z)$ is regular for all finite values of z and

$$\lim_{|z| \to \infty} \frac{f(z)}{|z|^k} = 0,$$

then $f(z)$ is a polynomial of degree $< k$. If $k = 1$ then $f(z)$ is constant.

Let us introduce the generating function

$$\Pi_i^{(n)}(s, z) = \sum_{j=0}^\infty \pi_{ij}^{(n)}(s) z^j,$$

which is convergent if $|z| \leq 1$ and $\Re(s) \geq 0$. We shall show that if $|z| = 1$ then $\Pi_i^{(n)}(s, z)$ $(n = 0, 1, 2, \ldots)$ satisfies the following recurrence formula

$$(13) \qquad \Pi_i^{(n+1)}(s, z) = z^m \phi \left(s + \mu \left(1 - \frac{1}{z} \right) \right) \Pi_i^{(n)}(s, z)$$

$$+ \sum_{j=0}^{\infty} C_{ij}^{(n+1)}(s) \left(1 - \frac{1}{z^j} \right),$$

where for every i and n

$$\sum_{j=0}^{\infty} |C_{ij}^{(n)}(s)| < 1.$$

We have

$$\Pi_i^{(n)}(s, z) = \mathbf{E}\{e^{-s\tau_n} z^{\xi_n} | \xi_0 = i\}$$

and further

$$(14) \qquad \tau_{n+1} = \tau_n + \theta_n,$$

and

$$(15) \qquad \xi_{n+1} = [\xi_n + m - \nu_n]^+,$$

where $\{(\theta_n, \nu_n)\}$ is a sequence of independent vector random variables with distributions $\mathbf{P}\{\theta_n \leq x\} = F(x)$, and

$$\mathbf{P}\{\nu_n = j | \theta_n = x\} = e^{-\mu x} \frac{(\mu x)^j}{j!} \qquad (j = 0, 1, 2, \ldots).$$

By (14) and (15) we obtain (13). The first term on the right-hand side of (13) is $\mathbf{E}\{e^{-s\tau_{n+1}} z^{\xi_n + m - \nu_n} | \xi_0 = i\}$. To obtain $\mathbf{E}\{e^{-s\tau_{n+1}} z^{\xi_{n+1}} | \xi_0 = i\}$ we have to omit from this the terms corresponding to the values $\xi_n + m - \nu_n = -1, -2, -3, \ldots$ and take into consideration that $\xi_{n+1} = 0$ if and only if $\xi_n + m - \nu_n \leq 0$. Thus we obtain the second term on the right-hand side of (13), where

$$C_{ij}^{(n+1)}(s) = \mathbf{P}\{\xi_n + m - \nu_n = -j | \xi_0 = i\}$$

$$\cdot \mathbf{E}\{e^{-s\tau_n} | \xi_n + m - \nu_n = -j, \xi_0 = i\}.$$

In (13) we used the relation

$$\mathbf{E}\{e^{-s\theta_n} z^{-\nu_n}\} = \phi \left(s + \mu \left(1 - \frac{1}{z} \right) \right)$$

if $|z| = 1$.

Now let $\Re(s) \geqq 0$, $|z| \leqq 1$, $|w| < 1$, $|y| < 1$ and define

$$A_i(z, s, w) = \sum_{n=0}^{\infty} \Pi_i^{(n)}(s, z)w^n$$

and

$$A(z, s, w, y) = \sum_{i=0}^{\infty} A_i(z, s, w)y^i.$$

Clearly,

(16)
$$A(z, s, w, y) = \sum_{i=0}^{\infty} \sum_{k=0}^{\infty} \sum_{n=0}^{\infty} \pi_{ik}^{(n)}(s)y^i z^k w^n$$

and by definition $A(z, s, w, y)$ is a regular function of z if $|z| \leqq 1$, $\Re(s) \geqq 0$, $|w| < 1$, and $|y| < 1$. If $|z| = 1$ then by (13) we have

$$A_i(z, s, w) = \frac{z^i + \sum\limits_{n=1}^{\infty} \sum\limits_{j=0}^{\infty} C_{ij}^{(n)}(s)w^n \left(1 - \dfrac{1}{z^j}\right)}{1 - wz^m \phi\left(s + \mu\left(1 - \dfrac{1}{z}\right)\right)} \, ;$$

and hence if $|z| = 1$

(17)
$$A(z, s, w, y) = \frac{\dfrac{1}{1 - zy} + \sum\limits_{j=0}^{\infty} C_j(s, w, y) \left(1 - \dfrac{1}{z^j}\right)}{1 - wz^m \phi\left(s + \mu\left(1 - \dfrac{1}{z}\right)\right)},$$

where the coefficients

$$C_j(s, w, y) = \sum_{n=1}^{\infty} \sum_{i=0}^{\infty} C_{ij}^{(n)}(s)w^n y^i \qquad (j = 0, 1, 2, \ldots)$$

satisfy the following condition

$$\sum_{j=0}^{\infty} |C_j(s, w, y)| < |w|/(1 - |w|)(1 - |y|).$$

Now let us define $A(z, s, w, y)$ also for $|z| > 1$ by (17) if $\Re(s) \geqq 0$, $|w| < 1$ and $|y| < 1$. Thus $A(z, s, w, y)$ has singularities only at $z = 1/y$ and at the zeros of the denominator of (17) outside the unit circle. These zeros evidently agree with the reciprocal values of the roots of (12) inside the unit circle. If we define

$$(18) \quad B(z, s, w, y) = A(z, s, w, y)(1 - zy) \prod_{r=1}^{m} \left(z - \frac{1}{\delta_r(s, w)} \right)$$

then $B(z, s, w, y)$ will be a regular function of z in the whole complex plane. Since obviously

$$\lim_{|z| \to \infty} \frac{B(z, s, w, y)}{|z|^2} = 0,$$

$B(z, s, w, y)$ is a linear function of z, that is,

$$(19) \quad\quad B(z, s, w, y) = B_0(s, w, y) + z B_1(s, w, y).$$

$B_0(s, w, y)$ and $B_1(s, w, y)$ can be determined as follows. We have clearly

$$A(1, s, w, y) = \sum_{i=0}^{\infty} \sum_{n=0}^{\infty} [\phi(s)]^n y^i w^n = \frac{1}{(1 - y)[1 - w\phi(s)]}$$

and hence by (19)

$$(20) \quad\quad B(1, s, w, y) = \frac{1}{[1 - w\phi(s)]} \prod_{r=1}^{m} \left(1 - \frac{1}{\delta_r(s, w)} \right).$$

Further by (17)

$$\lim_{z \to 1/y} (1 - zy) A(z, s, w, y) = \frac{y^m}{y^m - w\phi(s + \mu(1 - y))}$$

and hence by (19)

$$(21) \quad B\left(\frac{1}{y}, s, w, y \right) = \frac{1}{[y^m - w\phi(s + \mu(1 - y))]} \prod_{r=1}^{m} \left(1 - \frac{y}{\delta_r(s, w)} \right).$$

Thus (19) is determined by (20) and (21). Finally, $A(z, s, w, y)$ can be obtained by (18). So we get (11), which was to be proved. It is to be remarked that in the above proof we did not exploit the fact that the roots $\delta_r(s, w)$ are distinct.

REMARK 1. If we restrict ourselves to the case $y = 0$ in proving (11), then we have

$$\lim_{|z| \to \infty} \frac{B(z, s, w, 0)}{|z|} = 0,$$

that is, $B(z, s, w, 0)$ is independent of z and so it is determined by (20). In this case we obtain by (18) that

$$(22) \quad [1 - w\phi(s)] \sum_{k=0}^{\infty} \sum_{n=0}^{\infty} \pi_{0k}^{(n)}(s) z^k w^n = \prod_{r=1}^{m} \left(\frac{1 - \delta_r(s, w)}{1 - z\delta_r(s, w)} \right),$$

where $\delta_r(s, w)$ $(r = 1, 2, \ldots, m)$ are defined in Lemma 1.

To prove Theorem 1 let us note that $p_{ik}^{(n)} = \pi_{ik}^{(n)}(0)$ and thus if $s = 0$ in (11), then we get (9). In particular if $s = 0$ in (22), then we get

$$(23) \quad (1 - w) \sum_{k=0}^{\infty} \sum_{n=0}^{\infty} p_{0k}^{(n)} z^k w^n = \prod_{r=1}^{m} \left(\frac{1 - d_r(w)}{1 - z d_r(w)} \right),$$

where $d_r(w)$ $(r = 1, 2, \ldots, m)$ are defined in Lemma 1.

Using Theorem 1 we shall prove

THEOREM 3. *If* $\mu\beta > m$ *then the limiting probability distribution* $\lim_{n \to \infty} \mathbf{P}\{\xi_n = k\} = P_k$ $(k = 0, 1, 2, \ldots)$ *exists and is independent of the initial distribution. We have*

$$(24) \quad \sum_{k=0}^{\infty} P_k z^k = \prod_{r=1}^{m} \left(\frac{1 - \delta_r}{1 - z\delta_r} \right),$$

where δ_r $(r = 1, 2, \ldots, m)$ *are the* m *roots in* z *of the equation*

$$(25) \quad z^m = \phi(\mu(1 - z))$$

in the unit circle $|z| < 1$.

PROOF. Since $\{\xi_n\}$ is an irreducible and aperiodic Markov chain, the limit $\lim_{n \to \infty} p_{ik}^{(n)} = P_k$ always exists irrespective of i and either every $P_k > 0$ and P_k is a probability distribution or every $P_k = 0$. Let $i = 0$. Using (23) by Abel's theorem we get

$$\sum_{k=0}^{\infty} P_k z^k = \lim_{w \to 1} (1 - w) \sum_{k=0}^{\infty} \sum_{n=0}^{\infty} p_{0k}^{(n)} z^k w^n = \prod_{r=1}^{m} \left(\frac{1 - \delta_r}{1 - z\delta_r} \right).$$

If $\mu\beta > m$ then $\{P_k\}$ is a proper probability distribution, because $|\delta_r| < 1$ $(r = 1, 2, \ldots, m)$. If $\mu\beta \leqq m$ then $\delta_m = 1$ and therefore $P_k = 0$ for every k.

THE TRANSIENT BEHAVIOR OF THE WAITING TIME. If we suppose in particular that the batches will be served in the order of their arrival and if $\eta(t)$ denotes the occupation time of the server at the instant t, i.e. $\eta(t)$ is the time which elapses from t until the server becomes idle for the first time if no customers join the queue after time t, then we have

$$\eta(t) = \sum_{i=1}^{\xi(t)} \chi_i,$$

where $\{\chi_i\}$ is a sequence of identically distributed, independent random variables with distribution function $H(x)$ and independent of $\xi(t)$.

THE PROBABILITY LAW OF THE BUSY PERIOD. We need the following probability

$$F_{ik}^{(n)}(x) = \mathbf{P}\{\tau_n \leqq x, \xi_n = k, \xi_{n-1} > 0, \ldots, \xi_1 > 0 | \xi_0 = i\}.$$

The Laplace-Stieltjes transform of $F_{ik}^{(n)}(x)$,

$$\Phi_{ik}^{(n)}(s) = \int_0^\infty e^{-sx}\, dF_{ik}^{(n)}(x),$$

is given by

THEOREM 4. *If* $\Re(s) \geqq 0$ *and* $|w| < 1$ *then we have*

$$(26) \quad \sum_{n=1}^\infty \Phi_{ik}^{(n)}(s)w^n = \sum_{n=1}^\infty \pi_{ik}^{(n)}(s)w^n - \frac{\displaystyle\sum_{n=1}^\infty \pi_{0k}^{(n)}(s)w^n \sum_{n=1}^\infty \pi_{i0}^{(n)}(s)w^n}{1 + \displaystyle\sum_{n=1}^\infty \pi_{00}^{(n)}(s)w^n},$$

where the expressions on the right-hand side can be obtained by (11).

PROOF. By the theorem of total probability we get

$$P_{ik}^{(n)}(x) = F_{ik}^{(n)}(x) + \sum_{j=1}^{n-1} \int_0^x P_{0k}^{(n-j)}(x - y)\, dF_{i0}^{(j)}(y),$$

and forming Laplace-Stieltjes transforms we have

$$\Pi_{ik}^{(n)}(s) = \Phi_{ik}^{(n)}(s) + \sum_{j=1}^{n-1} \Pi_{0k}^{(n-j)}(s)\Phi_{i0}^{(j)}(s).$$

Hence

$$(27) \quad \sum_{n=1}^{\infty} \Pi_{ik}^{(n)}(s)w^n = \sum_{n=1}^{\infty} \Phi_{ik}^{(n)}(s)w^n + \sum_{n=1}^{\infty} \Pi_{0k}^{(n)}(s)w^n \cdot \sum_{n=1}^{\infty} \Phi_{i0}^{(n)}(s)w^n.$$

If $k = 0$ in (27), then we get (26) for $k = 0$, whence (26) follows for every k by (27).

By (26) and (11) we can prove the following

THEOREM 5. *If* $\Re(s) \geqq 0$ *and* $|w| < 1$ *then we have*

$$(28) \quad \sum_{n=1}^{\infty} \sum_{k=0}^{\infty} \Phi_{0k}^{(n)}(s)w^n z^k = \prod_{r=1}^{m} \frac{1}{[1 - z\delta_r(s, w)]} - \frac{1 - w\phi(s)}{\prod_{r=1}^{m} [1 - \delta_r(s, w)]},$$

where $\delta_r(s, w)$ $(r = 1, 2, \ldots, m)$ *are defined in Lemma 1.*

In particular if $z = 0$ in (28), then we have

$$(29) \quad \sum_{n=1}^{\infty} \Phi_{00}^{(n)}(s)w^n = 1 - \frac{1 - w\phi(s)}{\prod_{r=1}^{m} [1 - \delta_r(s, w)]}.$$

REMARK 2. If $F_{00}(x)$ denotes the probability that the distance between two consecutive transitions $E_0 \to E_m$ is at most x, then we have

$$F_{00}(x) = \sum_{n=1}^{\infty} F_{00}^{(n)}(x),$$

and if $\Phi_{00}(s)$ denotes its Laplace-Stieltjes transform, then by (29) we get

$$(30) \quad \Phi_{00}(s) = 1 - \frac{1 - \phi(s)}{\prod_{r=1}^{m} [1 - \delta_r(s)]},$$

where $\delta_r(s) = \delta_r(s, 1)$ $(r = 1, 2, \ldots, m)$.

Now denote by $\tilde{G}_n(x)$ the probability that a busy period consists in serving n batches and its length is at most x. Write

$$\Gamma_n(s) = \int_0^{\infty} e^{-sx} d\tilde{G}_n(x)$$

if $\Re(s) \geq 0$. We shall prove

THEOREM 6. *If $\Re(s) \geq 0$ and $|w| < 1$ then we have*

$$(31) \qquad \sum_{n=1}^{\infty} \Gamma_n(s)w^n = 1 - \frac{1 - w\left(\dfrac{\mu}{\mu + s}\right)^m}{\displaystyle\prod_{r=1}^{m}\left[1 - \frac{\mu}{\mu + s}\,\delta_r(s, w)\right]},$$

where the $\delta_r(s, w)$ $(r = 1, 2, \ldots, m)$ are the m roots in z of (3) in the unit circle $|z| < 1$.

PROOF. If $w = 0$ then (31) is evidently true. Thus we suppose that $w \neq 0$. By the theorem of total probability we can write that

$$\tilde{G}_1(x) = \mu \int_0^x [1 - F(y)]e^{-\mu y} \frac{(\mu y)^{m-1}}{(m - 1)!}\,dy,$$

and if $n = 2, 3, \ldots$ then

$$\tilde{G}_n(x) = \mu \sum_{k=1}^{\infty} \int_0^x F_{0k}^{(n-1)}(x - y)[1 - F(y)]e^{-\mu y} \frac{(\mu y)^{k-m+1}}{(k - m + 1)!}\,dy.$$

Hence

$$\Gamma_1(s) = \mu \int_0^{\infty} e^{-(\mu+s)x} \frac{(\mu x)^{m-1}}{(m - 1)!}[1 - F(x)]\,dx$$

and

$$\Gamma_n(s) = \mu \sum_{k=1}^{\infty} \Phi_{0k}^{(n-1)}(s) \int_0^{\infty} e^{-(\mu+s)x} \frac{(\mu x)^{k-m+1}}{(k - m + 1)!}[1 - F(x)]\,dx$$

if $n = 2, 3, \ldots$. Forming the generating function of $\{\Gamma_n(s)\}$ we get

$$(32) \qquad \sum_{n=1}^{\infty} \Gamma_n(s)w^n = \mu w \sum_{k=0}^{\infty} C_k(s, w) \int_0^{\infty} e^{-(\mu+s)x} \frac{(\mu x)^k}{k!}[1 - F(x)]\,dx,$$

where $C_k(s, w) \equiv 0$ if $k = 0, 1, \ldots, m - 2$, $C_{m-1}(s, w) \equiv 1$ and

$$C_{k+m-1}(s, w) = \sum_{n=0}^{\infty} \Phi_{0k}^{(n)}(s)w^n \qquad (k = 1, 2, \ldots).$$

Thus by (28) we get

$$(33) \qquad \sum_{k=0}^{\infty} C_k(s, w)z^k = \frac{1}{z}\prod_{r=1}^{m}\left(\frac{z}{1 - z\delta_r(s, w)}\right).$$

For fixed s and w write

$$(34) \qquad f(z) = \prod_{r=1}^{m} \left(\frac{z}{1 - z\delta_r(s, w)} \right).$$

Then

$$C_k(s, w) = \frac{1}{2\pi i} \oint_{|z|=1} \frac{f(z)}{z^{k+2}} \, dz \qquad (k = 0, 1, 2, \ldots)$$

and by (32) we get for $s \neq 0$

$$(35) \qquad \sum_{n=1}^{\infty} \Gamma_n(s)w^n = \frac{\mu w}{2\pi i} \oint_{|z|=1} f(z) \frac{\left[1 - \phi\left(s + \mu\left(1 - \frac{1}{z}\right)\right) \right]}{z[(\mu + s)z - \mu]} \, dz.$$

Now the integral on the right-hand side can be evaluated as $-2\pi i$ times the sum of the residues of the integrand at the poles $z = 1/\delta_r(s, w)$ $(r = 1, 2, \ldots, m)$ outside the unit circle. The residue at $z = 1/\delta_r(s, w)$ depends on the value $\phi\left(s + \mu\left(1 - \frac{1}{z}\right)\right)$ at $z = 1/\delta_r(s, w)$, but if $z = 1/\delta_r(s, w)$ then $\phi\left(s + \mu\left(1 - \frac{1}{z}\right)\right) = 1/wz^m$. Accordingly (35) remains unchanged by the substitution

$$\phi\left(s + \mu\left(1 - \frac{1}{z}\right)\right) = 1/wz^m.$$

Hence

$$(36) \qquad \sum_{n=1}^{\infty} \Gamma_n(s)w^n = \frac{\mu}{2\pi i} \oint_{|z|=1} f(z) \frac{\left(w - \frac{1}{z^m} \right)}{z[(\mu + s)z - \mu]} \, dz.$$

On the other hand this integral can be evaluated as $2\pi i$ times the sum of the residues of the integrand at the poles $z = 0$ and $z = \mu/(\mu + s)$ inside the unit circle. Proceeding in this way we get

$$\sum_{n=1}^{\infty} \Gamma_n(s)w^n = 1 - \left[\left(\frac{\mu + s}{\mu} \right)^m - w \right] f\left(\frac{\mu}{\mu + s} \right),$$

where $f(z)$ is defined by (34). This completes the proof of the theorem.

REMARK 3. Denote by $G(x)$ the distribution function of the length of the busy period and let $\Gamma(s)$ be its Laplace-Stieltjes transform. Evidently,

$$\Gamma(s) = \sum_{n=1}^{\infty} \Gamma_n(s)$$

and therefore if $w \to 1$ in (31) we get

$$(37) \qquad \Gamma(s) = 1 - \frac{1 - \left(\dfrac{\mu}{\mu + s}\right)^m}{\displaystyle\prod_{r=1}^{m} \left[1 - \dfrac{\mu}{\mu + s} \delta_r(s)\right]},$$

where $\delta_r(s) = \delta_r(s, 1)$ $(r = 1, 2, \ldots, m)$.

The probability that a busy period consists in serving n batches is $f_{00}^{(n)} = \Gamma_n(0)$ and therefore by (31)

$$(38) \qquad \sum_{n=1}^{\infty} f_{00}^{(n)} w^n = 1 - \frac{1 - w}{\displaystyle\prod_{r=1}^{m} [1 - d_r(w)]},$$

where $d_r(w) = \delta_r(0, w)$ $(r = 1, 2, \ldots, m)$.

THE PROBABILITY THAT THE SERVER IS IDLE. The Laplace transform of $P_{00}(t)$ is given by

THEOREM 7. *Denote by $P_{00}(t)$ the probability that the server is idle at the instant t given that he was idle at $t = 0$. If $\Re(s) > 0$ then*

$$(39) \qquad \int_0^{\infty} e^{-st} P_{00}(t) \, dt$$

$$= \frac{1}{s} - \frac{\left[1 - \left(\dfrac{\mu}{\mu + s}\right)^m\right]}{s[1 - \phi(s)]} \prod_{r=1}^{m} \left(\frac{1 - \delta_r(s)}{1 - \dfrac{\mu}{\mu + s} \delta_r(s)}\right),$$

where $\delta_r(s)$ $(r = 1, 2, \ldots, m)$ are the m roots in z of the equation

$$(40) \qquad z^m = \phi(s + \mu(1 - z))$$

in the unit circle $|z| < 1$.

PROOF. Clearly, $P_{00}(t) = \mathbf{P}\{\xi(t) = 0 | \xi(0) = 0\}$. Denote by $M_{00}(t)$ the expectation of the number of transitions $E_0 \rightarrow E_m$ occurring in the time interval $[0, t]$ given that $\xi(0) = 0$. Then we can write that

$$(41) \qquad P_{00}(t) = 1 - \int_0^t [1 - G(t - x)] \, dM_{00}(x),$$

where

$$M_{00}(t) = I(t) + F_{00}(t) + F_{00}(t) * F_{00}(t) + \cdots$$

and $I(t) = 1$ if $t \geqq 0$, $I(t) = 0$ if $t < 0$. Since

$$\int_0^\infty e^{-st} \, dM_{00}(t) = \frac{1}{1 - \Phi_{00}(s)},$$

we get by (41) that

$$\int_0^\infty e^{-st} P_{00}(t) \, dt = \frac{1}{s}\left[1 - \frac{1 - \Gamma(s)}{1 - \Phi_{00}(s)}\right],$$

where $\Phi_{00}(s)$ is defined by (30) and $\Gamma(s)$ by (37).

REMARK 4. Now let us consider the following queueing process: Customers arrive at a counter at the instants $\tau_0, \tau_1, \ldots,$ $\tau_n, \ldots$ where the inter-arrival times $\theta_n = \tau_{n+1} - \tau_n$ $(n = 0, 1, 2, \ldots;$ $\tau_0 = 0)$ are identically distributed, independent, positive random variables with distribution function $\mathbf{P}\{\theta_n \leqq x\} = F(x)$. The customers will be served by a single server. The server is idle if and only if there is no customer waiting at the counter, otherwise the order of the services is irrelevant. The service times are identically distributed, independent random variables with distribution function

$$(42) \qquad H_m(x) = \begin{cases} 1 - \sum_{j=0}^{m-1} e^{-\mu x} \dfrac{(\mu x)^j}{j!} & \text{if } x \geqq 0, \\ 0 & \text{if } x < 0, \end{cases}$$

and independent of $\{\tau_n\}$.

Denote by $\xi^*(t)$ the queue size at the instant t, i.e. the number of customers waiting or being served at the instant t. Further define $\xi_n^* = \xi^*(\tau_n - 0)$, i.e. ξ_n is the queue size immediately before the arrival of the nth customer.

Denote by $\eta^*(t)$ the occupation time of the server at the instant t, i.e. $\eta^*(t)$ is the time which elapses from t until the server becomes idle for the first time if no customers join the queue after time t.

If we suppose, in particular, that the customers will be served in the order of their arrival, then $\eta^*(t)$ agrees with the virtual waiting time at the instant t, i.e. the time that a customer would wait if he joined the queue at the instant t. In this case $\eta_n^* = \eta^*(\tau_n - 0)$ is the waiting time of the nth customer.

Denote by $G_n^*(x)$ the probability that the busy period consists of n services and its length is at most x.

We are interested in the investigation of the stochastic behavior of the queue size, the waiting time, and the busy period of this process. Now we shall show that if we know the stochastic behavior of the process defined in Section 6, then that of the above process can be deduced immediately. If we identify the arrivals of the batches of size m with the arrivals of individual customers and the total service time of a batch with the service time of an individual customer, then the first process reduces to the second one. For, the distribution function of the total service time of a batch in the first process is equal to $H_m(x)$, the mth iterated convolution of $H(x)$ with itself.

If we consider the second process then the occupation time and the busy period follow the same probability laws, i.e. $\eta^*(t) = \eta(t)$ and $G_n^*(x) = \tilde{G}_n(x)$, but the queue size will change to

$$\xi^*(t) = \left[\frac{\xi(t) + m - 1}{m} \right].$$

Problems for solution

PROBLEM 12. Find the stationary distribution of $\{\xi_n\}$.

PROBLEM 13. Find $\tilde{G}_n(x)$, the probability that the busy period consists in serving n batches and its length is at most x.

7. General results concerning single server queueing processes with recurrent input and general service times

Let us consider the queueing model $[F(x), H(x), 1]$ and write

$$\alpha = \int_0^\infty x \, dH(x)$$

and

$$\beta = \int_0^\infty x \, dF(x).$$

Denote by τ_n the arrival instant of the nth customer and by χ_n his service time. Let $\theta_n = \tau_{n+1} - \tau_n$ $(n = 1, 2, \ldots; \tau_0 = 0)$. If we suppose that the customers are served in the order of their arrival and if η_n denotes the waiting time of the nth customer, then we have

$$(1) \qquad \eta_{n+1} = [\eta_n + \chi_n - \theta_n]^+.$$

Starting from the distribution of η_1 we can determine the distribution of η_n for every n by the recurrence relation (1). If we suppose that $\mathbf{P}\{\chi_n = \theta_n\} < 1$ and α and β are finite, then $\lim_{n \to \infty} \mathbf{P}\{\eta_n \leq x\} = W(x)$ exists and is independent of the initial distribution. If $\alpha < \beta$ then $W(x)$ is a distribution function, whereas if $\alpha \geq \beta$ then $W(x) \equiv 0$. If $\alpha < \beta$ then the limiting distribution $W(x)$ is the unique solution of the integral equation

$$(2) \qquad W(x) = \int_0^x K(x - y) \, dW(y) \quad , \quad x \geq 0,$$

where

$$K(x) = \int_0^\infty H(x + y) \, dF(y).$$

This theorem was proved by *D. V. Lindley* [14]. (Cf. Theorem **13** of Section 2, Chapter 1, and *F. Spitzer* [56].)

The distribution of the random variables $\{\eta_n\}$ was determined by *F. Pollaczek* [48] and *F. Spitzer* [56]. Now we shall give another proof. We shall introduce an operator **A** as follows: Let $\rho(s)$ be the Laplace-Stieltjes transform of a function $R(x)$ of bounded variation in $-\infty < x < \infty$, that is,

$$\rho(s) = \int_{-\infty}^{\infty} e^{-sx} \, dR(x).$$

In any case $\rho(s)$ is convergent if $\Re(s) = 0$. Now define

$$\mathbf{A}\rho(s) = \int_{-0}^{\infty} e^{-sx} \, dR(x),$$

which is convergent if $\Re(s) \geqq 0$. $\mathbf{A}$ is evidently a linear operator which is continuous and satisfies the relation $\mathbf{A}^2 = \mathbf{A}$. The operator $\mathbf{A}$ possesses the following properties: If $\mathbf{A}\rho(s) = \rho(s)$ then $\mathbf{A} \log \rho(s) = \log \rho(s)$ and if $\mathbf{A}\rho(s) = 1$ then $\mathbf{A} \log \rho(s) = 0$. We remark that, for example, $\mathbf{A}\rho(s)$ can be calculated by the following integral

$$\mathbf{A}\rho(s) = \frac{s}{2\pi i} \int_{-\epsilon-i\infty}^{-\epsilon+i\infty} \frac{\rho(z)}{z(s+z)} \, dz$$

if the right-hand side is convergent for some $\epsilon > 0$. Now we shall prove the following

LEMMA 1. *If* $\mathbf{A}\{\Gamma(s)\} = \Gamma(s)$ *and*

(3) $$\mathbf{A}\{\Gamma(s)\gamma(s)\} = 1,$$

then

(4) $$\Gamma(s) = e^{-\mathbf{A} \log \gamma(s)}.$$

PROOF. By (3)

$$\mathbf{A}\{\log \Gamma(s)\gamma(s)\} = \mathbf{A}\{\log \Gamma(s)\} + \mathbf{A}\{\log \gamma(s)\} = 0$$

and further

$$\mathbf{A}\{\log \Gamma(s)\} = \log \Gamma(s).$$

Now define $\Omega_n(s) = \mathbf{E}\{e^{-s\eta_n}\}$, $\phi(s) = \mathbf{E}\{e^{-s\theta_n}\}$, $\psi(s) = \mathbf{E}\{e^{-sX_n}\}$, and suppose that $\eta_1 = 0$.

THEOREM 1. *If* $|w| < 1$ *then we have*

(5) $$\sum_{n=1}^{\infty} \Omega_n(s)w^n = we^{-\mathbf{A}\{\log [1-w\psi(s)\phi(-s)]\}}.$$

PROOF. By (1)

(6) $$\Omega_{n+1}(s) = \mathbf{A}\{\Omega_n(s)\psi(s)\phi(-s)\}.$$

If we introduce the generating function

$$\Gamma(s, w) = \sum_{n=1}^{\infty} \Omega_n(s)w^n,$$

then by (6) we get

(7) $$\Gamma(s, w) - 1 = w\mathbf{A}\{\Gamma(s, w)\psi(s)\phi(-s)\}.$$

Since evidently $\mathbf{A}\{\Gamma(s, w)\} = \Gamma(s, w)$, by (7)

(8) $$\mathbf{A}\{\Gamma(s, w)[1 - w\psi(s)\phi(-s)]\} = 1.$$

Thus (5) follows by Lemma 1.

Now let us denote by $Q(t)$ the probability that the server is idle at time t. We have

THEOREM 2. *If $F(x)$ is not a lattice distribution and $\alpha < \beta$ then*

(9) $$\lim_{t \to \infty} Q(t) = 1 - \frac{\alpha}{\beta}$$

irrespective of the initial state.

PROOF. Let us denote by $G(x)$ the distribution function of the busy period and denote by $\hat{G}(x)$ the distribution function of the initial busy period. Further denote by $M_0(t)$ the expected number of the transitions $E_0 \to E_1$ occurring in the time interval $(0, t]$. By using the theorem of total probability we can write that

(10) $$Q(t) = \hat{G}(t) - \int_0^t [1 - G(t - u)] \, dM_0(u).$$

Now denote by ρ the expected number of services during a busy period. Evidently, $\lim_{n \to \infty} \mathbf{P}\{\eta_n = 0\} = 1/\rho$. By Lindley's theorem we obtain that $\rho < \infty$ if $\alpha < \beta$ and $\rho = \infty$ if $\alpha \geq \beta$. Thus if $\alpha < \beta$ then

$$\int_0^{\infty} x \, dG(x) = \int_0^{\infty} [1 - G(x)] \, dx = \rho\alpha.$$

Since the transitions $E_0 \to E_1$ form a recurrent process and the expectation of the distance between two successive transitions $E_0 \to E_1$ is $\rho\beta$, we get by *Blackwell*'s theorem that

(11)
$$\lim_{t \to \infty} \frac{M_0(t + h) - M_0(t)}{h} = \lim_{t \to \infty} \frac{M_0(t)}{t} = \frac{1}{\rho\beta}$$

for every $h > 0$. If $\rho < \infty$ then clearly $G(\infty) = 1$ and thus $\hat{G}(\infty) = 1$ also holds. Now by using the fundamental theorem of recurrent processes (cf. Appendix) we get from (10) that

$$\lim_{t \to \infty} Q(t) = 1 - \frac{\rho\alpha}{\rho\beta} = 1 - \frac{\alpha}{\beta}.$$

It is interesting to see that ρ plays no role in the final formula. If $\alpha \geqq \beta$ then $\lim_{t \to \infty} Q(t) = 0$.

Let us denote by $\xi(t)$ the queue size at the instant t and write $\xi_n = \xi(\tau_n - 0)$ and $\zeta_n = \xi(\tau'_n + 0)$, where τ_n is the nth arrival instant and τ'_n is the nth departure instant, that is, ξ_n is the queue size immediately before the nth arrival and ζ_n is the queue size immediately after the nth departure. If we know the stochastic behavior of the sequence $\{\xi_n\}$, then that of $\{\zeta_n\}$ can be deduced immediately and conversely. If $\xi(0) = 0$ then we have

(12)
$$\mathbf{P}\{\zeta_n \leqq k\} = \mathbf{P}\{\xi_{n+k+1} \leqq k\} \qquad (k = 0, 1, \ldots)$$

because the event $\{\zeta_n \leqq k\}$ and also the event $\{\xi_{n+k+1} \leqq k\}$ occurs if and only if $\tau'_n < \tau_{n+k+1}$. If $\xi(0)$ is arbitrary then a similar relation holds between $\{\xi_n\}$ and $\{\zeta_n\}$. By (12) it follows that

$$\lim_{n \to \infty} \mathbf{P}\{\zeta_n = k\} = \lim_{n \to \infty} \mathbf{P}\{\xi_n = k\} \qquad (k = 0, 1, \ldots),$$

provided that one of the limits exists.

For this general case $F.$ $Pollaczek$ [47] has given a method for the determination of the joint distribution of the length of the busy period and the number of customers served during the busy period.

Bibliography

[1] *N. T. J. Bailey:* On queueing processes with bulk service. J. Roy. Statist. Soc. Ser. B. 16 (1954) 80–87.
[2] *N. T. J. Bailey:* A continuous time treatment of a simple queue using generating functions. J. Roy. Statist. Soc. Ser. B. 16 (1954) 288–91.
[3] *V. E. Beneš:* On queues with Poisson arrivals. Ann. Math. Statist. 28 (1957) 670–77.

[4] *V. E. Beneš:* Combinatory methods and stochastic Kolmogorov equations in the theory of queues with one server. Trans. Amer. Math. Soc. 94 (1960) 282–94.

[5] *V. E. Beneš:* General stochastic processes in traffic systems with one server. Bell System Tech. J. 39 (1960) 127–60.

[6] *D. Blackwell:* A renewal theorem. Duke Math. J. 15 (1948) 145–50.

[7] *P. J. Burke:* The output of queuing system. Operations Res. 4 (1956) 699–704.

[8] *D. G. Champernowne:* An elementary method of solution of the queueing problem with a single server and constant parameters. J. Roy. Statist. Soc. Ser. B. 18 (1956) 125–8.

[9] *K. L. Chung and W. H. J. Fuchs:* On the distribution of values of sums of random variables. Four papers on probability. Mem. Amer. Math. Soc. No. 6 (1950) 1–12.

[10] *A. B. Clarke:* A waiting line process of Markov type. Ann. Math. Statist. 27 (1956) 452–9.

[11] *B. W. Conolly:* A difference equation technique applied to the simple queue. J. Roy. Statist. Soc. Ser. B. 20 (1958) 165–7.

[12] *B. W. Conolly:* A difference equation technique applied to the simple queue with arbitrary arrival interval distribution. J. Roy. Statist. Soc. Ser. B. 20 (1958) 168–75.

[13] *B. W. Conolly:* The busy period in relation to the queueing process GI/M/1. Biometrika 46 (1959) 246–51.

[14] *B. W. Conolly:* The busy period in relation to the single-server queueing system with general independent arrivals and Erlangian service-time. J. Roy. Statist. Soc. Ser. B. 22 (1960) 89–96.

[15] *B. W. Conolly:* The busy period in relation to the queueing process $E_k/G/1$. To be published.

[16] *J. W. Cohen:* A survey of queueing problems occurring in telephone and telegraph traffic theory. Proc. First Intern. Conf. on Operat. Res., Oxford (1957) 138–46.

[17] *F. Downton:* Waiting times in bulk service queues. J. Roy. Statist. Soc. Ser. B. 17 (1955) 256–61.

[18] *F. Downton:* On limiting distributions arising in bulk service queues. J. Roy. Statist. Soc. Ser. B. 18 (1956) 265–74.

[19] *A. J. Fabens:* The solution of queueing and inventory models by semi-Markov processes. J. Roy. Statist. Soc. Ser. B. 23 (1961) 113–27.

[20] *W. Feller:* Zur Theorie der stochastischen Prozesse. Math. Ann. 113 (1936) 116–60.

[21] *W. Feller:* On theory of stochastic processes, with particular reference to applications. Proc. First Berkeley Symp. on Math. Stat. and Prob., Berkeley and Los Angeles, University of California Press (1949) 403–32.

[22] *P. D. Finch:* Balking in the queueing system GI/M/1. Acta Math. Acad. Sci. Hungar. 10 (1959) 241–7.

[23] *P. D. Finch:* On the distribution of queue size in queueing problems. Acta Math. Acad. Sci. Hungar. 10 (1959) 327–36.

[24] J. Gani: Some problems in the theory of provisioning and of dams. Biometrika 42 (1955) 179–200.

[25] J. Gani: Problems in the probability theory of storage systems. J. Roy. Stat. Soc. Ser. B. 19 (1957) 181–206.

[26] J. Gani: Elementary methods for an occupancy problem of storage. Math. Ann. 136 (1958) 454–65.

[27] J. Gani and N. U. Prabhu: Continuous time treatment of a storage problem. Nature 182 (1958) 39–40.

[28] J. Gani and N. U. Prabhu: The time-dependent solution for a storage model with Poisson input. J. Math. Mech. 8 (1959) 653–64.

[29] D. P. Graver: Imbedded Markov chain analysis of a waiting-line process in continuous time. Ann. Math. Statist. 30 (1959) 698–720.

[30] S. Karlin and J. McGregor: Many server queueing processes with Poisson input and exponential service times. Pacific J. Math. 8 (1958) 87–118.

[31] S. Karlin, R. G. Miller and N. U. Prabhu: Note on a moving single server problem. Ann. Math. Statist. 30 (1959) 243–6.

[32] J. Keilson and A. Kooharian: On time dependent queueing processes. Ann. Math. Statist. 31 (1960) 104–12.

[33] D. G. Kendall: Some problems in the theory of queues. J. Roy. Statist. Soc. Ser. B. 13 (1951) 151–85.

[34] D. G. Kendall: Stochastic processes occurring in the theory of queues and their analysis by the method of the imbedded Markov chain. Ann. Math. Statist. 24 (1953) 338–54.

[35] D. G. Kendall: Some problems in the theory of dams. J. Roy. Statist. Soc. Ser. B. 19 (1957) 207–12.

[36] H. Kesten and J. Th. Runnenburg: Priority in waiting line problems I-II. Nederl. Akad. Wetensch. Proc. Ser. A. 60 (1957) 312–24 and 325–36.

[37] A. Y. Khintchine: Mathematical theory of a stationary queue (in Russian). Mat. Sb. 39 No. 4 (1932) 73–84.

[38] A. Kolmogorov: Sur le problème d'attente. Math. Sb. 38, No. 1–2. (1931) 101–6.

[39] A. Kolmogorov: Über die analytischen Methoden in der Wahrscheinlichkeitsrechnung. Math. Ann. 104 (1931) 415–58.

[40] W. Lederman and G. E. H. Reuter: Spectral theory for the differential equations of simple birth and death processes. Philos. Trans. Roy. Soc. London Ser. A. 246 (1954) 321–69.

[41] D. V. Lindley: The theory of queues with a single server. Proc. Cambridge Philos. Soc. 48 (1952) 277–89.

[42] B. McMillan and J. Riordan: A moving single server problem. Ann. Math. Statist. 28 (1957) 471–8.

[43] R. G. Miller: A contribution to the theory of bulk queues. J. Roy. Statist. Soc. Ser. B. 21 (1959) 320–37.

[44] R. G. Miller: Priority queues. Ann. Math. Statist. 31 (1960) 86–103.

[45] P. M. Morse: Queues, inventories and maintenance. John Wiley and Sons, New York, 1958.

[46] F. Pollaczek: Über eine Aufgabe der Wahrscheinlichkeitstheorie I-II. Mat. Zeit. 32 (1930) 64–100 and 729–50.

[47] *F. Pollaczek:* Sur la répartition des périodes d'occupation ininterrompue d'un guichet. C. R. Acad. Sci. Paris 234 (1952) 2042–4.

[48] *F. Pollaczek:* Fonctions caractéristiques de certaines répartitions définies au moyen de la notion d'ordre. Application à la théorie des attentes. C. R. Acad. Sci. Paris 234 (1952) 2334–6.

[49] *F. Pollaczek:* Problèmes stochastiques posés par le phénomène de formation d'une queue d'attente à un guichet et par des phénomènes apparentés. Gauthier-Villars, Paris, 1957.

[50] *N. U. Prabhu:* On the integral equation for the finite dam. Quart. J. Math. Oxford Ser. (2) 9 (1958) 183–8.

[51] *N. U. Prahbu:* Some results for the queue with Poisson arrivals. J. Roy. Statist. Soc. Ser. B. 22 (1960) 104–7.

[52] *E. Reich:* Waiting times when queues are in tandem. Ann. Math. Statist. 28 (1957) 768–73.

[53] *E. Reich:* On the integrodifferential equation of Takács I–II. Ann. Math. Statist. 29 (1958) 563–70 and 30 (1959) 143–8.

[54] *J. Th. Runnenburg:* Probabilistic interpretation of some formulae in queueing theory. Bull. Inst. Internat. Statist. 37 (1960) 405–14.

[55] *W. L. Smith:* On the distribution of queueing times. Proc. Cambridge Philos. Soc. 49 (1953) 449–61.

[56] *F. Spitzer:* The Wiener-Hopf equation whose kernel is a probability density. Duke Math. J. 24 (1957) 327–43.

[57] *L. Takács:* Investigation of waiting time problems by reduction to Markov processes. Acta Math. Acad. Sci. Hungar. 6 (1955) 101–29.

[58] *L. Takács:* Transient behavior of single-server queuing processes with recurrent input and exponentially distributed service times. Operations Res. 8 (1960) 231–45.

[59] *L. Takács:* The transient behavior of a single server queuing process with recurrent input and gamma service time. Ann. Math. Statist. 32 (1961) 1286–98.

[60] *L. Takács:* Transient behavior of single-server queueing processes with Erlang input. Trans. Amer. Math. Soc. 100 (1961) 1–28.

[61] *L. Takács:* The transient behavior of a single server queueing process with a Poisson input. Proc. Fourth Berkeley Symp. on Math. Stat. and Prob., Berkeley and Los Angeles, University of California Press. 2 (1961) 535–67.

[62] *L. Takács:* The probability law of the busy period for two types of queuing processes. Operations Research 9 (1961) 402–7.

[63] *C. B. Winsten:* Geometric distributions in the theory of queues. J. Roy. Statist. Soc. Ser. B. 21 (1959) 1–35.

[64] *D. M. G. Wishart:* A queueing system with χ^2 service-time distribution. Ann. Math. Statist. 27 (1956) 768–79.

[65] *E. T. Whittaker and G. N. Watson:* A Course of Modern Analysis. Cambridge University Press, Cambridge, 1952.

[66] *A. Zygmund:* A remark on characteristic functions. Proc. Second Berkeley Symp. on Math. Stat. and Prob., Berkeley and Los Angeles, University of California Press. (1951) 369–72.

2

MANY SERVER QUEUEING PROCESSES

1. Many server queueing processes in the case of Palm input and exponentially distributed service times

Let us suppose that customers arrive at a counter at the instants $\tau_0, \tau_1, \ldots, \tau_n, \ldots$ where the inter-arrival times $\tau_{n+1} - \tau_n$ ($n = 0, 1, 2, \ldots; \tau_0 = 0$) are identically distributed, independent, positive random variables with distribution function

$$(1) \qquad \qquad \mathbf{P}\{\tau_{n+1} - \tau_n \leq x\} = F(x).$$

There are m servers. Let us suppose that there is no idle server if there is a waiting customer; otherwise the order of the services is irrelevant. It is supposed that the service times are identically distributed, independent random variables with distribution function

$$(2) \qquad \qquad H(x) = \begin{cases} 1 - e^{-\mu x} & \text{if } x \geq 0, \\ 0 & \text{if } x < 0, \end{cases}$$

and independent of $\{\tau_n\}$.

Denote by $\xi(t)$ the queue size at the instant t, i.e. $\xi(t)$ is the number of customers waiting or being served at the instant t. We say that the system is in state E_j at the instant t if $\xi(t) = j$.

Further define $\xi_n = \xi(\tau_n - 0)$ ($n = 0, 1, 2, \ldots$), i.e. ξ_n is the queue size immediately before the arrival of the nth customer.

In what follows we shall determine the asymptotic behavior of the stochastic sequence $\{\xi_n\}$ as $n \to \infty$, and that of the stochastic process $\{\xi(t)\}$ as $t \to \infty$.

REMARK 1. If we suppose that the customers will be served in the order of their arrival, then the investigation of the stochastic behavior of the waiting time can be reduced immediately to that of the

147

queue size. For, if η_n denotes the waiting time of the nth customer, then we have $\eta_n = 0$ if $\xi_n < m$ and $\eta_n = \chi_1 + \chi_2 + \cdots + \chi_{\xi_n - m + 1}$ if $\xi_n \geqq m$, where $\chi_1, \chi_2, \ldots$ are independent random variables with distribution function defined by (2) and independent of ξ_n.

We shall use the notation

$$\phi(s) = \int_0^\infty e^{-sx} \, dF(x)$$

and

$$\beta = \int_0^\infty x \, dF(x).$$

Furthermore we note that if $z = \omega$ is the root of the equation

$$z = \phi(\mu m(1 - z)),$$

which has the smallest absolute value, then ω is a positive real number and $\omega < 1$ if $m\beta\mu > 1$ and $\omega = 1$ if $m\beta\mu \leqq 1$. This follows from Lemma 1 of Section 3, Chapter 1.

We shall prove the following

THEOREM 1. *If* $m\beta\mu > 1$, *then the limiting distribution* $\lim_{n \to \infty} \mathbf{P}\{\xi_n = k\} = P_k$ $(k = 0, 1, 2, \ldots)$ *exists and is independent of the initial distribution. We have*

$$(3) \quad P_k = \begin{cases} \displaystyle\sum_{r=k}^{m-1} (-1)^{r-k} \binom{r}{k} U_r & (k = 0, 1, \ldots, m-1) \\ A\omega^{k-m} & (k = m, m+1, \ldots) \end{cases}$$

where ω is the only root of the equation

$$(4) \quad \omega = \phi(m\mu(1 - \omega))$$

in the unit circle,

$$(5) \quad U_r = AC_r \sum_{j=r+1}^{m} \frac{\binom{m}{j}}{C_j(1 - \phi_j)} \left(\frac{m(1 - \phi_j) - j}{m(1 - \omega) - j} \right),$$

$$(6) \quad A = 1 \bigg/ \left[\frac{1}{1 - \omega} + \sum_{j=1}^{m} \frac{\binom{m}{j}}{C_j(1 - \phi_j)} \left(\frac{m(1 - \phi_j) - j}{m(1 - \omega) - j} \right) \right],$$

(7) $\qquad C_j = \prod_{\nu=1}^{j} \left(\frac{\phi_\nu}{1 - \phi_\nu} \right),$

and

(8) $\qquad\qquad \phi_\nu = \phi(\nu\mu) \qquad (\nu = 0, 1, 2, \ldots).$

The rth binomial moment of the distribution $\{P_k\}$, that is

(9) $\qquad\qquad\qquad B_r = \sum_{k=r}^{\infty} \binom{k}{r} P_k,$

is given by

(10) $\qquad B_r = \begin{cases} U_r + \dfrac{A}{1 - \omega} \sum_{j=0}^{r} \binom{m}{j} \left(\dfrac{\omega}{1 - \omega} \right)^{r-j} & \text{if } r < m, \\[3ex] \dfrac{A\omega^{r-m}}{(1 - \omega)^{r+1}} & \text{if } r \geq m. \end{cases}$

If $m\beta\mu \leq 1$ then $\lim_{n\to\infty} \mathbf{P}\{\xi_n = k\} = 0$ for every k.

PROOF. It is easy to see that the sequence of random variables $\{\xi_n\}$ forms a Markov chain with transition probabilities

(11) $\qquad \mathbf{P}\{\xi_{n+1} = k \,|\, \xi_n = j\} = p_{jk} = \int_0^\infty \pi_{jk}(x)\, dF(x),$

where $\pi_{jk}(x)$ is the transition probability under the condition that the inter-arrival time $\tau_{n+1} - \tau_n = x$ and is given by the following formulas:

(12)

$\pi_{jk}(x) = \binom{j+1}{k} e^{-k\mu x}(1 - e^{-\mu x})^{j+1-k} \qquad \text{when } j < m,$

$\pi_{jk}(x) = \binom{m}{k} e^{-k\mu x} \left[\int_0^x \frac{(m\mu y)^{j-m}}{(j-m)!} (e^{-\mu y} - e^{-\mu x})^{m-k} m\mu\, dy \right]$

$\qquad\qquad\qquad\qquad\qquad\qquad \text{when } j \geq m \text{ and } k < m,$

$\pi_{jk}(x) = e^{-m\mu x} \frac{(m\mu x)^{j+1-k}}{(j+1-k)!} \qquad\qquad \text{when } j \geq m \text{ and } k \geq m.$

The Markov chain $\{\xi_n\}$ is irreducible and aperiodic. Therefore $\lim_{n\to\infty} \mathbf{P}\{\xi_n = k\} = P_k$ $(k = 0, 1, 2, \ldots)$ always exists and is independent of the initial distribution. There are two possibilities: either every $P_k > 0$ and $\{P_k\}$ is a probability distribution, or every $P_k = 0$. If the limiting distribution $\{P_k\}$ exists then it is uniquely determined by the following system of linear equations

$$(13) \qquad P_k = \sum_{j=k-1}^{\infty} p_{jk} P_j \qquad (k = 0, 1, \ldots)$$

and

$$(14) \qquad \sum_{k=0}^{\infty} P_k = 1.$$

Conversely, if the system (13) has a non-null solution $\{P_k\}$ which forms an absolutely convergent series then there exists a limiting distribution. First let us consider the equations (13) for $k \geqq m$. We have

$$(15) \qquad P_k = \sum_{\nu=0}^{\infty} P_{\nu+k-1} \int_0^{\infty} e^{-m\mu x} \frac{(m\mu x)^{\nu}}{\nu!} \, dF(x) \qquad \text{if } k \geqq m.$$

The solution of these equations can be written in the form

$$P_k = A\omega^{k-m} \qquad (k \geqq m),$$

where ω is a root of the equation

$$(16) \qquad \omega = \phi(m\mu(1 - \omega)).$$

This equation has a root $|\omega| < 1$ if and only if $m\beta\mu > 1$. Consequently the Markov chain $\{\xi_n\}$ is ergodic if and only if $m\beta\mu > 1$. In this case

$$(17) \qquad P_k = A\omega^{k-m},$$

where ω denotes the only root of (16) in the unit circle $|\omega| < 1$. If $k = m$ in (15) then we get $A = \omega P_{m-1}$. It remains only to determine the unknown probabilities $P_0, P_1, \ldots, P_{m-1}$. Let us introduce the following generating function

$$U(z) = \sum_{k=0}^{m-1} P_k z^k.$$

Then from (13) we obtain

$$(18) \quad U(z) = \int_0^\infty (1 - e^{-\mu x} + ze^{-\mu x})U(1 - e^{-\mu x} + ze^{-\mu x}) \, dF(x)$$

$$+ A \int_0^\infty \left[\int_0^x e^{m\mu\omega y}(e^{-\mu y} - e^{-\mu x} + ze^{-\mu x})^m m\mu \, dy \right] dF(x) - Az^m.$$

By (17)

$$(19) \qquad U(1) = \sum_{k=0}^{m-1} P_k = 1 - \sum_{k=m}^{\infty} P_k = 1 - \frac{A}{1 - \omega}.$$

Now let

$$U_j = \frac{1}{j!} \left(\frac{d^j U(z)}{dz^j} \right)_{z=1} \qquad (j = 0, 1, \ldots, m-1).$$

Then we obtain by (19) that

$$(20) \qquad\qquad U_0 = 1 - \frac{A}{1 - \omega},$$

and differentiating (18) j times and putting $z = 1$ we get for $j = 1, 2, \ldots, m - 1$ that

$$U_j = U_j\phi_j + U_{j-1}\phi_j - A \binom{m}{j} \left(\frac{m(1 - \phi_j) - j}{m(1 - \omega) - j} \right)$$

because $\phi(m\mu(1 - \omega)) = \omega$. Thus

$$(21) \qquad U_j = \frac{\phi_j}{1 - \phi_j} U_{j-1} - \frac{A \binom{m}{j}}{(1 - \phi_j)} \left(\frac{m(1 - \phi_j) - j}{m(1 - \omega) - j} \right).$$

This is a linear difference equation of the first order with variable coefficients which can be solved easily. Define $C_0 = 1$ and

$$C_j = \left(\frac{\phi_1}{1 - \phi_1} \right)\left(\frac{\phi_2}{1 - \phi_2} \right) \cdots \left(\frac{\phi_j}{1 - \phi_j} \right),$$

and divide both sides of (21) by C_j; then we obtain

$$\frac{U_j}{C_j} = \frac{U_{j-1}}{C_{j-1}} - \frac{A \binom{m}{j}}{C_j(1 - \phi_j)} \left(\frac{m(1 - \phi_j) - j}{m(1 - \omega) - j} \right).$$

Add these equations for $j = r + 1, \ldots, m - 1$; then we get for $r = 0, 1, \ldots, m - 1$

$$(22) \qquad \frac{U_r}{C_r} = A \sum_{j=r+1}^{m} \frac{\binom{m}{j}}{C_j(1 - \phi_j)} \left(\frac{m(1 - \phi_j) - j}{m(1 - \omega) - j} \right),$$

where we used that $U_{m-1} = P_{m-1} = A/\omega$. Now put $r = 0$ in (22) and take into consideration that by (20)

$$\frac{U_0}{C_0} = 1 - \frac{A}{1 - \omega};$$

then finally we obtain that

$$(23) \quad A = 1 \Bigg/ \left[\frac{1}{1 - \omega} + \sum_{j=1}^{m} \frac{\binom{m}{j}}{C_j(1 - \phi_j)} \left(\frac{m(1 - \phi_j) - j}{m(1 - \omega) - j} \right) \right].$$

Thus by (22) and (23) $U(z)$ is determined, namely

$$U(z) = \sum_{j=0}^{m-1} U_j(z - 1)^j.$$

The unknown probabilities P_k $(k = 0, 1, \ldots, m - 1)$ can be expressed as

$$(24) \quad P_k = \frac{1}{k!} \left(\frac{d^k U(z)}{dz^k} \right)_{z=0} = \sum_{r=k}^{m-1} (-1)^{r-k} \binom{r}{k} U_r$$

$$(r = 0, 1, \ldots, m - 1).$$

Thus the probability distribution $\{P_k\}$ is determined completely.

The binomial moments B_r $(r = 0, 1, 2, \ldots)$ can be determined by the generating function

$$U^*(z) = \sum_{k=0}^{\infty} P_k z^k = U(z) + \frac{Az^m}{1 - z}.$$

Hence

$$(25)$$
$$B_r = \frac{1}{r!} \left(\frac{d^r U^*(z)}{dz^r} \right)_{z=1} = U_r + \frac{A}{1 - \omega} \sum_{j=0}^{r} \binom{m}{j} \left(\frac{\omega}{1 - \omega} \right)^{r-j},$$

where $U_r = 0$ if $r \geqq m$. This completes the proof of the theorem. Now let

$$P_k(t) = \mathbf{P}\{\xi(t) = k\}.$$

THEOREM 2. *If $m\beta\mu > 1$ and $F(x)$ is not a lattice distribution, then the limiting distribution $\lim\limits_{t\to\infty} P_k(t) = P_k^*$ $(k = 0, 1, 2, \ldots)$ exists and is independent of the initial state. We have*

$$(26) \qquad P_0^* = 1 - \frac{1}{m\beta\mu} - \frac{1}{\beta\mu} \sum_{j=1}^{m-1} P_{j-1}\left(\frac{1}{j} - \frac{1}{m}\right),$$

$$(27) \qquad P_k^* = \frac{P_{k-1}}{k\beta\mu} \qquad \text{if } k = 1, 2, \ldots, m - 1,$$

$$(28) \qquad P_k^* = \frac{P_{k-1}}{m\beta\mu} \qquad \text{if } k = m, m + 1, \ldots,$$

where $\{P_k\}$ is defined by (3).

PROOF. It is easy to see that the time differences between consecutive transitions $E_k \to E_{k+1}$ are identically distributed, independent, positive random variables. If $F(x)$ is not a lattice distribution, then these random variables are not lattice distributed either. Now we shall show that if $m\beta\mu > 1$, then these random variables have a finite expectation β/P_k. If we consider the Markov chain $\{\xi_n\}$, then in this case the state E_k is recurrent and the expectation of the recurrence step number is $1/P_k$. Since transitions $E_k \to E_{k+1}$ occur only at such instants τ_n $(n = 1, 2, 3, \ldots)$ when $\xi_n = k$, therefore the expected number of steps between consecutive transitions $E_k \to E_{k+1}$ is $1/P_k$. The expectation of the length of each step is β. Now by using *Wald's* theorem (cf. Appendix) it follows that the expectation of the time differences between consecutive transitions $E_k \to E_{k+1}$ is β/P_k. Now denote by $M_k(t)$ the expectation of the number of transitions $E_k \to E_{k+1}$ $(k = 0, 1, 2, \ldots)$ occurring in the time interval $(0, t]$. If $m\beta\mu > 1$ and $F(x)$ is not a lattice distribution, then for all $h > 0$ we have

$$(29) \qquad \lim_{t\to\infty} \frac{M_k(t + h) - M_k(t)}{h} = \frac{P_k}{\beta},$$

irrespective of the distribution of $\xi(0)$. This follows from *Blackwell's* theorem (cf. Appendix).

Now we have

$$(30) \qquad P_k(t) = \sum_{j=k-1}^{\infty} \int_0^t \pi_{jk}(t-u)[1 - F(t-u)] \, dM_j(u),$$

where $\pi_{jk}(x)$ is defined by (12). For, the event $\xi(t) = k$ can occur in the following mutually exclusive ways: at the instant u (where $0 \leq u \leq t$) there occurs a transition $E_j \to E_{j+1}$ $(j = k - 1, k, \ldots)$ and the next customer arrives after the instant t (the probability of that is $1 - F(t-u)$) and in the time interval $(u, t]$ exactly $j + 1 - k$ services end (the probability of that is $\pi_{jk}(t-u)$). Finally (30) follows by the theorem of total probability.

By using the fundamental theorem of recurrent processes (cf. Appendix) we get that $\lim_{t\to\infty} P\{\xi(t) = k\} = P_k^*$ exists and is independent of the initial distribution. Further we have

$$(31) \qquad P_k^* = \sum_{j=k-1}^{\infty} p_{jk}^* P_j$$

where

$$(32) \qquad p_{jk}^* = \frac{1}{\beta} \int_0^{\infty} \pi_{jk}(x)[1 - F(x)] \, dx.$$

Thus we obtain an explicit form for the distribution $\{P_k^*\}$, but it can be expressed also in a simpler way.

Denote by $N_k(t)$ the expectation of the number of transitions $E_k \to E_{k-1}$ $(k = 1, 2, \ldots)$ occurring in the time interval $(0, t]$. Then we have

$$(33) \qquad N_k(t) = \begin{cases} k\mu \displaystyle\int_0^t P_k(u) \, du & \text{if } k \leq m \\[2ex] m\mu \displaystyle\int_0^t P_k(u) \, du & \text{if } k \geq m. \end{cases}$$

For, if we introduce a new time variable involved only when there is state E_k, then the transitions $E_k \to E_{k-1}$ form a Poisson process of density $k\mu$ (when $k \leq m$) or $m\mu$ (when $k \geq m$). If $\lim_{t\to\infty} P_k(t) = P_k^*$ exists then by (33)

$$(34) \qquad \lim_{t\to\infty} \frac{N_k(t)}{t} = \begin{cases} k\mu P_k^* & \text{if } k \leq m, \\ m\mu P_k^* & \text{if } k \geq m. \end{cases}$$

On the other hand by (29) we have

$$(35) \qquad \lim_{t \to \infty} \frac{M_k(t)}{t} = \frac{P_k}{\beta}, \qquad (k = 0, 1, 2, \ldots).$$

The difference between the number of transitions $E_{k-1} \to E_k$ and $E_k \to E_{k-1}$ occurring in the time interval $(0, t]$ is at most 1 and therefore

$$|M_{k-1}(t) - N_k(t)| \leqq 1$$

for all $t \geqq 0$. Hence

$$\lim_{t \to \infty} \frac{M_{k-1}(t)}{t} = \lim_{t \to \infty} \frac{N_k(t)}{t} \qquad (k = 1, 2, \ldots),$$

that is,

$$(36) \qquad \frac{P_{k-1}}{\beta} = \begin{cases} k\mu P_k^* & \text{if } k = 1, 2, \ldots, m, \\ m\mu P_k^* & \text{if } k = m, m+1, \ldots. \end{cases}$$

This proves (27) and (28), and (26) follows from $P_0^* = 1 - \sum_{k=1}^{\infty} P_k^*$.

THE DISTRIBUTION OF THE WAITING TIME. Let us suppose that the customers are served in the order of their arrival. Denote by η_n the waiting time of the nth customer. Let $\mathbf{P}\{\eta_n \leqq x\} = W_n(x)$. We shall prove

THEOREM 3. *If $m\beta\mu > 1$ then $\lim_{n \to \infty} W_n(x) = W(x)$ exists and is independent of the initial state. We have*

$$(37) \qquad W(x) = 1 - \frac{Ae^{-m\mu(1-\omega)x}}{(1-\omega)} \qquad (x \geqq 0)$$

where ω and A are defined by (4) and (6) respectively.

PROOF. We have

$$W_n(x) = \sum_{j=0}^{m-1} \mathbf{P}\{\xi_n = j\} + \sum_{j=m}^{\infty} \mathbf{P}\{\xi_n = j\} \int_0^x e^{-m\mu y} \frac{(m\mu y)^{j-m}}{(j-m)!} \, m\mu \, dy.$$

The nth arriving customer finds ξ_n customers in the queue. If $\xi_n = j$ and $j < m$ then his service starts without waiting; if $\xi_n = j$ and $j \geqq m$ then he must wait for $j + 1 - m$ successive departures and these departures follow a Poisson process of density $m\mu$. If $m\beta\mu > 1$ and n tends to infinity, then we get

$$W(x) = \sum_{j=0}^{m-1} P_j + \sum_{j=m}^{\infty} P_j \int_0^x e^{-m\mu y} \frac{(m\mu y)^{j-m}}{(j-m)!} m\mu \, dy.$$

Since $P_j = A\omega^{j-m}$ if $j \geqq m$ and $\sum_{j=0}^{m-1} P_j = 1 - \sum_{j=m}^{\infty} P_j = 1 - \dfrac{A}{1-\omega}$, we get (37).

REMARK 2. The expectation of the waiting time of the nth customer is given by

$$\mathbf{E}\{\eta_n\} = \frac{1}{m\mu} \sum_{j=m}^{\infty} (j+1-m)\mathbf{P}\{\xi_n = j\},$$

and is independent of the order of the services. Hence

$$\lim_{n \to \infty} \mathbf{E}\{\eta_n\} = \frac{1}{m\mu} \sum_{j=m}^{\infty} (j+1-m)P_j = \frac{A}{m\mu(1-\omega)^2},$$

which is in agreement with

$$\int_0^\infty x \, dW(x) = \int_0^\infty [1 - W(x)] \, dx = \frac{A}{m\mu(1-\omega)^2}.$$

Problems for solution

PROBLEM 14. Let us suppose that

$$F(x) = \begin{cases} 1 - e^{-\lambda x} & \text{if } x \geqq 0, \\ 0 & \text{if } x < 0. \end{cases}$$

In this special case find the stationary distribution of $\{\xi(t)\}$.

PROBLEM 15. Let us suppose that

$$F(x) = \begin{cases} 1 - e^{-\lambda x} & \text{if } x \geqq 0, \\ 0 & \text{if } x < 0. \end{cases}$$

In this special case find the stationary distribution of $\{\xi_n\}$.

2. General results concerning many server queueing processes with recurrent input and general service times

Let us consider the queueing model $[F(x), H(x), m]$ and write

$$\alpha = \int_0^\infty x \, dH(x)$$

and

$$\beta = \int_0^\infty x \, dF(x).$$

Denote by η_n the waiting time and χ_n the service time of the nth customer. Let θ_n be the inter-arrival time between the nth and $n + 1$st arrival. Now we shall mention the following theorem of J. Kiefer and J. Wolfowitz [4]. If $\mathbf{P}\{\chi_n = m\theta_n\} < 1$, and if α and β are finite, then the limiting distribution $\lim_{n \to \infty} \mathbf{P}\{\eta_n \leq x\} = W(x)$ exists when and only when $\alpha < m\beta$ and in this case the limiting distribution is independent of the initial distribution. If $\alpha \geq m\beta$ then $\lim_{n \to \infty} \mathbf{P}\{\eta_n \leq x\} = 0$ for every x. Further we remark that for this general case F. Pollaczek [7] has given a method for the determination of the limiting distribution $W(x)$.

Bibliography

[1] *P. D. Finch:* The effect of the size of the waiting room on a simple queue. J. Roy. Statist. Soc. Ser. B. 20 (1958) 182–6.

[2] *P. D. Finch:* On the distribution of queue size in queueing problems. Acta Math. Acad. Sci. Hungar. 10 (1959) 327–36.

[3] *S. Karlin and J. McGregor:* Many server queueing processes with Poisson input and exponential service times. Pacific J. Math. 8 (1958) 87–118.

[4] *J. Kiefer and J. Wolfowitz:* On the theory of queues with many servers. Trans. Amer. Math. Soc. 78 (1955) 1–18.

[5] *J. Kiefer and J. Wolfowitz:* On the characteristics of the general queueing process, with applications to random walk. Ann. Math. Statist. 27 (1956) 147–61.

[6] *D. G. Kendall:* Stochastic processes occurring in the theory of queues and their analysis by the method of the imbedded Markov chain. Ann. Math. Statist. 24 (1953) 338–54.

[7] *F. Pollaczek:* Sur une généralisation de la théorie des attentes. C. R. Acad. Sci. Paris 236 (1953) 578–80.

[8] *L. Takács:* On a queueing problem concerning telephone traffic. Acta Math. Acad. Sci. Hungar. 8 (1957) 325–35.

[9] *L. Takács:* On a combined waiting time and loss problem concerning telephone traffic. Ann. Univ. Sci. Budapest Eötvös. Sect. Math. 1 (1958) 73–82.

3

QUEUES WITH INFINITELY MANY SERVERS

1. Formulation of the problem

Let us suppose that customers arrive at a counter at the instants $\tau_1, \tau_2, \ldots, \tau_n, \ldots$ where the inter-arrival times $\theta_n = \tau_n - \tau_{n-1}$ $(n = 1, 2, \ldots; \tau_0 = 0)$ are identically distributed, independent random variables with the distribution function

$$\mathbf{P}\{\tau_n - \tau_{n-1} \leqq x\} = F(x) \qquad (n = 1, 2, \ldots).$$

Let us suppose that each customer starts being served as soon as he arrives, that is, there is no waiting time because there is a sufficient number of servers. Denote by χ_n the service time of the nth customer. It is supposed that $\chi_1, \chi_2, \ldots, \chi_n, \ldots$ are identically distributed, independent, positive random variables with distribution function

$$\mathbf{P}\{\chi_n \leqq x\} = H(x) \qquad (n = 1, 2, \ldots)$$

and independent of $\{\tau_n\}$.

Denote by $\xi(t)$ the queue size at the instant t, that is, the number of customers being served at the instant t. $\xi(0)$ is the initial queue size. We are interested in the investigation of the stochastic behavior of the queue size.

We shall consider two particular cases: when $\{\tau_n\}$ is a Poisson process of density λ, i.e.

$$(1) \qquad F(x) = \begin{cases} 1 - e^{-\lambda x} & \text{if } x \geqq 0, \\ 0 & \text{if } x < 0, \end{cases}$$

and when the $\{\chi_n\}$ are distributed exponentially, i.e.

$$(2) \qquad H(x) = \begin{cases} 1 - e^{-\mu x} & \text{if } x \geqq 0, \\ 0 & \text{if } x < 0. \end{cases}$$

159

2. Queues with infinitely many servers in the case of a Poisson input

Now we consider the case when $F(x)$ is defined by (1) of Section 1, i.e. $\{\tau_n\}$ is a Poisson process of density λ. Let $P\{\xi(t) = k\} = P_k(t)$ and denote by α the average service time,

$$\alpha = \int_0^\infty x \, dH(x).$$

We shall prove

THEOREM 1. *If* $\xi(0) = 0$ *then*

(1)

$$P_k(t) = e^{-\lambda \int_0^t [1 - H(x)] \, dx} \frac{[\lambda \int_0^t (1 - H(x)) \, dx]^k}{k!} \qquad (k = 0, 1, 2, \ldots)$$

and if $\alpha < \infty$ *then* $\lim_{t \to \infty} P_k(t) = P_k^* \ (k = 0, 1, 2, \ldots)$ *exists and we have*

(2)

$$P_k^* = e^{-\lambda \alpha} \frac{(\lambda \alpha)^k}{k!}.$$

PROOF. By the theorem of total probability we can write that

(3) $P_k(t)$

$$= \sum_{n=k}^\infty e^{-\lambda t} \frac{(\lambda t)^n}{n!} \binom{n}{k} \left[\frac{1}{t} \int_0^t (1 - H(x)) \, dx \right]^k \left[\frac{1}{t} \int_0^t H(x) \, dx \right]^{n-k}.$$

For, the event $\xi(t) = k$ can occur in several mutually exclusive ways: in the time interval $(0, t]$ $n = 0, 1, 2, \ldots$ customers arrive and if $n \geq k$ then among them the serving of k customers does not terminate by time t. The probability that n customers arrive in the time interval $(0, t]$ is

$$e^{-\lambda t} \frac{(\lambda t)^n}{n!},$$

and under this condition the joint distribution of the instants of arrivals agrees with the joint distribution of the co-ordinates arranged in increasing order of n independent random points distributed uniformly in the time interval $(0, t]$. Accordingly if exactly n customers arrive in the time interval $(0, t]$ then under this condition $\xi(t)$ has a Bernoulli distribution with parameters n and

$$p_t = \frac{1}{t} \int_0^t [1 - H(x)]\, dx,$$

p_t being the probability that a service does not terminate by time t given that its starting time has a uniform distribution in $(0, t]$. Thus we get (3) which agrees with (1). Since

$$\lim_{t \to \infty} \int_0^t [1 - H(x)]\, dx = \alpha,$$

therefore $\lim_{t \to \infty} \mathbf{P}\{\xi(t) = k\} = P_k^*$ $(k = 0, 1, 2, \ldots)$ exists and (2) holds.

If we consider an arbitrary initial distribution, instead of $\xi(0) = 0$, then $P_k(t)$ can be obtained similarly, and if $\alpha < \infty$ then $\lim_{t \to \infty} P_k(t) = P_k^*$ $(k = 0, 1, 2, \ldots)$ irrespective of the distribution of $\xi(0)$.

THE STATIONARY PROCESS. Under the condition that $\xi(t) = k$, denote by $\chi_1(t), \chi_2(t), \ldots, \chi_k(t)$ the times measured from time t which are required to complete the services in progress at the instant t.

THEOREM 2. *If $\alpha < \infty$ then*

(4) $\lim_{t \to \infty} \mathbf{P}\{\chi_1(t) \leqq x_1, \chi_2(t) \leqq x_2, \ldots, \chi_k(t) \leqq x_k \,|\, \xi(t) = k\}$

$$= H^*(x_1)H^*(x_2) \ldots H^*(x_k),$$

where

(5) $$H^*(x) = \begin{cases} \dfrac{1}{\alpha} \displaystyle\int_0^x [1 - H(y)]\, dy & \text{if } x \geqq 0, \\[2mm] 0 & \text{if } x < 0, \end{cases}$$

and the limiting distribution is independent of the initial state.

PROOF. First we suppose that $\xi(0) = 0$. In this case proceeding as in the proof of Theorem 1 we get that

$$\mathbf{P}\{\chi_1(t) \leqq x_1, \chi_2(t) \leqq x_2, \ldots, \chi_k(t) \leqq x_k; \xi(t) = k\}$$

$$= \sum_{n=k}^{\infty} e^{-\lambda t} \frac{(\lambda t)^n}{n!} \binom{n}{k} \left[\frac{1}{t!} \int_0^t H(x)\,dx\right]^{n-k}$$

$$\cdot \prod_{i=1}^{k} \left\{\frac{1}{t}\int_0^t [H(x+x_i) - H(x)]\,dx\right\}$$

$$= e^{-\lambda \int_0^t [1-H(x)]\,dx} \frac{\lambda^k}{k!} \prod_{i=1}^{k} \left\{\int_0^t [H(x+x_i) - H(x)]\,dx\right\},$$

whence, by (1),

$$\mathbf{P}\{\chi_1(t) \leqq x_1, \chi_2(t) \leqq x_2, \ldots, \chi_k(t) \leqq x_k | \xi(t) = k\}$$

$$= \prod_{i=1}^{k} \left[\frac{\displaystyle\int_0^t [H(x+x_i) - H(x)]\,dx}{\displaystyle\int_0^t [1 - H(x)]\,dx} \right].$$

If we let $t \to \infty$ then we obtain (4). If we consider an arbitrary initial state, then the only difference is that $\xi(t)$ contains an additional term which stochastically tends to zero when $t \to \infty$. Consequently the limiting distribution is independent of the initial distribution. This completes the proof.

Thus we have shown that the Markov process $\{\xi(t); \chi_1(t), \chi_2(t), \ldots\}$ is ergodic if $\alpha < \infty$. Accordingly there exists a uniquely determined stationary distribution. If we suppose that $\alpha < \infty$ and

$$\mathbf{P}\{\xi(0) = k; \chi_1(0) \leqq x_1, \chi_2(0) \leqq x_2, \ldots, \chi_k(0) \leqq x_k\}$$

$$= P_k^* H^*(x_1)H^*(x_2) \ldots H^*(x_k),$$

then we obtain the stationary process. In this case $\{\xi(t); \chi_1(t), \chi_2(t), \ldots\}$ has the same distribution for all $t \geqq 0$. For the stationary process let us denote by $\xi^*(t)$ the queue size at the instant t. Then we have

$$\mathbf{P}\{\xi^*(t) = k\} = P_k^* \qquad (k = 0, 1, 2, \ldots)$$

for all $t \geqq 0$.

3. Queues with infinitely many servers in the case of exponentially distributed service times

Now we shall suppose that $H(x)$, the distribution function of the service times, is defined by (2) of Section 1. Let

$$\phi(s) = \int_0^\infty e^{-sx}\, dF(x)$$

and

$$\beta = \int_0^\infty x\, dF(x).$$

Denote by $\xi(t)$ the queue size at the instant t. Define $\xi_n = \xi(\tau_n - 0)$, i.e. ξ_n is the queue size immediately before the arrival of the nth customer. The system is said to be in state E_k at the instant t if $\xi(t) = k$. In the following we shall determine the transient behavior of the stochastic sequence $\{\xi_n\}$ and that of the stochastic process $\{\xi(t)\}$ as as well as their asymptotic behavior when $n \to \infty$ and $t \to \infty$ respectively.

Let us introduce the notation

$$(1) \qquad P_k^{(n)} = \mathbf{P}\{\xi_n = k\} \qquad (n = 1, 2, \ldots)$$

and denote by

$$(2) \qquad B_r^{(n)} = \sum_{k=r}^\infty \binom{k}{r} P_k^{(n)} \qquad (r = 0, 1, 2, \ldots)$$

the rth binomial moment of the distribution $\{P_k^{(n)}\}$.

Similarly let

$$(3) \qquad P_k(t) = \mathbf{P}\{\xi(t) = k\}$$

and

$$(4) \qquad B_r(t) = \sum_{k=r}^\infty \binom{k}{r} P_k(t).$$

Finally define

$$(5) \qquad C_r(s, w) = \prod_{i=0}^r \left(\frac{w\phi(s + i\mu)}{1 - w\phi(s + i\mu)} \right) \qquad (r = 0, 1, 2, \ldots)$$

and $C_{-1}(s, w) = 1$. If $s = 0$ then let us write $C_r(0, w) = C_r(w)$, and let $\lim_{w \to 1} (1 - w) C_r(0, w) = C_r$, that is,

$$(6) \qquad C_r = \prod_{i=1}^{r} \left(\frac{\phi(i\mu)}{1 - \phi(i\mu)} \right) \qquad (r = 1, 2, 3, \ldots)$$

and $C_0 = 1$.

THEOREM 1. *Let us suppose that $\xi(0) = i$ is fixed. Then the probabilities* $\mathbf{P}\{\xi_n = k\} = P_k^{(n)}$ *are given by the generating function*

$$(7) \qquad \sum_{n=1}^{\infty} P_k^{(n)} w^n = \sum_{r=k}^{\infty} (-1)^{r-k} \binom{r}{k} \Phi_r(w) \qquad (k = 0, 1, 2, \ldots)$$

where

$$(8) \qquad \Phi_r(w) = \sum_{j=0}^{r} \binom{i}{j} \prod_{i=j}^{r} \left(\frac{w\phi(i\mu)}{1 - w\phi(i\mu)} \right) \qquad (r = 0, 1, 2, \ldots).$$

PROOF. It is easy to see that the sequence of random variables $\{\xi_n\}$ forms a homogeneous Markov chain with transition probabilities

$$p_{jk} = \mathbf{P}\{\xi_{n+1} = k \,|\, \xi_n = j\} = \int_0^{\infty} \pi_{jk}(x) \, dF(x),$$

where

$$(9) \qquad \pi_{jk}(x) = \binom{j+1}{k} e^{-k\mu x} (1 - e^{-\mu x})^{j+1-k}$$

is the transition probability given that the inter-arrival time $\theta_{n+1} = x$ (constant). For, if $\xi_n = j$ and $\theta_{n+1} = x$ then ξ_{n+1} has a Bernoulli distribution with parameters $j + 1$ and $e^{-\mu x}$. If $\xi(0) = i$ and $\theta_1 = x$ then similarly ξ_1 has a Bernoulli distribution with parameters i and $e^{-\mu x}$. Now let us introduce the binomial moments

$$B_r^{(n)} = \mathbf{E}\left\{ \binom{\xi_n}{r} \right\} = \sum_{k=r}^{\infty} \binom{k}{r} P_k^{(n)}.$$

Our next aim is to determine the binomial moments $B_r^{(n)}$ ($r = 0, 1, 2, \ldots$). Knowing these moments the distribution $\{P_k^{(n)}\}$ can easily be determined. We shall use the fact that the rth binomial moment of the Bernoulli distribution $p_k = \binom{n}{k} p^k (1 - p)^{n-k}$ ($k =$

$0, 1, \ldots, n)$ is equal to

$$b_r = \sum_{k=r}^{n} \binom{k}{r} p_k = \binom{n}{r} p^r \qquad (r = 0, 1, \ldots, n).$$

If we suppose that $\xi(0) = i$ is fixed, then

$$\mathbf{E}\left\{\binom{\xi_1}{r} \Big| \theta_1 = x\right\} = \binom{i}{r} e^{-r\mu x},$$

whence unconditionally

$$(10) \qquad B_r^{(1)} = \mathbf{E}\left\{\binom{\xi_1}{r}\right\} = \binom{i}{r} \phi(r\mu).$$

Similarly

$$\mathbf{E}\left\{\binom{\xi_{n+1}}{r} \Big| \xi_n = j, \theta_{n+1} = x\right\} = \binom{j+1}{r} e^{-r\mu x},$$

whence

$$\mathbf{E}\left\{\binom{\xi_{n+1}}{r} \Big| \xi_n = j\right\} = \phi(r\mu) \binom{j+1}{r} = \phi(r\mu)\left[\binom{j}{r} + \binom{j}{r-1}\right].$$

Multiply this equation by $\mathbf{P}\{\xi_n = j\}$ and add for every j; then we get

$$(11) \qquad B_r^{(n+1)} = \phi(r\mu)(B_r^{(n)} + B_{r-1}^{(n)}).$$

By (10) and (11) $B_r^{(n)}$ can be determined recursively for every n and r. It is more convenient to introduce the generating function

$$\Phi_r(w) = \sum_{n=1}^{\infty} B_r^{(n)} w^n.$$

Then by (10) and (11) we obtain

$$(12) \qquad \Phi_r(w) = \frac{w\phi(r\mu)}{1 - w\phi(r\mu)} \left[\Phi_{r-1}(w) + \binom{i}{r}\right].$$

Let

$$(13) \qquad C_r(w) = \prod_{i=0}^{r} \left(\frac{w\phi(i\mu)}{1 - w\phi(i\mu)}\right) \qquad (r = 0, 1, 2, \ldots)$$

and $C_{-1}(w) = 1$. Divide both sides of (12) by $C_r(w)$; then we get

$$\frac{\Phi_r(w)}{C_r(w)} = \frac{\Phi_{r-1}(w)}{C_{r-1}(w)} + \frac{\binom{i}{r}}{C_{r-1}(w)} \qquad (r = 1, 2, \ldots)$$

whence

$$\frac{\Phi_r(w)}{C_r(w)} = \sum_{j=0}^{r} \frac{\binom{i}{j}}{C_{j-1}(w)}$$

because $\Phi_0(w)/C_0(w) = 1$. This proves (8). From the definition of the binomial moment $B_r^{(n)}$ $(r = 0, 1, 2, \ldots)$, it follows immediately that

$$P_k^{(n)} = \sum_{r=k}^{\infty} (-1)^{r-k} \binom{r}{k} B_r^{(n)},$$

whence for $|w| < 1$

$$\sum_{n=1}^{\infty} P_k^{(n)} w^n = \sum_{r=k}^{\infty} (-1)^{r-k} \binom{r}{k} \Phi_r(w),$$

which proves (7).

THEOREM 2. *The limiting distribution* $\lim\limits_{n \to \infty} P_k^{(n)} = P_k$ $(k = 0, 1, 2, \ldots)$ *always exists and is independent of the distribution of* $\xi(0)$. *We have*

$$(14) \qquad P_k = \sum_{r=k}^{\infty} (-1)^{r-k} \binom{r}{k} B_r,$$

where B_r $(r = 0, 1, 2, \ldots)$, *the rth binomial moment of* $\{P_k\}$, *is given by*

$$(15) \qquad B_r = \prod_{i=1}^{r} \left(\frac{\phi(i\mu)}{1 - \phi(i\mu)} \right) \qquad (r = 1, 2, \ldots)$$

and $B_0 = 1$.

PROOF. The Markov chain $\{\xi_n\}$ is irreducible and aperiodic, therefore $\lim\limits_{n \to \infty} P_k^{(n)} = P_k$ always exists and is independent of the initial distribution. There are two possibilities: either every $P_k > 0$

and $\{P_k\}$ is a probability distribution, or every $P_k = 0$. By using Abel's theorem we have

(16)
$$P_k = \lim_{w \to 1} (1 - w) \sum_{n=1}^{\infty} P_k^{(n)} w^n = \lim_{w \to 1} (1 - w) \sum_{r=k}^{\infty} (-1)^{r-k} \binom{r}{k} \Phi_r(w)$$

and

(17)
$$\lim_{w \to 1} (1 - w) \Phi_r(w) = B_r,$$

where B_r is defined by (15). It is easy to see that the limit can be formed term by term in (16).

To determine the probabilities $\mathbf{P}\{\xi(t) = k\} = P_k(t)$ we need the following auxiliary theorem.

LEMMA 1. *Let us suppose that $\xi(0) = i$ is fixed, and define*

(18)
$$A_r^{(n)}(s) = \mathbf{E}\left\{ e^{-s\tau_n} \binom{\xi_n}{r} \right\} \qquad (\Re(s) \geqq 0);$$

then we have for $|w| \leqq 1$ and $\Re(s) > 0$ that

(19) $\Phi_r(s, w) = \sum_{n=1}^{\infty} A_r^{(n)}(s) w^n = \sum_{j=0}^{r} \binom{i}{j} \prod_{i=j}^{r} \left(\dfrac{w\phi(s + i\mu)}{1 - w\phi(s + i\mu)} \right).$

PROOF. We have

$$\mathbf{E}\left\{ e^{-s\tau_{n+1}} \binom{\xi_{n+1}}{r} \Big| \xi_n = j, \tau_{n+1} - \tau_n = x \right\} = e^{-(s+r\mu)} \binom{j+1}{r}$$

$$\cdot \mathbf{E}\left\{ e^{-s\tau_n} | \xi_n = j \right\} = e^{-(s+r\mu)x} \mathbf{E}\left\{ e^{-s\tau_n} \left[\binom{\xi_n}{r} + \binom{\xi_n}{r-1} \right] \Big| \xi_n = j \right\},$$

because under the given condition ξ_{n+1} has a Bernoulli distribution with parameters $j + 1$ and $e^{-\mu x}$, and $\tau_{n+1} = \tau_n + x$. Dropping the condition $\tau_{n+1} - \tau_n = x$ we get

$$\mathbf{E}\left\{ e^{-s\tau_{n+1}} \binom{\xi_{n+1}}{r} \Big| \xi_n = j \right\}$$

$$= \phi(s + r\mu) \mathbf{E}\left\{ e^{-s\tau_n} \left[\binom{\xi_n}{r} + \binom{\xi_n}{r-1} \right] \Big| \xi_n = j \right\}.$$

Multiplying this equation by $\mathbf{P}\{\xi_n = j\}$ and adding for every j we obtain

$$A_r^{(n+1)}(s) = \phi(s + r\mu)\,[A_r^{(n)}(s) + A_{r-1}^{(n)}(s)],$$

and if $\xi(0) = i$ then evidently

$$A_r^{(1)}(s) = \binom{i}{r}\phi(s + r\mu).$$

Forming generating functions we get

(20) $$\Phi_r(s, w) = \frac{w\phi(s + r\mu)}{1 - w\phi(s + r\mu)}\left[\Phi_{r-1}(s, w) + \binom{i}{r}\right].$$

Now dividing both sides of this equation by $C_r(s, w)$, defined by (5), we get

$$\frac{\Phi_r(s, w)}{C_r(s, w)} = \frac{\Phi_{r-1}(s, w)}{C_{r-1}(s, w)} + \frac{\binom{i}{r}}{C_{r-1}(s, w)},$$

whence

$$\frac{\Phi_r(s, w)}{C_r(s, w)} = \sum_{j=0}^{r} \frac{\binom{i}{j}}{C_{j-1}(s, w)},$$

because

$$\Phi_0(s, w) = \sum_{n=1}^{\infty} [\phi(s)]^n w^n = \frac{w\phi(s)}{1 - w\phi(s)}.$$

This proves (19).

THEOREM 3. *Let $\xi(0) = i$ be fixed. Then the Laplace transform of $P_k(t)$ is given by*

(21) $$\int_0^{\infty} e^{-st} P_k(t)\,dt = \sum_{r=k}^{\infty} (-1)^{r-k}\binom{r}{k}\beta_r(s) \qquad (\Re(s) > 0)$$

where

(22) $$\beta_r(s) = \frac{1}{(s + r\mu)}\sum_{j=0}^{r}\binom{i}{j}\prod_{\nu=j}^{r-1}\left(\frac{1 - \phi(s + \nu\mu)}{\phi(s + \nu\mu)}\right).$$

PROOF. From the definition of the binomial moments $B_r(t)$ $(r = 0, 1, 2, \ldots)$ it follows immediately that

$$(23) \qquad P_k(t) = \sum_{r=k}^{\infty} (-1)^{r-k} \binom{r}{k} B_r(t).$$

If

$$\beta_r(s) = \int_0^{\infty} e^{-st} B_r(t)\, dt \qquad (\Re(s) > 0)$$

and we form the Laplace transform of (23), then we get (21). Thus $\beta_r(s)$ remains to be determined. By using the theorem of total expectation we can write that

$$(24) \quad B_r(t) = \binom{i}{r} e^{-r\mu t}[1 - F(t)]$$

$$+ \sum_{j=0}^{\infty} \binom{j+1}{r} \int_0^t e^{-r\mu(t-u)}[1 - F(t-u)]\, dM_j(u),$$

where

$$(25) \qquad M_j(t) = \sum_{n=1}^{\infty} \mathbf{P}\{\tau_n \leqq t, \xi_n = j\}$$

is the expected number of the transitions $E_j \to E_{j+1}$ occurring in the time interval $(0, t]$. If no customer arrives during the time interval $(0, t]$ then $\xi(t)$ has a Bernoulli distribution with parameters i and $e^{-\mu t}$. If the last customer in the time interval $(0, t]$ arrives at the instant u $(0 < u \leqq t)$ and finds j customers in the queue, then $\xi(t)$ has the Bernoulli distribution with parameters $j + 1$ and $e^{-\mu(t-u)}$. If we also take into consideration that the last customer arriving in the time interval $(0, t]$ may be the 1st, 2nd, $\ldots$, nth, $\ldots$ then we get (24).

Now let us introduce the Laplace-Stieltjes transform

$$\mu_j(s) = \int_0^{\infty} e^{-st}\, dM_j(t),$$

which is convergent if $\Re(s) > 0$. By (24) we get

$$\beta_r(s) = \frac{[1 - \phi(s + r\mu)]}{(s + r\mu)} \left[\binom{i}{r} + \sum_{j=0}^{\infty} \binom{j+1}{r} \mu_j(s) \right].$$

On the other hand we can write by (25) that

$$\mu_j(s) = \sum_{n=1}^{\infty} \mathbf{P}\{\xi_n = j\}\mathbf{E}\{e^{-s\tau_n}|\xi_n = j\},$$

whence

$$\sum_{j=r}^{\infty} \binom{j}{r} \mu_j(s) = \sum_{n=1}^{\infty} \mathbf{E}\left\{e^{-s\tau_n}\binom{\xi_n}{r}\right\} = \Phi_r(s, 1),$$

where $\Phi_r(s, 1)$ is defined by (19). Thus

$$\beta_r(s) = \frac{[1 - \phi(s + r\mu)]}{(s + r\mu)}\left[\binom{i}{r} + \Phi_r(s, 1) + \Phi_{r-1}(s, 1)\right].$$

Since by (20)

$$\Phi_r(s, 1) = \frac{\phi(s + r\mu)}{[1 - \phi(s + r\mu)]}\left[\Phi_{r-1}(s, 1) + \binom{i}{r}\right],$$

we obtain finally that

$$\beta_r(s) = \frac{[1 - \phi(s + r\mu)]}{(s + r\mu)} \frac{\Phi_r(s, 1)}{\phi(s + r\mu)} \qquad (r = 0, 1, 2, \ldots),$$

where $\Phi_r(s, 1)$ is defined by (19). This completes the proof of the theorem.

THEOREM 4. *Suppose that $F(x)$ is not a lattice distribution and its mean $\beta < \infty$; then the limiting distribution* $\lim_{t\to\infty} P_k(t) = P_k^*$ *($k = 0, 1, 2, \ldots$) exists and is independent of the initial queue size. We have*

(26)
$$P_k^* = \frac{P_{k-1}}{k\beta\mu} \qquad (k = 1, 2, \ldots)$$

and

(27)
$$P_0^* = 1 - \frac{1}{\beta\mu} \sum_{k=1}^{\infty} \frac{P_{k-1}}{k},$$

where $\{P_k\}$ is defined by (14) and (15).

PROOF. Let us suppose that $\xi(0) = i$ is fixed; then by the theorem of total probability we can write that

(28)
$$P_k(t) = \binom{i}{k}e^{-k\mu t}(1 - e^{-\mu t})^{i-k}[1 - F(t)]$$
$$+ \sum_{j=k-1}^{\infty} \int_0^t \pi_{jk}(t - u)[1 - F(t - u)]\,dM_j(u),$$

where $M_j(t)$ denotes the expectation of the number of transitions $E_j \to E_{j+1}$ occurring in the time interval $(0, t]$.

If $F(x)$ is not a lattice distribution and $\beta < \infty$, then for all $h > 0$ we have

$$(29) \qquad \lim_{t \to \infty} \frac{M_j(t + h) - M_j(t)}{h} = \frac{P_j}{\beta} \qquad (j = 0, 1, 2, \ldots),$$

where $\{P_j\}$ is defined by (14) and (15). This can be proved as follows. The time differences between consecutive transitions $E_j \to E_{j+1}$ are identically distributed, independent, positive random variables. If $F(x)$ is not a lattice distribution function, then these random variables have no lattice distribution function either. If $\beta < \infty$, then these random variables have a finite expectation β/P_j. Under these conditions according to *Blackwell's* theorem (cf. Appendix), we get (29) and this limit is independent of the initial queue size. It remains only to prove that the expectation in question is β/P_j. Let us consider the Markov chain $\{\xi_n\}$. The state E_j is a recurrent state and the expectation of the recurrence step number is $1/P_j$. Since transitions $E_j \to E_{j+1}$ occur at such instants τ_n $(n = 1, 2, \ldots)$ for which $\xi_n = j$, the expected number of steps between consecutive transitions $E_j \to E_{j+1}$ is $1/P_j$. The expectation of the length of each step is β. Thus by *Wald's* theorem (cf. Appendix) we get that the expectation of the time differences between consecutive transitions $E_j \to E_{j+1}$ is β/P_j.

By applying the fundamental theorem of recurrent processes (cf. Appendix) and using (29), we can conclude from (28) that $\lim_{t \to \infty} P_k(t) = P_k^*$ $(k = 0, 1, 2, \ldots)$ exists irrespective of the initial queue size. By (28) and (29) we get

$$(30) \qquad P_k^* = \sum_{j=k-1}^{\infty} p_{jk}^* P_j$$

where

$$p_{jk}^* = \frac{1}{\beta} \int_0^{\infty} \pi_{jk}(x)[1 - F(x)] \, dx.$$

It is easy to see that $\{P_k^*\}$ is a probability distribution. The formula (30) yields $\{P_k^*\}$ explicitly, but it can also be obtained in a simpler way.

Denote by $N_k(t)$ the expectation of the number of transitions

$E_k \to E_{k-1}$ occurring in the time interval $(0, t]$. Then we have

$$(31) \qquad N_k(t) = k\mu \int_0^t P_k(u)\, du.$$

For, if we introduce a new time variable involved only when there is state E_k then the transitions $E_k \to E_{k-1}$ form a Poisson process of density $k\mu$. Now if $\lim_{t\to\infty} P_k(t) = P_k^*$ exists, then by (31) we get

$$(32) \qquad \lim_{t\to\infty} \frac{N_k(t)}{t} = k\mu P_k^*, \qquad (k = 0, 1, 2, \ldots).$$

To prove Theorem 4 we note that the difference of the number of transitions $E_{k-1} \to E_k$ and $E_k \to E_{k-1}$ occurring in the time interval $(0, t]$ is at most 1. Consequently $|M_{k-1}(t) - N_k(t)| \leqq 1$ and hence

$$\lim_{t\to\infty} \frac{M_{k-1}(t)}{t} = \lim_{t\to\infty} \frac{N_k(t)}{t}.$$

By (29) we get

$$(33) \qquad \lim_{t\to\infty} \frac{M_{k-1}(t)}{t} = \frac{P_{k-1}}{\beta} \qquad (k = 1, 2, \ldots).$$

Comparing (32) and (33) we have

$$P_k^* k\mu = \frac{P_{k-1}}{\beta} \qquad (k = 1, 2, \ldots)$$

and $P_0^* = 1 - \sum_{k=1}^{\infty} P_k^*$. This completes the proof of the theorem.

Problems for solution

PROBLEM 16. Let us denote by $G_k(x)$ $(k = 0, 1, 2, \ldots)$ the distribution function of the distance between two consecutive transitions $E_{k-1} \to E_k$ and $E_k \to E_{k+1}$. (Suppose that a transition $E_{-1} \to E_0$ takes place at time $t = 0$.) Find $\gamma_k(s)$, the Laplace-Stieltjes transform of $G_k(x)$.

PROBLEM 17. Find the expectation

$$\Gamma_k = \int_0^\infty x\, dG_k(x).$$

Bibliography

[1] *L. Takács:* On a coincidence problem concerning telephone traffic. Acta Math. Acad. Sci. Hungar. 9 (1958) 45–81.

[2] *L. Takács:* On the limiting distribution of the number of coincidences concerning telephone traffic. Ann. Math. Statist. 30 (1959) 134–42.

4

TELEPHONE TRAFFIC PROCESSES

1. Formulation of the problem

Let us suppose that at a telephone exchange calls are arriving at the instants $\tau_1, \tau_2, \ldots, \tau_n, \ldots$, where the inter-arrival times $\theta_n = \tau_n - \tau_{n-1}$ $(n = 1, 2, \ldots; \tau_0 = 0)$ are identically distributed, independent, positive random variables with distribution function

$$(1) \qquad \mathbf{P}\{\theta_n \leqq x\} = F(x).$$

There are m available lines. Suppose that a connection is realized if the incoming call finds a free line. If all lines are busy then the incoming call is lost. It is supposed that the holding times are identically distributed, independent, positive random variables with distribution function $H(x)$ and independent of the input process $\{\tau_n\}$.

Let us denote by $\zeta(t)$ the number of busy lines at the instant t. The system is said to be in state E_k at the instant t if $\zeta(t) = k$. Define $\zeta_n = \zeta(\tau_n - 0)$, that is, ζ_n is the number of busy lines immediately before the arrival of the nth call. Let $\mathbf{P}\{\zeta_n = k\} = P_k^{(n)}$, $\mathbf{P}\{\zeta(t) = k\} = P_k(t)$ and

$$\Pi_k(s) = \int_0^\infty e^{-st} P_k(t)\, dt,$$

which is convergent whenever $\Re(s) > 0$.

In what follows we shall deal with the particular case when the holding times are distributed exponentially, that is,

$$(2) \qquad H(x) = \begin{cases} 1 - e^{-\mu x} & \text{if } x \geqq 0, \\ 0 & \text{if } x < 0, \end{cases}$$

and we shall mention briefly the results concerning the particular case when $\{\tau_n\}$ is a Poisson process of density λ.

174

2. *Exponentially distributed holding times*

Now we shall suppose that $H(x)$ has the form (2) of Section 1. The Laplace-Stieltjes transform of $F(x)$ will be denoted by

$$\phi(s) = \int_0^\infty e^{-sx}\, dF(x)$$

and its mean by

$$\beta = \int_0^\infty x\, dF(x).$$

We shall investigate the stochastic behavior of the stochastic sequence $\{\zeta_n\}$ and that of the stochastic process $\{\zeta(t)\}$. We need the following

LEMMA 1. *Let us suppose that $\zeta(0) = i$. For $n = 0, 1, \ldots,$ $r = 0, 1, \ldots, m$ and $\Re(s) \geqq 0$ let us define*

$$(1) \qquad A_r^{(n)}(s) = \mathbf{E}\left\{ e^{-s\tau_n}\binom{\zeta_n}{r}\right\},$$

and for $r = 0, 1, \ldots, m$ and $|w| \leqq 1$ and $\Re(s) > 0$,

$$(2) \qquad \Phi_r(s, w) = \sum_{n=1}^\infty A_r^{(n)}(s)w^n.$$

Then we have

$$(3) \quad \Phi_r(s, w) = \frac{C_r(s, w)}{\displaystyle\sum_{j=0}^m \binom{m}{j}\frac{1}{C_j(s, w)}}$$

$$\cdot\left\{\left[\sum_{j=r}^m \binom{m}{j}\frac{1}{C_j(s, w)}\right]\left[\sum_{j=0}^r \binom{i}{j}\frac{1}{C_{j-1}(s, w)}\right]\right.$$

$$\left. - \left[\sum_{j=0}^{r-1} \binom{m}{j}\frac{1}{C_j(s, w)}\right]\left[\sum_{j=r+1}^m \binom{i}{j}\frac{1}{C_{j-1}(s, w)}\right]\right\},$$

where

(4) $$C_r(s, w) = \prod_{i=0}^{r} \left(\frac{w\phi(s + \mu i)}{1 - w\phi(s + i\mu)} \right) \qquad (r = 0, 1, 2, \ldots)$$

and $C_{-1}(s, w) \equiv 1$.

PROOF. We have

$$\mathbf{E}\left\{ e^{-s\tau_{n+1}} \binom{\zeta_{n+1}}{r} \Big| \zeta_n = j, \tau_{n+1} - \tau_n = x \right\}$$

$$= \begin{cases} e^{-(s+r\mu)x} \dbinom{j+1}{r} \mathbf{E}\{e^{-s\tau_n}|\zeta_n = j\} \text{ if } j < m, \\[2ex] e^{-(s+r\mu)x} \dbinom{m}{r} \mathbf{E}\{e^{-s\tau_n}|\zeta_n = m\} \quad \text{if } j = m, \end{cases}$$

because under the given conditions ζ_{n+1} has a Bernoulli distribution with parameters $j + 1$ $(j = 0, 1, \ldots, m - 1)$ or m $(j = m)$ and $e^{-\mu x}$. Dropping the condition $\tau_{n+1} - \tau_n = x$ we get

$$\mathbf{E}\left\{ e^{-s\tau_{n+1}} \binom{\zeta_{n+1}}{r} \Big| \zeta_n = j \right\} = \phi(s + r\mu) \binom{j+1}{r} \mathbf{E}\{e^{-s\tau_n}|\zeta_n = j\}$$

when $j = 0, 1, \ldots, m - 1$ and

$$\mathbf{E}\left\{ e^{-s\tau_{n+1}} \binom{\zeta_{n+1}}{r} \Big| \zeta_n = m \right\} = \phi(s + r\mu) \binom{m}{r} \mathbf{E}\{e^{-s\tau_n}|\zeta_n = m\}.$$

If we multiply the corresponding equations by $\mathbf{P}\{\zeta_n = j\}$ and add them for $j = 0, 1, \ldots, m$, then we get

(5)

$$A_r^{(n+1)}(s) = \phi(s + r\mu) \left[A_r^{(n)}(s) + A_{r-1}^{(n)}(s) - \binom{m}{r-1} A_m^{(n)}(s) \right]$$

for $r = 1, 2, \ldots, m$ and evidently

$$A_0^{(n)}(s) = [\phi(s)]^n.$$

If we suppose that $\zeta(0) = i$ is fixed, then

$$A_r^{(1)}(s) = \binom{i}{r} \phi(s + r\mu).$$

Forming the generating function $\Phi_r(s, w)$ we get

$$\Phi_r(s, w) - w \binom{i}{r} \phi(s + r\mu) = w\phi(s + r\mu)[\Phi_r(s, w)$$

$$+ \Phi_{r-1}(s, w) - \binom{m}{r-1} \Phi_m(s, w)],$$

that is,

(6) $\Phi_r(s, w)$

$$= \frac{w\phi(s + r\mu)}{[1 - w\phi(s + r\mu)]} \left[\binom{i}{r} + \Phi_{r-1}(s, w) - \binom{m}{r-1} \Phi_m(s, w) \right].$$

Now dividing both sides of this equation by $C_r(s, w)$ we get

$$\frac{\Phi_r(s, w)}{C_r(s, w)} = \frac{\Phi_{r-1}(s, w)}{C_{r-1}(s, w)} + \frac{\binom{i}{r} - \binom{m}{r-1} \Phi_m(s, w)}{C_{r-1}(s, w)}.$$

If we write down this equation also for $r - 1$, $r - 2$, ..., 1 and add them, we obtain for $r = 1, 2, \ldots, m$ that

(7)

$$\frac{\Phi_r(s, w)}{C_r(s, w)} = \sum_{j=0}^{r} \binom{i}{j} \frac{1}{C_{j-1}(s, w)} - \Phi_m(s, w) \sum_{j=1}^{r} \binom{m}{j-1} \frac{1}{C_{j-1}(s, w)}.$$

Putting $r = m$ in (7) we get

(8) $$\Phi_m(s, w) = \frac{\displaystyle\sum_{j=0}^{m} \binom{i}{j} \frac{1}{C_{j-1}(s, w)}}{\displaystyle\sum_{j=0}^{m} \binom{m}{j} \frac{1}{C_j(s, w)}}.$$

Substituting (8) into (7) we obtain $\Phi_r(s, w)$ for $r = 1, 2, \ldots, m$. If $r = 0$ then

$$\Phi_0(s, w) = \sum_{n=1}^{\infty} [\phi(s)]^n w^n = \frac{w\phi(s)}{1 - w\phi(s)}.$$

This completes the proof of the lemma.

THEOREM 1. *Let us suppose that* $\zeta(0) = i$ *is fixed. Then the probabilities* $\mathbf{P}\{\zeta_n = k\} = P_k^{(n)}$ $(k = 0, 1, \ldots, m)$ *are given by the generating function*

$$(9) \qquad \sum_{n=1}^{\infty} P_k^{(n)} w^n = \sum_{r=k}^{m} (-1)^{r-k} \binom{r}{k} \Phi_r(w),$$

where

$$(10) \quad \Phi_r(w) = \frac{C_r(w)}{\sum_{j=0}^{m} \binom{m}{j} \dfrac{1}{C_j(w)}}$$

$$\cdot \left\{ \left[\sum_{j=r}^{m} \binom{m}{j} \frac{1}{C_j(w)} \right] \left[\sum_{j=0}^{r} \binom{i}{j} \frac{1}{C_{j-1}(w)} \right] \right.$$

$$\left. - \left[\sum_{j=0}^{r-1} \binom{m}{j} \frac{1}{C_j(w)} \right] \left[\sum_{j=r+1}^{m} \binom{i}{j} \frac{1}{C_{j-1}(w)} \right] \right\},$$

and $C_{-1}(w) \equiv 1,$

$$(11) \qquad C_r(w) = \prod_{i=0}^{r} \left(\frac{w\phi(i\mu)}{1 - w\phi(i\mu)} \right) \qquad (r = 0, 1, 2, \ldots).$$

PROOF. If

$$B_r^{(n)} = \sum_{k=r}^{m} \binom{k}{r} P_k^{(n)} \qquad (r = 0, 1, \ldots, m)$$

is the rth binomial moment of the distribution $\{P_k^{(n)}\}$ then by (2) we obtain that

$$\sum_{n=1}^{\infty} B_r^{(n)} w^n = \Phi_r(0, w) = \Phi_r(w).$$

Evidently

$$P_k^{(n)} = \sum_{r=k}^{m} (-1)^{r-k} \binom{r}{k} B_r^{(n)} \qquad (k = 0, 1, \ldots, m),$$

and forming the generating function we get (9), which was to be proved.

THEOREM 2. *The limiting distribution* $\lim_{n \to \infty} P_k^{(n)} = P_k$ $(k = 0, 1, \ldots, m)$ *always exists and is independent of the initial state.*

We have

(12)
$$P_k = \sum_{r=k}^{m} (-1)^{r-k} \binom{r}{k} B_r,$$

where B_r is the rth binomial moment of $\{P_k\}$ and is given by

(13)
$$B_r = C_r \frac{\sum_{j=r}^{m} \binom{m}{j} \frac{1}{C_j}}{\sum_{j=0}^{m} \binom{m}{j} \frac{1}{C_j}},$$

where $C_0 = 1$ and

(14)
$$C_r = \prod_{i=1}^{r} \left(\frac{\phi(i\mu)}{1 - \phi(i\mu)} \right) \qquad (r = 1, 2, \ldots).$$

PROOF. The sequence of random variables $\{\zeta_n\}$ forms an irreducible and aperiodic Markov chain. Thus $\lim_{n \to \infty} \mathbf{P}\{\zeta_n = k\} = P_k$ $(k = 0, 1, \ldots, m)$ exists irrespective of the initial distribution and $\{P_k\}$ is a probability distribution. If B_r denotes the rth binomial moment of $\{P_k\}$, that is,

$$B_r = \sum_{k=r}^{m} \binom{k}{r} P_k,$$

then clearly

$$P_k = \sum_{r=k}^{m} (-1)^{r-k} \binom{r}{k} B_r.$$

Further in this case

$$\lim_{n \to \infty} B_r^{(n)} = B_r.$$

By using Abel's theorem we have that

$$\lim_{n \to \infty} B_r^{(n)} = \lim_{w \to 1} (1 - w) \sum_{n=1}^{\infty} B_r^{(n)} w^n = B_r,$$

where B_r is defined by (13) and the limit is independent of i. This proves (12).

THEOREM 3. *Let $\zeta(0) = i$. Then the Laplace transform of* $P_k(t) = \mathbf{P}\{\zeta(t) = k\}$ $(k = 0, 1, \ldots, m)$ *is given by*

(15) $$\int_0^\infty e^{-st} P_k(t)\, dt = \sum_{r=k}^m (-1)^{r-k} \binom{r}{k} \beta_r(s),$$

where

(16) $$\beta_r(s) = \frac{[1 - \phi(s + r\mu)]}{\phi(s + r\mu)} \frac{\Phi_r(s, 1)}{(s + r\mu)}$$

and $\Phi_r(s, 1)$ is defined by (3) *if we put $w = 1$ in it.*

PROOF. From the definition of the binomial moments $B_r(t)$ $(r = 0, 1, \ldots, m)$ it follows immediately that

(17) $$P_k(t) = \sum_{r=k}^m (-1)^{r-k} \binom{r}{k} B_r(t),$$

and if

$$\beta_r(s) = \int_0^\infty e^{-st} B_r(t)\, dt$$

then forming the Laplace transform of (17) we get (15). Only $\beta_r(s)$ remains to be determined. By using the theorem of total expectation we can write that

(18) $$B_r(t) = \binom{i}{r} e^{-r\mu t}[1 - F(t)]$$

$$+ \sum_{j=0}^{m-1} \binom{j+1}{r} \int_0^t e^{-r\mu(t-u)}[1 - F(t - u)]\, dM_j(u)$$

$$+ \binom{m}{r} \int_0^t e^{-r\mu(t-u)}[1 - F(t - u)]\, dM_m(u),$$

where

(19) $$M_j(t) = \sum_{n=1}^\infty \mathbf{P}\{\tau_n \leqq t, \zeta_n = j\}$$

is the expected number of those calls which arrive in the time interval $(0, t]$ and find exactly j lines busy. In particular, $M_m(t)$ is the expected number of lost calls occurring in $(0, t]$. To prove (18) we note that, if there is no call in the time interval $(0, t]$, then $\zeta(t)$ has the Bernoulli distribution with parameters i and $e^{-\mu t}$; if the last call in the time interval $(0, t]$ occurs at the instant u and in that instant the number of busy lines is j ($j = 0, 1, \ldots, m$), then $\zeta(t)$ has the Bernoulli distribution with parameters $j + 1$ (if $j = 0, 1, \ldots, m - 1$) or m (if $j = m$) and $e^{-\mu(t-u)}$. If we also take into consideration that the last call occurring in the time interval $(0, t]$ may be the 1st, 2nd, $\ldots$, nth, $\ldots$, then we get (18).

Now let us introduce the Laplace-Stieltjes transform

$$\mu_j(s) = \int_0^\infty e^{-st}\, dM_j(t),$$

which is convergent if $\Re(s) > 0$. By (18) we have

(20)
$$\beta_r(s) = \frac{[1 - \phi(s + r\mu)]}{(s + r\mu)} \left[\binom{i}{r} + \sum_{j=0}^{m-1} \binom{j+1}{r} \mu_j(s) + \binom{m}{r} \mu_m(s) \right].$$

By (19)
$$\mu_j(s) = \sum_{n=1}^\infty \mathbf{P}\{\zeta_n = j\} \mathbf{E}\{e^{-s\tau_n} | \zeta_n = j\}$$

and hence by (2) we get

(21)
$$\sum_{j=r}^m \binom{j}{r} \mu_j(s) = \sum_{n=1}^\infty \mathbf{E}\left\{ e^{-s\tau_n} \binom{\zeta_n}{r} \right\} = \Phi_r(s, 1),$$

where $\Phi_r(s, w)$ is defined by (3). Thus $\beta_r(s)$ can be written in the following form

$$\beta_r(s) = \frac{[1 - \phi(s + r\mu)]}{(s + r\mu)} \left[\binom{i}{r} + \Phi_r(s, 1) \right.$$
$$\left. + \Phi_{r-1}(s, 1) - \binom{m}{r-1} \Phi_m(s, 1) \right].$$

If we take into consideration the relation (6) having put $w = 1$ in it, then this formula can be simplified to

(22)
$$\beta_r(s) = \frac{[1 - \phi(s + r\mu)]}{\phi(s + r\mu)} \frac{\Phi_r(s, 1)}{(s + r\mu)},$$

which was to be proved.

REMARK 1. If specifically $\zeta(0) = 0$ then

$$(23) \qquad \beta_r(s) = \frac{\sum_{j=r}^{m} \binom{m}{j} \prod_{i=0}^{j} \left(\frac{1 - \phi(s + i\mu)}{\phi(s + i\mu)} \right)}{(s + r\mu) \sum_{j=0}^{m} \binom{m}{j} \prod_{i=0}^{j} \left(\frac{1 - \phi(s + i\mu)}{\phi(s + i\mu)} \right)}.$$

In the particular case when $\{\tau_n\}$ is a Poisson process of density λ, i.e. $F(x) = 1 - e^{-\lambda x}$ $(x \geqq 0)$ and $\phi(s) = \lambda/(\lambda + s)$, then (23) reduces to

$$(24) \qquad \beta_r(s) = \frac{\dfrac{1}{(s + r\mu)} \sum_{j=r}^{m} \binom{m}{j} \dfrac{(s + r\mu)\dots(s + j\mu)}{\lambda^{j+1-r}}}{\sum_{j=0}^{m} \binom{m}{j} \dfrac{s(s + \mu)\dots(s + j\mu)}{\lambda^{j+1}}}.$$

Thus

$$\Pi_m(s) = \beta_m(s) = \frac{\lambda^m}{\sum_{j=0}^{m} \binom{m}{j} \lambda^{m-j} s(s + \mu)\dots(s + j\mu)}$$

is the Laplace transform of the probability that every line is busy at time t.

THEOREM 4. *If $F(x)$ is not a lattice distribution and its mean $\beta < \infty$, then the limiting distribution $\lim_{t \to \infty} P_k(t) = P_k^*$ $(k = 0, 1, \dots, m)$ exists and is independent of the initial distribution. The probability distribution $\{P_k^*\}$ can be expressed by the distribution $\{P_k\}$ as follows:*

$$(25) \qquad P_k^* = \frac{P_{k-1}}{k\mu\beta} \qquad (k = 1, 2, \dots, m)$$

and

$$(26) \qquad P_0^* = 1 - \frac{1}{\mu\beta} \sum_{k=1}^{m} \frac{P_{k-1}}{k}.$$

PROOF. First we shall prove that there exists a unique limiting distribution $\{P_k^*\}$ and then we show that if $\{P_k^*\}$ exists it can be expressed simply by the distribution $\{P_k\}$.

Let us suppose that $\zeta(0) = i$. By using the theorem of total probability we get

$$(27) \quad P_k(t) = \binom{i}{k} e^{-k\mu t}(1 - e^{-\mu t})^{i-k}[1 - F(t)] + \sum_{j=k-1}^{m-1} \binom{j+1}{k}$$

$$\cdot \int_0^t e^{-k\mu(t-u)}(1 - e^{-\mu(t-u)})^{j+1-k}[1 - F(t - u)]\, dM_j(u)$$

$$+ \binom{m}{k} \int_0^t e^{-k\mu(t-u)}(1 - e^{-\mu(t-u)})^{m-k}[1 - F(t - u)]\, dM_m(u).$$

For, the event $\zeta(t) = k$ can occur in the following mutually exclusive ways: in the time interval $(0, t]$ no call occurs and $i - k$ conversations terminate or the last call in the time interval $(0, t]$ occurs at the instant u and finds j $(j = 0, 1, \ldots, m)$ lines busy, and in the time interval $(u, t]$ $j + 1 - k$ (if $j = 0, 1, \ldots, m - 1$) or $m - 1$ (if $j = m$) conversations terminate. If we also take into consideration that the last call occurring in the time interval $(0, t]$ may be the 1st, 2nd, $\ldots$, nth, $\ldots$ one, then we get (27).

Now we shall prove that if $F(x)$ is not a lattice distribution and its mean $\beta < \infty$, then for all $h > 0$ we have

$$(28) \quad \lim_{t \to \infty} \frac{M_k(t + h) - M_k(t)}{h} = \frac{P_k}{\beta} \qquad (k = 0, 1, \ldots, m),$$

irrespective of the initial state. The time differences between consecutive calls, which find exactly k lines busy, are identically distributed, independent, positive random variables. If $F(x)$ is not a lattice distribution function, then these random variables have no lattice distribution function either. If $\beta < \infty$, then these random variables have a finite expectation β/P_k. Under these conditions according to *Blackwell*'s theorem (cf. Appendix), we get (28) and this limit is independent of the initial state. It remains only to prove that the expectation in question is β/P_k. Let us consider the Markov chain $\{\zeta_n\}$. The state E_k is a recurrent state and the expectation of the recurrence step number is $1/P_k$. The expectation of the length of each step is β. Thus by *Wald*'s theorem (cf. Appendix) we get that the expectation of the time differences between consecutive calls which find exactly k lines busy is β/P_k.

By applying the fundamental theorem of recurrent processes (cf. Appendix) and using (28), we can conclude from (27) that $\lim_{t \to \infty} P_k(t) = P_k^*$ $(k = 0, 1, \ldots, m)$ exists irrespective of the initial state. We have

$$(29) \qquad P_k^* = \sum_{j=k-1}^{m} p_{jk}^* P_j,$$

where

$$p_{jk}^* = \frac{1}{\beta} \binom{j+1}{k} \int_0^\infty e^{-k\mu x}(1 - e^{-\mu x})^{j+1-k}[1 - F(x)] \, dx$$

$$(j = 0, 1, \ldots, m - 1)$$

and

$$p_{m,k}^* = p_{m-1,k}^*.$$

The relation (29) gives P_k^* explicitly but it can be obtained also in a simpler form. Let us denote by $N_k(t)$ the expectation of the number of transitions $E_k \to E_{k-1}$ $(k = 1, 2, \ldots, m)$ occurring in the time interval $(0, t]$. Then we have

$$N_k(t) = k\mu \int_0^t P_k(u) \, du.$$

For, if we introduce a new time variable, involved only when there is state E_k, then the transitions $E_k \to E_{k-1}$ form a Poisson process of density $k\mu$. If we suppose that $\lim_{t \to \infty} P_k(t) = P_k^*$ then we get

$$\lim_{t \to \infty} \frac{N_k(t)}{t} = k\mu P_k^* \qquad (k = 1, 2, \ldots, m).$$

On the other hand by (28)

$$\lim_{t \to \infty} \frac{M_k(t)}{t} = \frac{P_k}{\beta} \qquad (k = 0, 1, \ldots, m).$$

Since evidently $|M_{k-1}(t) - N_k(t)| \leq 1$ for all $t \geq 0$ and for $k = 1, 2, \ldots, m$, therefore

$$\lim_{t \to \infty} \frac{N_k(t)}{t} = \lim_{t \to \infty} \frac{M_{k-1}(t)}{t} \qquad (k = 1, 2, \ldots, m)$$

that is,

$$k\mu P_k^* = \frac{P_{k-1}}{\beta} \qquad (k = 1, 2, \ldots, m)$$

and hence

$$P_0^* = 1 - \sum_{k=1}^{m} P_k^* = 1 - \frac{1}{\mu\beta} \sum_{k=1}^{m} \frac{P_{k-1}}{k}.$$

This completes the proof of the theorem.

THE PROCESS OF LOST CALLS. It is easy to see that the successive lost calls form a recurrent process. The distances between consecutive lost calls are identically distributed, independent random variables. Let us denote by $G_m(x)$ their common distribution function and let

$$\gamma_m(s) = \int_0^\infty e^{-sx} \, dG_m(x).$$

THEOREM 5. *The Laplace-Stieltjes transform of $G_m(x)$ is given by*

$$(30) \qquad \gamma_m(s) = \frac{\displaystyle\sum_{j=0}^{m} \binom{m}{j} \prod_{i=0}^{j-1} \left(\frac{1 - \phi(s + i\mu)}{\phi(s + i\mu)} \right)}{\displaystyle\sum_{j=0}^{m+1} \binom{m+1}{j} \prod_{i=0}^{j-1} \left(\frac{1 - \phi(s + i\mu)}{\phi(s + i\mu)} \right)},$$

where the empty product is 1.

PROOF. If we suppose specifically that $\zeta(0) = m$ then by the theory of recurrent processes we have

$$M_m(t) = G_m(t) + G_m(t) * G_m(t) + \cdots,$$

whence

$$\mu_m(s) = \int_0^\infty e^{-st} \, dM_m(t) = \frac{\gamma_m(s)}{1 - \gamma_m(s)}.$$

Thus

$$(31) \qquad \gamma_m(s) = \frac{\mu_m(s)}{1 + \mu_m(s)}.$$

By (21) $\mu_m(s) = \Phi_m(s, 1)$ and if we put $w = 1$ and $i = m$ in (3) we get

$$(32) \qquad \mu_m(s) = \frac{\displaystyle\sum_{j=0}^{m} \binom{m}{j} \frac{1}{C_{j-1}(s, 1)}}{\displaystyle\sum_{j=0}^{m} \binom{m}{j} \frac{1}{C_j(s, 1)}},$$

where $C_j(s, 1)$ is defined by (4). By (31) and (32) we obtain (30), which was to be proved.

REMARK 2. The mean of $G_m(x)$ is given by

$$(33) \qquad \int_0^\infty x \, dG_m(x) = \beta \sum_{j=0}^m \binom{m}{j} \prod_{i=1}^j \left(\frac{\phi(i\mu)}{1 - \phi(i\mu)} \right)$$

where the empty product is equal to 1. This can be obtained by calculating $-\gamma_m'(0)$ if we use that $\phi'(0) = -\beta$.

3. Poisson input

Now let us suppose that $\{\tau_n\}$ is a Poisson process of density λ, that is,

$$(1) \qquad F(x) = \begin{cases} 1 - e^{-\lambda x} & \text{if } x \geqq 0, \\ 0 & \text{if } x < 0, \end{cases}$$

and that the holding times have an arbitrary distribution function $H(x)$ with mean

$$\alpha = \int_0^\infty x \, dH(x).$$

In this case the following theorem is valid.

THEOREM 1. *If* $\alpha < \infty$ *then* $\lim_{t \to \infty} P_k(t) = P_k^*$ $(k = 0,$ $1, \ldots, m)$ *exists and is independent of the initial distribution. We have*

$$(2) \qquad P_k^* = \frac{e^{-\lambda\alpha} \dfrac{(\lambda\alpha)^k}{k!}}{\displaystyle\sum_{j=0}^m e^{-\lambda\alpha} \dfrac{(\lambda\alpha)^j}{j!}} \qquad (k = 0, 1, \ldots, m).$$

This theorem first was stated by *A. K. Erlang* [4]; however, he proved it only in the special case when the holding times are distributed exponentially. For the general case intuitive proofs were given by *F. Pollaczek* [9], *C. Palm* [7], *L. Kosten* [6], and others. The exact proof of Erlang's formula (2) was given by *B. A. Sevastyanov* [11].

Problems for solution

PROBLEM 18. Let us suppose that $F(x) = 1 - e^{-\lambda x}$ if $x \geq 0$, that is, the input process is a Poisson process of density λ, $H(x) = 1 - e^{-\mu x}$ if $x \geq 0$, that is, the holding times are distributed exponentially, and that $\zeta(0) = 0$, that is, initially every line is free. Find the probability $\mathbf{P}\{\zeta(t) = m\} = P_m(t)$.

PROBLEM 19. Prove Erlang's formula (2) in the case when the holding times have the distribution function

$$
H(x) = \begin{cases} 1 - \displaystyle\sum_{j=0}^{s-1} e^{-\mu x}\frac{(\mu x)^j}{j!} & \text{if } x \geq 0, \\ 0 & \text{if } x < 0. \end{cases}
$$

In this case $\alpha = s/\mu$.

Bibliography

[1] V. E. Beneš: On trunks with negative exponential holding times serving a renewal process. Bell System Tech. Jour. 38 (1959) 211–58.

[2] V. E. Beneš: Transition probabilities for telephone traffic. Bell System Tech. Jour. 39 (1960) 1297–320.

[3] J. W. Cohen: The full availability group of trunks with an arbitrary distribution of the inter-arrival times and a negative exponential holding time distribution. Simon Stevin Wis-en Natuurkundig Tijdschrift 31 (1957) 169–81.

[4] A. K. Erlang: Solution of some problems in the theory of probabilities of significance in automatic telephone exchanges. Post Office Electrical Engineer's Journal 10 (1917–18) 189–97.

[5] A. Y. Khintchine: Mathematical Methods of the Theory of Mass Service (in Russian). Trudy Mat. Inst. Steklov No. 49 (1955); Mathematical Methods in the Theory of Queueing. Ch. Griffin, London (1960).

[6] L. Kosten: On the validity of the Erlang and Engset loss-formulae. Het. P.T.T. Bedrijf 2 (1948–49) 42–5.

[7] C. Palm: Analysis of the Erlang traffic formulae for busy-signal arrangements. Ericsson Technics, No. 4 (1938) 39–58.

[8] C. Palm: Intensitätsschwankungen im Fernsprechverkehr. Ericsson Technics No. 44 (1943) 1–189.

[9] F. Pollaczek: Lösung eines geometrischen Wahrscheinlichkeitsproblems. Math. Zeit. 35 (1932) 230–78.

[10] *F. Pollaczek:* Généralisation de la théorie probabiliste des systèmes téléphoniques sans dispositif d'attente. C. R. Acad. Sci. Paris 236 (1953) 1469–70.

[11] *B. A. Sevastyanov:* An ergodic theorem for Markov processes and its application to telephone systems with refusals (in Russian). Teor. Veroyatnost. i Primenen 2 (1957) 106–16; Theory of Probability and its Applications 2 (1957) 104–12.

[12] *R. Syski:* Introduction to Congestion Theory in Telephone Systems. Oliver and Boyd, Edinburgh, 1960.

[13] *L. Takács:* On the generalization of Erlang's formula. Acta Math. Acad. Sci. Hungar. 7 (1956) 419–33.

[14] *L. Takács:* On a probability problem concerning telephone traffic. Acta Math. Acad. Sci. Hungar. 8 (1957) 319–24.

[15] *L. Takács:* On a coincidence problem concerning telephone traffic. Acta Math. Acad. Sci. Hungar. 9 (1958) 45–81.

[16] *L. Takács:* On the limiting distribution of the number of coincidences concerning telephone traffic. Ann. Math. Statist. 30 (1959) 134–42.

[17] *L. Takács:* The time dependence of Palm's loss formula. J. Math. Ann. and Appl. 2 (1961) 58–71.

[18] *L. Takács:* Stochastic processes with balking in the theory of telephone traffic. Bell System Tech. Journ. 40 (1961) 795–820.

5

A PROCESS OF SERVICING MACHINES

1. Formulation of the problem

Let us suppose that $m + 1$ machines are serviced by a single repairman. The machines work continuously; however, at any time a machine may break down and need service. The machines are assumed to work independently. Let us suppose that if at time t a machine is in working state, the probability that it will call for service in the time interval $(t, t + \Delta t)$ is $\mu \, \Delta t + o(\Delta t)$. If a machine breaks down it will be serviced immediately unless the repairman is servicing another machine, in which case a waiting line is formed. It is supposed that the repairman is idle if and only if there is no machine in the waiting line; otherwise the order of the servicing is irrelevant. Suppose that the times required for servicing the machines are independent, positive random variables with common distribution function $F(x)$.

Let us denote by $\xi(t)$ the number of machines working at the instant t. The system is said to be in state E_k at the instant t if $\xi(t) = k$. Denote by $\tau_1', \ldots, \tau_n', \ldots$ the termination points of the successive servicings. Suppose that a service ends at time $t = -0$. Define $\xi_n = \xi(\tau_n' - 0)$, that is, ξ_n is the number of machines working immediately before the termination of the nth servicing. Let $\mathbf{P}\{\xi(t) = k\} = Q_k(t)$ $(k = 0, 1, \ldots, m + 1)$.

This process is in close connection with the telephone traffic process investigated in Section 2 of the previous chapter. We shall show that the stochastic sequences $\{\xi_n\}$ and $\{\zeta_n\}$ follow exactly the same stochastic law if $\xi(0) = \zeta(0)$ or $\xi(0) = m + 1$ and $\zeta(0) = m$ and, further, that if we know the stochastic behavior of $\{\zeta(t)\}$, that of $\{\xi(t)\}$ can be deduced easily.

The analogy between the telephone traffic process and the servicing process can be seen as follows.

In the case of the *telephone traffic process* each call starts a conversation with distribution function $H(x) = 1 - e^{-\mu x}$ $(x \geqq 0)$ if there is a free line. If all the lines are busy, the calls will still continue to come in but they will be lost. The incoming calls form a recurrent process in which the inter-arrival times have the distribution function $F(x)$. (Cf. Fig. 4.)

In the case of the *servicing process* the termination of each servicing is the starting point of a working period with distribution function $H(x) = 1 - e^{-\mu x}$ $(x \geqq 0)$. If all machines are working then the process of the servicing is stopped and starts again only at the next breakdown. If we leave out all the times when every machine is working, then the endpoints of the successive servicings form a recurrent process in which the distances between two consecutive endpoints have the distribution function $F(x)$. (Cf. Fig. 3.)

If in the servicing process we introduce a new time variable involved only when there are machines which do not work, then this new process shows exactly the same stochastic behavior as the telephone process when $\zeta(0) = \xi(0)$ and $\xi(0) \leqq m$ or $\zeta(0) = m$ and $\xi(0) = m + 1$. By this correspondence with every transition $E_{m+1} \to E_m$ is associated a lost call. If $\xi(0) = m + 1$ in the servicing process then it is supposed that $\zeta(0) = m$ in the telephone traffic process and with the first transition $E_{m+1} \to E_m$ is associated the instant $t = 0$.

In particular if we consider the number of working machines immediately before the termination of each servicing, that is, $\{\xi_n\}$, and the number of busy lines immediately before each arrival, that is, $\{\zeta_n\}$, then these two stochastic sequences follow exactly the same stochastic law whenever $\zeta(0) = \xi(0)$ and $\xi(0) \leqq m$ or $\zeta(0) = m$ and $\xi(0) = m + 1$.

If we introduce the notation $\mathbf{P}\{\xi_n = k\} = Q_k^{(n)}$ and $\lim\limits_{n \to \infty} Q_k^{(n)} = Q_k$, then the probability distributions $\{Q_k^{(n)}\}$ and $\{Q_k\}$ agree with the respective distributions $\{P_k^{(n)}\}$ and $\{P_k\}$ defined by (9) and (12) of Section 2, Chapter 4.

In determining the probabilities $\mathbf{P}\{\xi(t) = k\} = Q_k(t)$ $(k = 0, 1, \ldots, m + 1)$ we shall restrict ourselves to the case when $\xi(0) =$

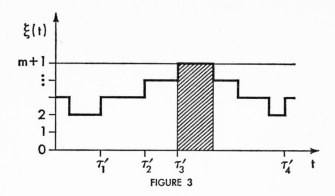

FIGURE 3

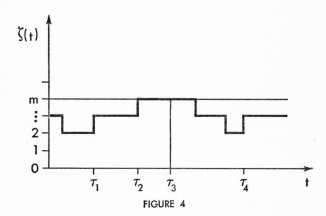

FIGURE 4

$m + 1$, that is, when initially every machine is working. We shall prove

THEOREM 1. *If $\xi(0) = m + 1$ then for $\Re(s) \geqq 0$ we have*

(1)

$$\int_0^\infty e^{-st} Q_k(t)\, dt = \sum_{j=r}^{m+1} (-1)^{r-k} \binom{r}{k} \theta_r(s) \qquad (k = 0, 1, \ldots, m + 1),$$

where

(2) $\theta_r(s)$

$$
= \frac{(m+1)\mu C_{r-1}(s,1)}{(s+r\mu)\left\{(m+1)\mu \sum_{j=0}^{m}\binom{m}{j}\frac{1}{C_j(s,1)} + s\sum_{j=0}^{m+1}\binom{m+1}{j}\frac{1}{C_{j-1}(s,1)}\right\}}
$$

$$
\cdot\left\{\left[\sum_{j=r}^{m}\binom{m}{j}\frac{1}{C_j(s,1)}\right]\left[\sum_{j=0}^{r}\binom{m}{j}\frac{1}{C_{j-1}(s,1)}\right]\right.
$$

$$
\left. -\left[\sum_{j=0}^{r-1}\binom{m}{j}\frac{1}{C_j(s,1)}\right]\left[\sum_{j=r+1}^{m}\binom{m}{j}\frac{1}{C_{j-1}(s,1)}\right]\right\}
$$

$$
+ \frac{\binom{m+1}{r}\sum_{j=0}^{m+1}\binom{m+1}{j}\frac{1}{C_{j-1}(s,1)}}{(m+1)\mu \sum_{j=0}^{m}\binom{m}{j}\frac{1}{C_j(s,1)} + s\sum_{j=0}^{m+1}\binom{m+1}{j}\frac{1}{C_{j-1}(s,1)}}.
$$

PROOF. In the case of the servicing process denote by $\hat{N}_{m+1}(t)$ the expectation of the number of transitions $E_{m+1} \to E_m$ occurring in the time interval $(0, t]$ given that $\xi(0) = m + 1$. The successive transitions $E_{m+1} \to E_m$ form a recurrent process in which the distribution function of the time of the first transition $E_{m+1} \to E_m$ is

$$
\hat{H}(x) = \begin{cases} 1 - e^{-(m+1)\mu x} & \text{if } x \geqq 0, \\ 0 & \text{if } x < 0, \end{cases}
$$

and the distribution function of the distance between two consecutive transitions $E_{m+1} \to E_m$ is $H(x) * G_m(x)$, where $G_m(x)$ is defined by Theorem 5 of Section 2, Chapter 4. Therefore by the renewal theory we can write that

(3) $$\int_0^\infty e^{-st}\, d\hat{N}_{m+1}(t) = \frac{\dfrac{(m+1)\mu}{[(m+1)\mu + s]}}{1 - \dfrac{(m+1)\mu}{[(m+1)\mu + s]}\gamma_m(s)},$$

where $\gamma_m(s)$ is defined by (30) of Section 2, Chapter 4. Further we can write that

$$(4) \qquad Q_k(t) = \int_0^t R_k(t - u) \, d\hat{N}_{m+1}(u) \qquad (k = 0, 1, \ldots, m),$$

where $R_k(t)$ is the probability that the system is in state E_k after a period t measured from a transition $E_{m+1} \rightarrow E_m$ and during this time interval of length t no new transition $E_{m+1} \rightarrow E_m$ occurs. $R_k(t)$ can be determined as follows. Let us consider the telephone traffic process $\{\zeta(t)\}$ with initial condition $\zeta(0) = m$. Under this condition let $\mathbf{P}\{\zeta(t) = k\} = P_k(t)$ and denote by $M_m(t)$ the expected number of the lost calls occurring in the time interval $(0, t]$. Then we have

$$(5) \quad P_k(t) = \int_0^t R_k(t - u) \, dM_m(u) + R_k(t) \qquad (k = 0, 1, \ldots, m),$$

where $R_k(t)$ is the probability that the system is in state E_k after a period t measured from a lost call and during this time interval of length t no call is lost. Evidently the probability $R_k(t)$ is the same in both processes. Forming the Laplace transform of (4) and that of (5) and comparing them, we get

$$\int_0^\infty e^{-st} Q_k(t) \, dt = \frac{\int_0^\infty e^{-st} \, d\hat{N}_{m+1}(t)}{1 + \int_0^\infty e^{-st} \, dM_m(t)} \int_0^\infty e^{-st} P_k(t) \, dt$$

for $k = 0, 1, \ldots, m$. Since

$$\sum_{k=0}^{m+1} Q_k(t) = 1$$

for all $t \geqq 0$, we have also

$$\int_0^\infty e^{-st} Q_{m+1}(t) \, dt = \frac{1}{s} \left[1 - \frac{\int_0^\infty e^{-st} \, d\hat{N}_{m+1}(t)}{1 + \int_0^\infty e^{-st} \, dM_m(t)} \right].$$

In this particular case

$$\int_0^\infty e^{-st} \, dM_m(t) = \frac{\gamma_m(s)}{1 - \gamma_m(s)}$$

and consequently

$$(6) \quad \int_0^\infty e^{-st} Q_k(t) \, dt = \frac{(m+1)\mu[1 - \gamma_m(s)]}{s + (m+1)\mu[1 - \gamma_m(s)]} \int_0^\infty e^{-st} P_k(t) \, dt$$

if $k = 0, 1, \ldots, m$ and

$$(7) \quad \int_0^\infty e^{-st} Q_{m+1}(t) \, dt = \frac{1}{s + (m+1)\mu[1 - \gamma_m(s)]}.$$

Here $\gamma_m(s)$ is defined by (30) of Section 2, Chapter 4, and it remains only to determine

$$\int_0^\infty e^{-st} P_k(t) \, dt,$$

which can be obtained by formulas (15), (16), and (3) of Section 2, Chapter 4, if we put $i = m$ and $w = 1$ in the latter one.

If we denote by $\beta_r(s)$ the Laplace transform of the rth binomial moment of $\{P_k(t)\}$ then the Laplace transform of the rth binomial moment of $\{Q_k(t)\}$ is given by

$$(8) \quad \theta_r(s) = \frac{(m+1)\mu[1 - \gamma_m(s)]\beta_r(s) + \binom{m+1}{r}}{s + (m+1)\mu[1 - \gamma_m(s)]}$$

$$(r = 0, 1, \ldots, m+1)$$

if we agree that $\beta_{m+1}(s) = 0$. By (16) and (3) of Section 2, Chapter 4,

$$(9) \quad \beta_r(s) = \frac{C_{r-1}(s, 1)}{(s + r\mu) \sum_{j=0}^m \binom{m}{j} \frac{1}{C_j(s, 1)}}$$

$$\cdot \left\{ \left[\sum_{j=r}^m \binom{m}{j} \frac{1}{C_j(s, 1)} \right] \left[\sum_{j=0}^r \binom{m}{j} \frac{1}{C_{j-1}(s, 1)} \right] \right.$$

$$\left. - \left[\sum_{j=0}^{r-1} \binom{m}{j} \frac{1}{C_j(s, 1)} \right] \left[\sum_{j=r+1}^m \binom{m}{j} \frac{1}{C_{j-1}(s, 1)} \right] \right\}$$

and this formula is valid for $r = 0, 1, \ldots, m+1$ too. Knowing the Laplace transforms of the binomial moments, i.e.

$$\theta_r(s) = \sum_{k=r}^{m+1} \binom{k}{r} \int_0^\infty e^{-st} Q_k(t)\, dt \qquad (r = 0, 1, \ldots, m+1)$$

we obtain by inversion that

$$\int_0^\infty e^{-st} Q_k(t)\, dt = \sum_{j=r}^{m+1} (-1)^{r-k} \binom{r}{k} \theta_r(s) \qquad (k = 0, 1, \ldots, m+1)$$

which was to be proved.

REMARK 1. In the special case when $F(x) = 1 - e^{-\lambda x}$ $(x \geq 0)$, the telephone process $\{\zeta(t)\}$ and the servicing process $\{\xi(t)\}$ have exactly the same stochastic behavior if the number of available lines agrees with the number of machines and if the initial conditions are the same.

THEOREM 2. *If $\beta < \infty$ then the limiting distribution* $\lim_{t\to\infty} Q_k(t) = Q_k^*$ $(k = 0, 1, \ldots, m+1)$ *exists and is independent of the initial distribution. We have*

$$(10) \qquad Q_k^* = \sum_{r=k}^{m+1} (-1)^{r-k} \binom{r}{k} S_r^*,$$

where S_r^* is the rth binomial moment of the distribution $\{Q_k^*\}$. $S_0^* = 1$ and

$$(11) \qquad S_r^* = \frac{(m+1)C_{r-1}}{r} \cdot \frac{\displaystyle\sum_{j=r-1}^{m} \binom{m}{j} \frac{1}{C_j}}{\left[1 + (m+1)\beta\mu \displaystyle\sum_{j=0}^{m} \binom{m}{j} \frac{1}{C_j}\right]}$$

$$(r = 1, 2, \ldots, m+1),$$

where $C_0 = 1$ and

$$(12) \qquad C_j = \prod_{i=1}^{j} \left(\frac{\phi(i\mu)}{1 - \phi(i\mu)}\right) \qquad (j = 1, 2, \ldots).$$

PROOF. By using a well-known Tauberian theorem (cf. Appendix) we get that the following limit exists and equals the right-hand side

$$\lim_{t\to\infty} \frac{1}{t} \int_0^t Q_k(u)\, du = \lim_{s\to 0} s \int_0^\infty e^{-st} Q_k(t)\, dt.$$

Thus by (1) we obtain that

(13) $$\lim_{t \to \infty} \frac{1}{t} \int_0^t Q_k(u)\, du = Q_k^* \qquad (k = 0, 1, \ldots, m + 1),$$

where Q_k^* is defined by (10). Now if we prove that $\lim_{t \to \infty} Q_k(t)$ exists, then by (13) it follows that $\lim_{t \to \infty} Q_k(t) = Q_k^*$. The existence of the limit can be proved by *Blackwell*'s theorem (cf. Appendix). Let $\xi(0)$ be an arbitrary random variable and denote by $\hat{M}_j(t)$ the expected number of the transitions $E_j \to E_{j+1}$ occurring in the time interval $(0, t]$ and by $\hat{N}_j(t)$ the expected number of transitions $E_j \to E_{j-1}$ occurring in the time interval $(0, t]$. Then we can write that

$$
\begin{aligned}
(14) \quad Q_k(t) = {} & \sum_{j=k}^{m} q_j(t) \binom{j}{k} e^{-k\mu t} (1 - e^{-\mu t})^{j-k} \\
& + \delta_{k, m+1} \left[Q_{m+1}(0) e^{-(m+1)\mu t} + \int_0^t e^{-(m+1)\mu(t-u)} d\hat{M}_m(u) \right] \\
& + \sum_{j=k-1}^{m-1} \binom{j+1}{k} \int_0^t e^{-k\mu(t-u)} \\
& \qquad \cdot (1 - e^{-\mu(t-u)})^{j+1-k} [1 - F(t - u)]\, d\hat{M}_j(u) \\
& + \binom{m}{k} \int_0^t e^{-k\mu(t-u)} (1 - e^{-\mu(t-u)})^{m-k} \\
& \qquad \cdot [1 - F(t - u)]\, d\hat{N}_{m+1}(u),
\end{aligned}
$$

where $q_j(t)$ is the probability that initially there is state E_j and no servicing terminates in the time interval $(0, t]$; $\delta_{k, m+1} = 1$ if $k \neq m + 1$ and $\delta_{k, m+1} = 0$ if $k \neq m + 1$. For, the event $\xi(t) = k$ can occur in the following mutually exclusive ways: the initial state is E_j ($j = k, k + 1, \ldots, m$) and in the time interval $(0, t]$ no servicing terminates and $j - k$ machines break down, or at the instant u ($0 \leq u \leq t$) a transition $E_j \to E_{j+1}$ ($j = k - 1, k, \ldots, m - 1$) occurs and the servicing starting at time u does not terminate in the time interval $(u, t]$ and in the time interval $(u, t]$ exactly $j + 1 - k$ machines break down, or at the instant u ($0 \leq u \leq t$) a transition $E_{m+1} \to E_m$ occurs and the servicing starting at time u does not terminate in the time interval $(u, t]$ and in the time interval $(u, t]$ exactly $m - k$ machines break down. The time differences between successive transitions

$E_j \to E_{j+1}$ $(j = 0, 1, \ldots, m)$ and $E_{m+1} \to E_m$ are identically distributed, independent random variables with nonlattice distribution. Thus by *Blackwell's* theorem we can conclude that the following limits exist for every $h > 0$

$$(15) \qquad \lim_{t \to \infty} \frac{\hat{M}_j(t + h) - \hat{M}_j(t)}{h} = \lim_{t \to \infty} \frac{\hat{M}_j(t)}{t} = \hat{M}_j$$

$$(j = 0, 1, \ldots, m)$$

and

$$(16) \qquad \lim_{t \to \infty} \frac{\hat{N}_{m+1}(t + h) - \hat{N}_{m+1}(t)}{h} = \lim_{t \to \infty} \frac{\hat{N}_{m+1}(t)}{t} = \hat{N}_{m+1}.$$

Hence by (14)

$$(17) \qquad \lim_{t \to \infty} Q_k(t) = \sum_{j=k-1}^{m-1} p_{jk}^* \hat{M}_j + p_{mk}^* \hat{N}_{m+1} + \frac{\delta_{k,m+1} \hat{M}_m}{(m + 1)\mu},$$

where

$$p_{jk}^* = \binom{j + 1}{k} \int_0^\infty e^{-k\mu x}(1 - e^{-\mu x})^{j+1-k}[1 - F(x)]\, dx$$

and

$$p_{mk}^* = p_{m-1,k}^*.$$

The limit $\lim_{t \to \infty} Q_k(t) = Q_k^*$ is independent of the initial state. The rth binomial moment of $\{Q_k^*\}$ is clearly

$$S_r^* = \lim_{s \to 0} s\theta_r(s) \qquad (r = 0, 1, \ldots, m + 1).$$

REMARK 2. It can easily be proved that

$$(18) \qquad \hat{M}_j = \frac{(m + 1)\mu Q_j}{(m + 1)\beta\mu + Q_m} \qquad (j = 0, 1, \ldots, m)$$

and

$$(19) \qquad \hat{N}_j = j\mu Q_j^*.$$

For, $\hat{M}_m$ is equal to the reciprocal value of the sum of the average length of the idle period, $1/(m + 1)\mu$, and the average length of the busy period, β/Q_m, which proves (18) for $j = m$. By using the theory of Markov chains we can conclude that $\hat{M}_j$ $(j = 0, 1, \ldots, m)$ is proportional to Q_j and the particular case $j = m$ yields the proportionality factor. The formula (19) is a consequence of the relation

$$\hat{N}_j(t) = j\mu \int_0^t Q_j(u) \, du \qquad (j = 1, 2, \ldots, m).$$

Now if we take into consideration that the difference of the number of transitions $E_{k-1} \rightarrow E_k$ and $E_k \rightarrow E_{k-1}$ occurring in the time interval $(0, t]$ is at most 1, then we get

$$|\hat{M}_{k-1}(t) - \hat{N}_k(t)| \leqq 1 \qquad (k = 1, 2, \ldots, m + 1)$$

for all $t \geqq 0$, whence

$$\hat{M}_{k-1} = \hat{N}_k \qquad (k = 1, 2, \ldots, m + 1).$$

Thus

$$(20) \qquad Q_k^* = \frac{(m + 1)Q_{k-1}}{k[(m + 1)\beta\mu + Q_m]} \qquad (k = 1, 2, \ldots, m + 1)$$

and

$$(21) \qquad Q_0^* = 1 - \sum_{k=1}^{m+1} Q_k^*.$$

The distribution $\{Q_k\}$ agrees with the distribution $\{P_k\}$ defined by (12) of Section 2, Chapter 4.

THE DISTRIBUTION FUNCTION OF THE WAITING TIME. Let us denote by $\eta(t)$ the occupation time of the server at the instant t, i.e. $\eta(t)$ is the time which elapses from t until the server becomes idle for the first time if no machines stop after time t. If we suppose, in particular, that the machines will be served in the order of their breakdown then $\eta(t)$ is the virtual waiting time, that is, the time a machine would wait if it stopped at the instant t. Denote by $\chi(t)$ the time needed to complete the current servicing at the instant t if there is such a servicing. Let $\chi(t) = 0$ if there is no service at time t. The process $\{\xi(t), \chi(t)\}$ is a Markov process and $\eta(t)$ can be expressed as follows

$$\eta(t) = \chi(t) + \sum_{i=1}^{[m-\xi(t)]^+} \chi_i,$$

where $\chi_1, \chi_2, \ldots$ are identically distributed, independent random variables with distribution function $F(x)$ and independent of $\xi(t)$ and $\chi(t)$.

THEOREM 3. *The limiting distribution*

(22)

$$\lim_{t \to \infty} \mathbf{P}\{\chi(t) \leq x, \xi(t) = k\} = F_k^*(x) \qquad (k = 0, 1, \ldots, m + 1)$$

exists and we have for $x \geq 0$

(23)
$$F_{m+1}^*(x) = Q_{m+1}^*$$

and

(24)

$$F_k^*(x) = \frac{(m + 1)\mu}{(m + 1)\beta\mu + Q_m} \left\{ \sum_{j=k-1}^{m-1} \binom{j + 1}{k} Q_j \right.$$

$$\cdot \int_0^\infty e^{-k\mu u}(1 - e^{-\mu u})^{j+1-k}[F(u + x) - F(u)] \, du$$

$$\left. + \binom{m}{k} Q_m \int_0^\infty e^{-k\mu u}(1 - e^{-\mu u})^{m-k}[F(u + x) - F(u)] \, du \right\}$$

when $k = 0, 1, \ldots, m.$

PROOF. By the theorem of total probability we can write for $k = 0, 1, \ldots, m$ that

(25)

$$\mathbf{P}\{\chi(t) \leq x, \xi(t) = k\} = \sum_{j=k}^{m} [q_j(t) - q_j(t + x)] \binom{j}{k} e^{-k\mu t}$$

$$\cdot (1 - e^{-\mu t})^{j-k} + \sum_{j=k-1}^{m-1} \binom{j + 1}{k}$$

$$\cdot \int_0^t e^{-k\mu(t-u)}(1 - e^{-\mu(t-u)})^{j+1-k}$$

$$\cdot [F(t - u + x) - F(t - u)] \, d\hat{M}_j(u)$$

$$+ \binom{m}{k} \int_0^t e^{-k\mu(t-u)}(1 - e^{-\mu(t-u)})^{m-k}$$

$$\cdot [F(t - u + x) - F(t - u)] \, d\hat{N}_{m+1}(u),$$

where $q_j(t)$ is the probability that initially there is state E_j and no servicing terminates in the time interval $(0, t]$. This can be proved in the same way as (14). The same argument that we used in the proof of Theorem 2 shows that

$$\lim_{t \to \infty} \mathbf{P}\{\chi(t) \leq x, \xi(t) = k\} = \sum_{j=k-1}^{m-1} \binom{j+1}{k} \hat{M}_j$$

$$\cdot \int_0^\infty e^{-k\mu u}(1 - e^{-\mu u})^{j+1-k} \cdot [F(u+x) - F(u)] \, du$$

$$+ \binom{m}{k} \hat{M}_m \int_0^\infty e^{-k\mu u}(1-e^{-\mu u})^{m-k}[F(u+x) - F(u)] \, du$$

because $\hat{N}_{m+1} = \hat{M}_m$. Here

(26)
$$\hat{M}_j = \frac{(m+1)\mu Q_j}{(m+1)\beta\mu + Q_m} = (j+1)\mu Q_{j+1}^* \qquad (j = 0, 1, \ldots, m).$$

THEOREM 4. *We have*

(27)
$$\lim_{t \to \infty} \mathbf{P}\{\chi(t) \leq x \,|\, \xi(t) \leq m\} = F^*(x),$$

where

(28)
$$F^*(x) = \begin{cases} \dfrac{1}{\beta} \displaystyle\int_0^x [1 - F(y)] \, dy & \text{if } x \geq 0, \\ 0 & \text{if } x < 0. \end{cases}$$

PROOF. By (24)

$$\lim_{t \to \infty} \mathbf{P}\{\chi(t) \leq x, \xi(t) \leq m\} = \sum_{k=0}^m F_k^*(x)$$

$$= \frac{(m+1)\mu}{(m+1)\beta\mu + Q_m} \int_0^x [1 - F(y)] \, dy$$

if $x \geq 0$ and clearly

$$\lim_{t \to \infty} \mathbf{P}\{\xi(t) \leq m\} = 1 - Q_{m+1}^* = \frac{(m+1)\beta\mu}{(m+1)\beta\mu + Q_m}.$$

Hence the theorem follows, since

$$\mathbf{P}\{\chi(t) \leq x \,|\, \xi(t) \leq m\} = \frac{\mathbf{P}\{\chi(t) \leq x, \xi(t) \leq m\}}{\mathbf{P}\{\xi(t) \leq m\}}.$$

If we suppose that the machines are serviced in the order of their breakdown, then the distribution function of the virtual waiting time $\eta(t)$ is given by

$$\mathbf{P}\{\eta(t) \leq x\} = \sum_{k=0}^{m+1} \mathbf{P}\{\chi(t) \leq x, \xi(t) = k\} * F_{m-k}(x),$$

where $F_k(x)$ denotes the kth iterated convolution of $F(x)$ with itself and $F_0(x) = F_{-1}(x) = 1$ if $x \geq 0$ and $F_0(x) = F_{-1}(x) = 0$ if $x < 0$. Hence follows

THEOREM 5. *If $\beta < \infty$ then*

$$(29) \qquad \lim_{t \to \infty} \mathbf{P}\{\eta(t) \leq x\} = \sum_{k=0}^{m+1} F_k^*(x) * F_{m-k}(x).$$

STATIONARY PROCESS. If we suppose that $\beta < \infty$ and the initial distribution of the process $\{\xi(t), \chi(t)\}$ is given by $\mathbf{P}\{\chi(0) \leq x, \xi(0) = k\} = F_k^*(x)$ $(k = 0, 1, \ldots, m + 1)$, where $F_k^*(x)$ is defined by (23) and (24), then $\mathbf{P}\{\chi(t) \leq x, \xi(t) = k\} = F_k^*(x)$ for all $t \geq 0$. In this case $\{\xi(t), \chi(t)\}$ will be a stationary process. The distribution function of the virtual waiting time is given by

$$(30) \qquad \mathbf{P}\{\eta(t) \leq x\} = \sum_{k=0}^{m+1} F_k^*(x) * F_{m-k}(x).$$

If σ_β^2, the variance of $F(x)$, is finite then

(31)
$$\mathbf{E}\{\eta(t)\} = \frac{(m+1)\beta\mu}{(m+1)\beta\mu + Q_m} \left\{ \frac{\sigma_\beta^2 + \beta^2}{2} + m\beta - \frac{1 - Q_m}{\mu} \right\},$$

where

$$(32) \qquad Q_m = \frac{1}{\displaystyle\sum_{j=0}^{m} \binom{m}{j} \frac{1}{C_j}}.$$

This can be proved as follows. We have

$$\eta(t) = \chi(t) + \sum_{i=1}^{[m-\xi(t)]^+} \chi_i,$$

where for every t, $\mathbf{P}\{\xi(t) = k\} = Q_k^*$ and

$$\mathbf{P}\{\chi(t) \leq x \,|\, \xi(t) \leq m\} = F^*(x).$$

Thus

$$\mathbf{E}\{\chi(t) \,|\, \xi(t) \leq m\} = \int_0^\infty x \, dF^*(x) = \frac{\sigma_\beta^2 + \beta^2}{2\beta}$$

and consequently

$$\mathbf{E}\{\chi(t)\} = \frac{(\sigma_\beta^2 + \beta^2)}{2\beta} \sum_{k=0}^m Q_k^*.$$

Since $\mathbf{E}\{\chi_i\} = \beta$ $(i = 1, 2, \ldots)$ we get finally

$$\mathbf{E}\{\eta(t)\} = \sum_{k=0}^m Q_k^* \left[\frac{\sigma_\beta^2 + \beta^2}{2\beta} + (m - k)\beta \right].$$

Here

$$\sum_{k=0}^m Q_k^* = 1 - Q_{m+1}^* = \frac{(m + 1)\beta\mu}{(m + 1)\beta\mu + Q_m}$$

and

$$\sum_{k=0}^m k Q_k^* = S_1^* - (m + 1)Q_{m+1}^* = \frac{(m + 1)(1 - Q_m)}{(m + 1)\beta\mu + Q_m}.$$

This completes the proof of (31).

Denote by A_t the event that there is a breakdown at time t. The conditional probability distribution of the waiting time at the instant t given that a machine breaks down at that time is given by

$$(33) \qquad \mathbf{P}\{\eta(t) \leq x \,|\, A_t\} = \frac{\mu \sum\limits_{k=0}^{m+1} k F_k^*(x) * F_{m-k}(x)}{\mu \sum\limits_{k=0}^{m+1} k Q_k^*}.$$

Hence

$$(34)$$

$$\mathbf{E}\{\eta(t) \,|\, A_t\} = \frac{\sum\limits_{k=0}^m k \left[\int_0^\infty x \, dF_k^*(x) + Q_k^*(m - k)\beta \right]}{\sum\limits_{k=0}^{m+1} k Q_k^*} = m\beta - \frac{1 - Q_m}{\mu}.$$

For,

$$\sum_{k=0}^{m} kF_k^*(x) = G^*(x) \frac{(m+1)(1-Q_m)}{(m+1)\beta\mu + Q_m} = G^*(x) \sum_{k=0}^{m} kQ_k^*,$$

where

$$G^*(x) = \frac{\int_0^\infty e^{-\mu u}[F(u+x) - F(u)]\, du}{\int_0^\infty e^{-\mu u}[1 - F(u)]\, du}.$$

Now

$$\int_0^\infty x\, dG^*(x) = \frac{\beta}{1 - \phi(\mu)} - \frac{1}{\mu}$$

and since

$$kQ_k^* = \frac{[1 - Q_{m+1}^*]}{\beta\mu} Q_{k-1}$$

we get

$$\sum_{k=0}^{m+1} kQ_k^* = \frac{1 - Q_{m+1}^*}{\beta\mu};$$

and further

$$\sum_{k=0}^{m} kQ_k = \frac{\phi(\mu)}{1 - \phi(\mu)}(1 - Q_m).$$

Using these formulas we get (34).

Problems for solution

PROBLEM 20. Find the expectation of the waiting time of a machine in the case of the stationary process.

PROBLEM 21. Let us suppose that $m + r$ machines are serviced by r repairmen. The machines work continuously; however, at any time a machine may break down and call for service. The machines are assumed to work independently. Let us suppose that if at time t a machine is in working state, the probability that it will call for service in the time interval $(t, t + \Delta t)$ is $\mu\, \Delta t + o(\Delta t)$. It is supposed that there is no repairman idle if a machine is on the waiting line. Suppose that the times required for servicing the machines are independent random variables with the common distribution function

$$F(x) = \begin{cases} 1 - e^{-x/\beta} & \text{if } x \geqq 0, \\ 0 & \text{if } x < 0. \end{cases}$$

Let us denote by $\xi(t)$ the number of machines working at the instant t. Find the limiting distribution $\lim_{t \to \infty} \mathbf{P}\{\xi(t) = k\} = Q_k^*$ ($k = 0, 1, \ldots, m + r$).

Bibliography

[1] *H. Ashcroft:* The productivity of several machines under the care of one operator. J. Roy. Statist. Soc. Ser. B. 12 (1950) 145–51.

[2] *F. Benson and D. R. Cox:* The productivity of machines requiring attention at random intervals. J. Roy. Statist. Soc. Ser. B. 13 (1951) 65–82.

[3] *A. Y. Khintchine:* On the average stopping time of machines (in Russian) Mat. Sb. 40 (1933) 119–23.

[4] *R. Kronig:* On time losses in machinery undergoing interruption I. Physica 10 (1943) 215–24.

[5] *R. Kronig and H. Mondria:* On time losses in machinery undergoing interruption II. Physica 10 (1943) 331–36.

[6] *C. Mack, T. Murphy and N. L. Webb:* The efficiency of N machines unidirectionally patrolled by one operative when walking time and repair times are constants. J. Roy. Statist. Soc. Ser. B. 19 (1957) 166–72.

[7] *P. Naor:* Some problems of machine interference. Proc. First Intern. Conf. Oper. Res. Oxford (1957) 147–64.

[8] *C. Palm:* The distribution of repairmen in servicing automatic machines (in Swedish). Industritidningen Norden 75 (1947) 75–80, 90–94, 119–23.

[9] *C. Palm:* The assignment of workers in servicing automatic machines. Journal of Industrial Engineering 9, No. 1 (1958) 28–42.

[10] *L. Takács:* On a stochastic process concerning some waiting time problems. Teor. Veroyatnost. i Primenen 2 (1957) 92–105; Theory of Probability and its Applications 2 (1957) 90–103.

[11] *L. Takács:* The time dependence of Palm's loss formula. J. Math. Analysis and Appl. 2 (1961) 58–71.

A PROCESS OF PARTICLE COUNTING

1. Formulation of the problem

Let us suppose that particles arrive at a counting device at the instants $\tau_1, \tau_2, \ldots, \tau_n, \ldots$ where the inter-arrival times $\tau_n - \tau_{n-1}$ ($n = 1, 2, \ldots; \tau_0 = 0$) are identically distributed, independent, positive random variables with the distribution function

$$\mathbf{P}\{\tau_n - \tau_{n-1} \leqq x\} = F(x).$$

Suppose that each particle independently of the others on its arrival gives rise to an impulse with probability p_r if r ($r = 0, 1, 2, \ldots$) impulses are present. Let $p_0 = 1$. Let us suppose that the durations of the impulses are identically distributed, independent, positive random variables with distribution function $H(x)$ and they are independent of $\{\tau_n\}$ and the events of realizations of the impulses. We define as "registered particles" those particles which arrive at an instant when there is no impulse present.

Denote by $\xi(t)$ the number of impulses present at the instant t. We suppose that $\xi(0) = 0$. The system is said to be in state E_k at the instant t if $\xi(t) = k$. Let $\mathbf{P}\{\xi(t) = k\} = P_k(t)$ and denote by $M_k(t)$ the expected number of the transitions $E_k \to E_{k+1}$ occurring in the time interval $(0, t]$.

Clearly the arrivals of the registered particles and the transitions $E_0 \to E_1$ coincide. Let us denote by $\nu_1, \nu_2, \ldots, \nu_n, \ldots$ the serial numbers of the registered particles. We are interested in the investigation of the stochastic behavior of the sequence $\{\tau_{\nu_n}\}$ and that of the stochastic process $\{\xi(t)\}$.

The following particular cases have special interest.

TYPE I COUNTER. In this case $p_0 = 1$ and $p_r = 0$ ($r = 1, 2, \ldots$). This model can be applied for Geiger-Müller counters when the duration of an impulse is replaced by the dead time.

TYPE II COUNTER. In this case $p_r = 1$ $(r = 0, 1, 2, \ldots)$. This model can be applied for electron multipliers or crystal counters.

TYPE III COUNTER. In this case $p_0 = 1$ and $p_r = p$ $(r = 1, 2, 3, \ldots)$ where $0 \leq p \leq 1$. This type of counter contains as special cases the former two types.

In what follows we shall consider only these three types of counters and we shall restrict ourselves to special forms of $F(x)$ and $H(x)$ respectively. For the sake of brevity we speak about process of type $[F(x), H(x), p]$ if Type III counter is the case and then Type I counter and Type II counter correspond to the particular cases when $p = 0$ and $p = 1$ respectively.

It is valid even in the general case, that $\{\tau_{\nu_n}\}$ forms a recurrent process in which $\mathbf{P}\{\tau_{\nu_1} \leq x\} = F(x)$ and $\tau_{\nu_{n+1}} - \tau_{\nu_n}$ $(n = 1, 2, \ldots)$ are identically distributed, independent random variables. Define $\mathbf{P}\{\tau_{\nu_{n+1}} - \tau_{\nu_n} \leq x\} = R(x)$ $(n = 1, 2, \ldots)$. If we know the distribution function $R(x)$ then the stochastic behavior of $\{\tau_{\nu_n}\}$ can be determined by the theory of recurrent processes.

Let us introduce the following transforms

$$\phi(s) = \int_0^\infty e^{-sx} \, dF(x),$$

$$\psi(s) = \int_0^\infty e^{-sx} \, dH(x),$$

$$\rho(s) = \int_0^\infty e^{-sx} \, dR(x),$$

$$\mu_j(s) = \int_0^\infty e^{-st} \, dM_j(t)$$

and

$$\Pi_k(s) = \int_0^\infty e^{-st} P_k(t) \, dt.$$

2. Type I counter

THEOREM 1. *We have*

(1) $$R(x) = \int_0^x [1 - F(x - u)] H(u) \, dm(u)$$

where $m(t)$ is the expected number of the particles arriving in the time interval $(0, t]$, that is

$$(2) \qquad m(t) = \sum_{n=1}^{\infty} F_n(t),$$

where $F_n(t)$ denotes the nth iterated convolution of $F(t)$ with itself.

PROOF. We can write that

$$R(x) = \mathbf{P}\{\tau_{\nu_2} - \tau_{\nu_1} \leqq x\} = \int_0^{\infty} \mathbf{P}\{\tau_{\nu_2} - \tau_{\nu_1} \leqq x \mid \chi_1 = y\} \, dH(y),$$

where χ_1 denotes the length of the first impulse. Evidently

$$\mathbf{P}\{\tau_{\nu_2} - \tau_{\nu_1} \leqq x \mid \chi_1 = y\} = 0$$

when $x < y$ and

$$\mathbf{P}\{\tau_{\nu_2} - \tau_{\nu_1} \leqq x \mid \chi_1 = y\} = \sum_{n=1}^{\infty} \int_y^x [1 - F(x - u)] \, dF_n(u)$$

$$= \int_y^x [1 - F(x - u)] \, dm(u)$$

when $x \geqq y$. For, the event in question is realized if at least one particle arrives in the time interval $(\tau_{\nu_1} + y, \tau_{\nu_1} + x]$ and this can occur in the following mutually exclusive ways: during this time interval $n = 1, 2, 3, \ldots$ particles arrive at the counter. Thus we get

$$(3) \qquad R(x) = \int_0^x \left\{ \int_y^x [1 - F(x - u)] \, dm(u) \right\} dH(y).$$

We can write also that

$$(4) \quad \mathbf{E}\{\exp[-s(\tau_{\nu_2} - \tau_{\nu_1})] \mid \chi_1 = y\} = [1 - \phi(s)] \int_y^{\infty} e^{-su} \, dm(u),$$

whence unconditionally

$$(5) \quad \rho(s) = \mathbf{E}\{\exp[-s(\tau_{\nu_2} - \tau_{\nu_1})]\} = [1 - \phi(s)] \int_0^{\infty} e^{-sy} H(y) \, dm(y).$$

This formula proves (1).

THEOREM 2. *Let*

$$(6) \qquad \beta = \int_0^{\infty} x \, dF(x)$$

and

(7)
$$\sigma_\beta^2 = \int_0^\infty (x - \beta)^2 \, dF(x).$$

Then

(8)
$$\int_0^\infty x \, dR(x) = \beta \int_0^\infty [1 + m(x)] \, dH(x)$$

and

(9)
$$\int_0^\infty x^2 \, dR(x) = (\sigma_\beta^2 + \beta^2) \int_0^\infty [1 + m(x)] \, dH(x)$$
$$+ 2\beta \int_0^\infty \left[\int_0^x u \, dm(u) \right] dH(x).$$

PROOF. Since

$$\int_0^\infty e^{-su} \, dm(u) = \frac{\phi(s)}{1 - \phi(s)}$$

we can write by (4) that

$$\mathbf{E}\{\exp[-s(\tau_{\nu_2} - \tau_{\nu_1})] | \chi_1 = y\} = \phi(s) - [1 - \phi(s)] \int_0^y e^{-su} \, dm(u),$$

whence

$$\mathbf{E}\{\tau_{\nu_2} - \tau_{\nu_1} | \chi_1 = y\} = \beta[1 + m(y)]$$

and

$$\mathbf{E}\{(\tau_{\nu_2} - \tau_{\nu_1})^2 | \chi_1 = y\} = (\sigma_\beta^2 + \beta^2)[1 + m(y)] + 2\beta \int_0^y u \, dm(u).$$

Dropping the condition $\chi_1 = y$ we get (8) and (9).

The random variable $\xi(t)$ assumes only the values 0 and 1 and thus $P_0(t) + P_1(t) = 1$. We shall prove

THEOREM 3. *We have*

(10)
$$P_1(t) = \int_0^t [1 - H(t - u)] \, dM_0(u)$$

where

(11) $$M_0(t) = F(t) + F(t) * R(t) + F(t) * R(t) * R(t) + \cdots$$

is the expected number of the registrations occurring in the time interval $(0, t]$.

If α, the mean of $H(x)$, is finite and $F(x)$ is not a lattice distribution, then

$$(12) \qquad \lim_{t \to \infty} P_1(t) = \frac{\alpha}{\beta \int_0^\infty [1 + m(x)]\, dH(x)},$$

where $m(x)$ is defined by (2).

PROOF. Let us denote by χ_n the length of the nth impulse. It is easy to see that

$$P_1(t) = \sum_{n=1}^\infty \mathbf{P}\{\tau_{\nu_n} < t \leq \tau_{\nu_n} + \chi_n\}$$

$$= \sum_{n=1}^\infty \int_0^t [1 - H(t - u)]\, d\mathbf{P}\{\tau_{\nu_n} \leq u\}$$

and clearly

$$\mathbf{P}\{\tau_{\nu_n} \leq u\} = F(u) * R_{n-1}(u)$$

where $R_n(u)$ is the nth iterated convolution of $R(u)$ with itself and $R_0(u) = 1$ if $u \geq 0$ and $R_0(u) = 0$ if $u < 0$.

If $F(t)$ is not a lattice distribution then $R(t)$ is not one either. Thus by *Blackwell*'s theorem

$$\lim_{t \to \infty} \frac{M_0(t + h) - M_0(t)}{h} = \lim_{t \to \infty} \frac{M_0(t)}{t} = \frac{1}{\int_0^\infty x\, dR(x)},$$

for every $h > 0$. Since

$$\int_0^\infty [1 - H(x)]\, dx = \alpha,$$

we get (12) by (10).

REMARK 1. The Laplace transform of $P_1(t)$ can be expressed as follows

$$\Pi_1(s) = \phi(s) \frac{[1 - \psi(s)]}{[1 - \rho(s)]},$$

where $\rho(s)$ is defined by (5).

3. Type II counter

POISSON INPUT. First let us consider the case when

$$F(x) = \begin{cases} 1 - e^{-\lambda x} & \text{if } x \geqq 0, \\ 0 & \text{if } x < 0, \end{cases}$$

that is, when $\{\tau_n\}$ is a Poisson process of density λ. In this case we have proved earlier (Theorem 1 of Section 2, Chapter 3) that

$$(1) \quad P_k(t) = e^{-\lambda \int_0^t [1 - H(x)] \, dx} \frac{[\lambda \int_0^t (1 - H(x)) \, dx]^k}{k!} \qquad (k = 0, 1, \ldots).$$

Now we shall prove

THEOREM 1. *The Laplace-Stieltjes transform of the distribution function $R(x)$ is given by*

$$(2) \quad \rho(s) = 1 - \frac{1}{\lambda + s} \left\{ \int_0^\infty e^{-st - \lambda \int_0^t [1 - H(x)] \, dx} \, dt \right\}^{-1}.$$

PROOF. Since

$$M_0(t) = F(t) + F(t) * R(t) + F(t) * R(t) * R(t) + \cdots$$

therefore

$$\mu_0(s) = \frac{\lambda}{(\lambda + s)} \frac{1}{[1 - \rho(s)]},$$

whence

$$\rho(s) = 1 - \frac{\lambda}{(\lambda + s)\mu_0(s)}.$$

On the other hand, evidently

$$M_0(t) = \lambda \int_0^t P_0(u) \, du,$$

whence

$$\mu_0(s) = \lambda \Pi_0(s).$$

Thus finally

$$\rho(s) = 1 - \frac{1}{(\lambda + s)\Pi_0(s)}$$

where by (1)

$$\Pi_0(s) = \int_0^\infty e^{-st} P_0(t)\, dt = \int_0^\infty e^{-st - \lambda \int_0^t [1 - H(x)]\, dx}\, dt.$$

THEOREM 2. *We have*

(3)
$$\int_0^\infty x\, dR(x) = \frac{e^{\lambda \alpha}}{\lambda}$$

and

(4)
$$\int_0^\infty x^2\, dR(x) = \frac{2e^{2\lambda \alpha}}{\lambda} \int_0^\infty [P_0(t) - e^{-\lambda \alpha}]\, dt + \frac{2e^{\lambda \alpha}}{\lambda^2}.$$

PROOF. Knowing the Laplace-Stieltjes transform $\rho(s)$ the mean, variance, and higher moments of $R(x)$ can easily be determined.

EXPONENTIALLY DISTRIBUTED IMPULSE TIMES. Now let us suppose that

(5)
$$H(x) = \begin{cases} 1 - e^{-\mu x} & \text{if } x \geqq 0, \\ 0 & \text{if } x < 0. \end{cases}$$

In this case we have proved earlier (Theorem 3 of Section 3, Chapter 3) that

(6)
$$\Pi_k(s) = \sum_{r=k}^\infty \frac{(-1)^{r-k} \binom{r}{k}}{s + r\mu} \prod_{i=0}^{r-1} \left(\frac{1 - \phi(s + i\mu)}{\phi(s + i\mu)} \right),$$

where the empty product means 1. Furthermore it follows easily that

(7)
$$\mu_k(s) = \sum_{r=k}^\infty (-1)^{r-k} \binom{r}{k} \prod_{i=0}^r \left(\frac{\phi(s + i\mu)}{1 - \phi(s + i\mu)} \right).$$

THEOREM 3. *We have*

(8)
$$\rho(s) = 1 - \phi(s) \left[\sum_{r=0}^\infty (-1)^r \prod_{i=0}^r \left(\frac{\phi(s + i\mu)}{1 - \phi(s + i\mu)} \right) \right]^{-1}.$$

PROOF. Since

$$M_0(t) = F(t) + F(t) * R(t) + F(t) * R(t) * R(t) + \cdots,$$

therefore

$$\mu_0(s) = \frac{\phi(s)}{1 - \rho(s)},$$

whence

$$\rho(s) = 1 - \frac{\phi(s)}{\mu_0(s)}$$

and $\mu_0(s)$ is defined by (7) with $k = 0$.

CONSTANT IMPULSE TIMES. If we suppose that

$$(9) \qquad H(x) = \begin{cases} 1 & \text{if } x \geqq \alpha, \\ 0 & \text{if } x < \alpha, \end{cases}$$

and $F(\alpha) < 1$, then we have

THEOREM 4. *The distribution function $R(x)$ can be obtained by the following Laplace-Stiltjes transform*

$$(10) \qquad \int_0^\infty e^{-sx} \, dR(x) = \frac{\int_\alpha^\infty e^{-sx} \, dF(x)}{1 - \int_0^\alpha e^{-sx} \, dF(x)}.$$

Further

$$(11) \qquad \int_0^\infty x \, dR(x) = \frac{\beta}{1 - F(\alpha)}$$

and

$$(12) \qquad \int_0^\infty x^2 \, dR(x) = \frac{\sigma_\beta^2 + \beta^2}{1 - F(\alpha)} + 2 \frac{\beta \int_0^\alpha x \, dF(x)}{[1 - F(\alpha)]^2}.$$

PROOF. It is easy to see that

$$R(x) = \begin{cases} 0 & \text{when } x \leqq \alpha, \\ F(x) - F(\alpha) + \int_0^\alpha R(x - y) \, dF(y) & \text{when } x \geqq \alpha. \end{cases}$$

Forming the Laplace-Stieltjes transform we get

$$\int_0^\infty e^{-sx} \, dR(x) = \int_\alpha^\infty e^{-sx} \, dF(x) + \int_0^\alpha e^{-sx} \, dF(x) \int_0^\infty e^{-sx} \, dR(x),$$

which proves (10). Knowing the Laplace-Stieltjes transform of $R(x)$, the mean and variance of $R(x)$ can easily be obtained.

4. Type III counter

Now we shall investigate the process of type $[F(x), H(x), p]$ when $0 < p < 1$. We shall show that if we know the stochastic behavior of the process of type $[\hat{F}(x), H(x), 1]$, where

$$\hat{F}(x) = p \sum_{n=1}^{\infty} q^{n-1} F_n(x),$$

$q = 1 - p$, and $F_n(x)$ denotes the nth iterated convolution of the distribution function $F(x)$ with itself, then that of $[F(x), H(x), p]$ can easily be deduced. For, if we associate a new process with the process of type $[F(x), H(x), p]$ by supposing that *each* particle independently of the others gives rise to an impulse with probability p, but otherwise every assumption remains unchanged, then we arrive at a process of type $[\hat{F}(x), H(x), 1]$. It is easy to see that the only difference between the process of type $[F(x), H(x), p]$ and $[\hat{F}(x), H(x), 1]$ is that the latter contains an additional interval spent in state E_0 immediately before every transition $E_0 \to E_1$ and the lengths of these intervals are identically distributed, independent random variables with distribution function

$$(1) \qquad \hat{Q}(x) = \sum_{n=0}^{\infty} q^n F_n(x)$$

and these random variables are independent of any other random variables involved.

Specifically, if $\hat{R}(x)$ denotes the distribution function of the distance between successive transitions $E_0 \to E_1$ in the process of type $[\hat{F}(x), H(x), 1]$, then we have

$$(2) \qquad \hat{R}(x) = R(x) * \hat{Q}(x),$$

whence

$$(3) \qquad \rho(s) = \int_0^{\infty} e^{-sx} \, dR(x) = \hat{\rho}(s)[1 - q\phi(s)],$$

where

(4) $$\hat{\rho}(s) = \int_0^\infty e^{-sx}\, d\hat{R}(x),$$

and we used the fact that

(5) $$\int_0^\infty e^{-sx}\, d\hat{Q}(x) = \sum_{n=0}^\infty q^n [\phi(s)]^n = \frac{1}{1 - q\phi(s)}.$$

In the particular case when $F(x) = 1 - e^{-\lambda x}$ $(x \geqq 0)$ we obtain easily that $\hat{F}(x) = 1 - e^{-\lambda p x}$ $(x \geqq 0)$, and hence by (2) of Section 3 we get

(6) $$\hat{\rho}(s) = 1 - \frac{1}{\lambda p + s} \left\{ \int_0^\infty e^{-st - \lambda p \int_0^t [1 - H(x)]\, dx}\, dt \right\}^{-1},$$

having replaced λ by λp in (2) of Section 3.

In the particular case when $H(x) = 1 - e^{-\mu x}$ $(x \geqq 0)$ we have by (8) of Section 3 that

(7) $$\hat{\rho}(s) = 1 - \frac{p\phi(s)}{1 - q\phi(s)} \left[\sum_{r=0}^\infty (-1)^r \prod_{i=0}^r \left(\frac{p\phi(s + i\mu)}{1 - \phi(s + i\mu)} \right) \right]^{-1},$$

for,

$$\hat{\phi}(s) = \int_0^\infty e^{-sx}\, d\hat{F}(x) = \frac{p\phi(s)}{1 - q\phi(s)},$$

and (7) can be obtained by (8) of Section 3 if we replace $\phi(s)$ by $\hat{\phi}(s)$.

Now let us denote by $\hat{P}_k(t)$ the probability that there are k impulses present at the instant t in the process of type $[\hat{F}(x), H(x), 1]$ and let

$$\hat{\Pi}_k(s) = \int_0^\infty e^{-st} \hat{P}_k(t)\, dt.$$

Then we have

(8) $$\Pi_k(s) = \frac{p[1 - \hat{\rho}(s)][1 - q\phi(s)]}{1 - p[1 - \hat{\rho}(s)][1 - q\phi(s)]} \hat{\Pi}_k(s) \qquad (k = 1, 2, 3, \ldots)$$

and

(9) $$\Pi_0(s) = \frac{1}{s} + \frac{p[1 - \hat{\rho}(s)][1 - q\phi(s)]}{1 - p[1 - \hat{\rho}(s)][1 - q\phi(s)]} \left[\hat{\Pi}_0(s) - \frac{1}{s} \right].$$

This can be proved as follows. Denote by $\hat{M}_0(t)$ the expected number of the transitions $E_0 \to E_1$ occurring in the time interval $(0, t]$ in the process of type $[\hat{F}(x), H(x), 1]$. Then we have

$$\hat{M}_0(t) = \hat{F}(t) + \hat{F}(t) * \hat{R}(t) + \hat{F}(t) * \hat{R}(t) * \hat{R}(t) + \cdots,$$

whence

(10) $$\hat{\mu}_0(s) = \frac{\hat{\phi}(s)}{1 - \hat{\rho}(s)} = \frac{p\phi(s)}{[1 - q\phi(s)][1 - \hat{\rho}(s)]}.$$

In the process of type $[F(x), H(x), p]$

$$M_0(t) = F(t) + F(t) * R(t) + F(t) * R(t) * R(t) + \cdots,$$

whence

(11) $$\mu_0(s) = \frac{\phi(s)}{1 - \rho(s)}.$$

Now consider the process of type $[F(x), H(x), p]$ and denote by $C_k(t)$ $(k = 1, 2, \ldots)$ the probability that the system is in state E_k after a time t measured from a point of transition $E_0 \to E_1$ and during this time interval of length t there is no other transition $E_0 \to E_1$. Clearly this probability is the same for the process of type $[\hat{F}(x), H(x), 1]$. Thus by the theorem of total probability we obtain

(12) $$P_k(t) = \int_0^t C_k(t - u) \, dM_0(u) \qquad (k = 1, 2, \ldots),$$

and similarly

(13) $$\hat{P}_k(t) = \int_0^t C_k(t - u) \, d\hat{M}_0(u) \qquad (k = 1, 2, \ldots),$$

by taking into consideration that the event that there is a state E_k at the instant t can occur in several mutually exclusive ways: the last transition $E_0 \to E_1$ in the time interval $(0, t]$ is the 1st, 2nd, ..., nth, ... and this transition takes place at the instant u $(0 \leq u \leq t)$.

Forming the Laplace-Stieltjes transforms of (12) and (13) we get

(14) $$\Pi_k(s) = \mu_0(s) \int_0^\infty e^{-st} \, dC_k(t)$$

and

(15) $$\hat{\Pi}_k(s) = \hat{\mu}_0(s) \int_0^\infty e^{-st} \, dC_k(t).$$

Comparing (14) and (15) we obtain

$$(16) \qquad \Pi_k(s) = \hat{\Pi}_k(s) \frac{\mu_0(s)}{\hat{\mu}_0(s)} \qquad (k = 1, 2, \ldots)$$

and thus

$$(17) \qquad \Pi_0(s) = \hat{\Pi}_0(s) \frac{\mu_0(s)}{\hat{\mu}_0(s)} + \frac{1}{s}\left(1 - \frac{\mu_0(s)}{\hat{\mu}_0(s)}\right)$$

because

$$\sum_{k=0}^{\infty} \Pi_k(s) = \sum_{k=0}^{\infty} \hat{\Pi}_k(s) = \frac{1}{s}.$$

In the particular case when $H(x) = 1 - e^{-\mu x}$ $(x \geqq 0)$ we have by (7) of Section 3 that

$$(18) \quad \Pi_k(s) = \frac{\displaystyle\sum_{r=k}^{\infty} (-1)^{r-k} \binom{r}{k} \frac{1}{(s+r\mu)} \prod_{i=0}^{r-1}\left(\frac{p\phi(s+i\mu)}{1-\phi(s+i\mu)}\right)}{1 - q\displaystyle\sum_{r=0}^{\infty} (-1)^r \prod_{i=1}^{r}\left(\frac{p\phi(s+i\mu)}{1-\phi(s+i\mu)}\right)}$$

if $k = 1, 2, \ldots$ and

$$(19) \qquad \Pi_0(s) = \frac{1}{s} - \frac{\displaystyle\sum_{r=1}^{\infty} \frac{(-1)^{r-1}}{s+r\mu} \prod_{i=0}^{r-1}\left(\frac{p\phi(s+i\mu)}{1-\phi(s+i\mu)}\right)}{1 - q\displaystyle\sum_{r=0}^{\infty} (-1)^r \prod_{i=1}^{r}\left(\frac{p\phi(s+i\mu)}{1-\phi(s+i\mu)}\right)}.$$

Problems for solution

PROBLEM 22. Let us consider the counter of Type I in the case of Poisson input of density λ and constant α impulse time. Determine $R(x)$ and the probability $W(t, n)$ that at most n particles will be registered in the time interval $(0, t]$.

PROBLEM 23. Let us consider the counter of Type II in the case of Poisson input of density λ and constant α impulse time. Determine $R(x)$ and the probability $W(t, n)$ that at most n particles will be registered in the time interval $(0, t]$.

PROBLEM 24. Let us consider the counter of Type III in the case of Poisson input of density λ and constant α impulse time. Determine the asymptotic distribution of the number of registered particles during the time interval $(0, t]$.

Bibliography

[1] *G. E. Albert and L. Nelson:* Contributions to the statistical theory of counter data. Ann. Math. Statist. 24 (1953) 9–22.

[2] *W. Feller:* On probability problems in the theory of counters. Courant Anniversary Volume (1948) 105–15.

[3] *J. Giltay:* A counter arrangement with constant resolving time. Physica 10 (1943) 725–34.

[4] *J. M. Hammersley:* On counters with random dead time I. Proc. Cambridge Philos. Soc. 49 (1953) 623–37.

[5] *L. Kosten:* On the frequency distribution of the number of discharges counted by a Geiger-Müller counter in a constant interval. Physica 10 (1943) 749–56.

[6] *C. Levert and W. L. Scheen:* Probability fluctuations of discharges in a Geiger-Müller counter produced by cosmic radiation. Physica 10 (1943) 225–38.

[7] *S. Malmquist:* A statistical problem connected with the counting of radioactive particles. Ann. Math. Statist. 18 (1947) 255–65.

[8] *F. Pollaczek:* Sur la théorie stochastique des compteurs électroniques. C. R. Acad. Sci. Paris 238 (1954) 766–8.

[9] *R. Pyke:* On renewal processes related to Type I and Type II counter models. Ann. Math. Statist. 29 (1958) 737–54.

[10] *W. L. Smith:* On renewal theory, counter problems, and quasi-Poisson processes. Proc. Cambridge Philos. Soc. 53 (1957) 175–93.

[11] *W. L. Smith:* Renewal theory and its ramifications. Roy. Statist. Soc. Ser. B. 20 (1958) 243–302.

[12] *L. Takács:* On a probability problem arising in the theory of counters. Proc. Cambridge Philos. Soc. 52 (1956) 488–98.

[13] *L. Takács:* On the sequence of events, selected by a counter from a recurrent process of events. Teor. Veroyatnos. i. Primenen 1 (1956) 90–102; Theory of Probability and its Applications 1 (1956) 81–91.

[14] *L. Takács:* On some probability problems concerning the theory of counters. Acta Math. Acad. Sci. Hungar. 8 (1957) 127–38.

[15] *L. Takács:* On a probability problem in the theory of counters. Ann. Math. Statist. 29 (1958) 1257–63.

[16] *L. Takács:* On a coincidence problem concerning particle counters. Ann. Math. Statist. 32 (1961) 739–56.

APPENDIX

1. Markov chains

Let us consider the sequence of random variables $\xi_0, \xi_1, \ldots, \xi_n, \ldots$ where every random variable may assume the values $0, 1, 2, \ldots$. We say that the sequence $\{\xi_n\}$ forms a Markov chain if for all n $(n = 1, 2, \ldots)$ and for all possible values of the random variables,

$$\mathbf{P}\{\xi_n = j \,|\, \xi_0 = i_0, \xi_1 = i_1, \ldots, \xi_{n-1} = i_{n-1}\}$$
$$= \mathbf{P}\{\xi_n = j \,|\, \xi_{n-1} = i_{n-1}\}.$$

If $\xi_n = j$ then the system is said to be in state E_j at the nth step. The probability distribution $\mathbf{P}\{\xi_0 = j\}$ $(j = 0, 1, 2, \ldots)$ of the random variable ξ_0 is called the *initial distribution*, and the conditional probabilities $\mathbf{P}\{\xi_n = j \,|\, \xi_{n-1} = i\}$ are called *transition probabilities*. Furthermore if $\xi_{n-1} = i$ and $\xi_n = j$, then we say that the system made *a transition $E_i \to E_j$ at the nth step.*

If we know the initial distribution and transition probabilities of a Markov chain, then we can uniquely determine the probability distribution of each random variable ξ_n $(n = 1, 2, \ldots)$.

We speak about a *homogeneous Markov chain* if the transition probabilities are independent of n. In this case we can write that

$$\mathbf{P}\{\xi_n = j \,|\, \xi_{n-1} = i\} = p_{ij}.$$

In the case of a homogeneous Markov chain the n-step transition probabilities

$$\mathbf{P}\{\xi_{m+n} = j \,|\, \xi_m = i\} = p_{ij}^{(n)}$$

are independent of m. In what follows we shall consider only homogeneous Markov chains.

We say that the state E_k can be reached from the state E_j if there is a number $n \geqq 0$ such that $p_{jk}^{(n)} > 0$. A Markov chain is called *irreducible* if every state can be reached from every other state.

Let us consider an arbitrary but fixed state E_j. Suppose that the system initially is in state E_j. Denote by $f_j^{(n)}$ the probability that the *first return* to E_j occurs at the nth step. The probability that *the system ever returns* to the state E_j is

$$f_j = \sum_{n=1}^{\infty} f_j^{(n)}.$$

If $f_j = 1$, that is, the system returns to E_j with probability 1, then E_j is said to be a *recurrent state;* if $f_j < 1$ then E_j is said to be a *transient state.*

The state E_j is called *periodic* with period t if a return to E_j can occur only at steps $t, 2t, 3t, \ldots$ and $t > 1$ is the greatest integer with this property. Then $p_{ij}^{(n)} = 0$ whenever n is not divisible by t.

If $f_j = 1$ then

$$\mu_j = \sum_{n=1}^{\infty} n f_j^{(n)}$$

is the *mean recurrence time* of the state E_j. If $\mu_j < \infty$ then we say that E_j is a *recurrent non-null state*, whereas if $\mu_j = \infty$ then we say that E_j is a *recurrent null state.*

All states of an irreducible Markov chain are either transient or recurrent null states or recurrent non-null states. Their periods are always the same.

A probability distribution $\{P_j\}$ is called *stationary* if

$$P_j = \sum_{i=0}^{\infty} P_i p_{ij} \qquad (j = 0, 1, \ldots).$$

If the initial distribution $\mathbf{P}\{\xi_0 = j\}$ $(j = 0, 1, 2, \ldots)$ is a stationary distribution, then $\mathbf{P}\{\xi_n = j\}$ $(j = 0, 1, 2, \ldots)$ coincides with the initial distribution for every n.

In an irreducible and aperiodic Markov chain the limiting probabilities $\lim_{n \to \infty} \mathbf{P}\{\xi_n = j\} = P_j$ $(j = 0, 1, 2, \ldots)$ always exist and are independent of the initial distribution. There are two possibilities:

1. The states are all transient or all recurrent null states; in this case $P_j = 0$ for every j and there exists no stationary distribution.

2. All states are recurrent non-null states; in this case $P_j > 0$ for every j and $\{P_j\}$ is a probability distribution. $P_j = 1/\mu_j$. The limiting distribution $\{P_j\}$ is uniquely determined as the solution of the following system of linear equations

$$P_j = \sum_{i=0}^{\infty} P_i p_{ij} \qquad (j = 0, 1, 2, \ldots)$$

and

$$\sum_{i=0}^{\infty} P_i = 1.$$

In this case $\{P_j\}$ is a stationary distribution and there exists no other stationary distribution. Then the Markov chain is said to be *ergodic*.

According to a theorem of *A. A. Markov* all states of a finite, aperiodic, and irreducible Markov chain are recurrent non-null states.

According to a theorem of *F. G. Foster* all states of an aperiodic and irreducible Markov chain are recurrent non-null states if the following system of linear equations

$$\sum_{i=0}^{\infty} x_i p_{ij} = x_j \qquad (j = 0, 1, 2, \ldots)$$

has a non-null solution for which

$$\sum_{i=0}^{\infty} |x_i| < \infty.$$

2. *Poisson process*

Let us suppose that in the time interval $[0, \infty)$ random events occur at the instants $\tau_1, \tau_2, \ldots, \tau_n, \ldots$ where the time differences $\tau_n - \tau_{n-1}$ $(n = 1, 2, \ldots; \tau_0 = 0)$ are identically distributed, independent random variables with the distribution function

$$F(x) = \begin{cases} 1 - e^{-\lambda x} & \text{if } x \geqq 0, \\ 0 & \text{if } x < 0. \end{cases}$$

Let us denote by $\nu(t)$ the number of the events occurring in the time interval $(0, t]$. Thus $\nu(0) = 0$. In this case the stochastic process $\{\nu(t), 0 \leqq t < \infty\}$ is a Markov process with independent increments;

that is, for every $k \geqq 2$ and $0 \leqq t_0 < t_1 < \cdots < t_k < \infty$ the differences

$$\nu(t_1) - \nu(t_0), \nu(t_2) - \nu(t_1), \ldots, \nu(t_k) - \nu(t_{k-1})$$

are mutually independent random variables, and further $\{\nu(t)\}$ is homogeneous, that is, the distribution of $\nu(s + t) - \nu(s)$ depends only on t when $0 \leqq s$ and $0 \leqq t$. The process $\{\nu(t), 0 \leqq t < \infty\}$ is said to be a *homogeneous Poisson process* of density λ. We have

$$\mathbf{P}\{\nu(s + t) - \nu(s) = n\} = e^{-\lambda t} \frac{(\lambda t)^n}{n!} \qquad (n = 0, 1, 2, \ldots)$$

and

$$\mathbf{E}\{\nu(s + t) - \nu(s)\} = \lambda t$$

when $0 \leqq s$ and $0 \leqq t$.

Evidently $\mathbf{P}\{\nu(s + t) - \nu(s) = 0\} = 1 - \lambda t + o(t)$, $\mathbf{P}\{\nu(s + t) - \nu(s) = 1\} = \lambda t + o(t)$ and $\mathbf{P}\{\nu(s + t) - \nu(s) \geqq 2\} = o(t)$ where $o(t)/t \to 0$ as $t \to 0$.

THEOREM 1. *Under the condition $\nu(s + t) - \nu(s) = n$ the joint distribution of the instants of the events occurring in the time interval $(s, s + t]$ agrees with the joint distribution of the co-ordinates arranged in increasing order of n independently and uniformly distributed random points in the interval $(s, s + t]$.*

PROOF. Let $s = t_0 < t_1 < \cdots < t_k = s + t$ be a subdivision of the interval $(s, s + t]$. The probability that $n_1, n_2, \ldots, n_k$ events occur respectively in the non-overlapping time intervals $(t_0, t_1]$, $(t_1, t_2], \ldots, (t_{k-1}, t_k]$ given that $n = n_1 + n_2 + \cdots + n_k$ events occur in $(s, s + t]$ is

$$\frac{\displaystyle\prod_{j=1}^{k} e^{-\lambda(t_j - t_{j-1})} \frac{[\lambda(t_j - t_{j-1})]^{n_j}}{n_j!}}{e^{-\lambda(t_k - t_0)} \dfrac{[\lambda(t_k - t_0)]^n}{n!}} = \frac{n!}{n_1! n_2! \ldots n_k!} \prod_{j=1}^{k} \left(\frac{t_j - t_{j-1}}{t_k - t_0}\right)^{n_j},$$

whence the theorem follows.

3. Recurrent processes

Let us suppose that in the time interval $[0, \infty)$ random events occur at the instants $\tau_1, \tau_2, \ldots, \tau_n, \ldots$ where the time differences $\tau_n - \tau_{n-1}$

$(n = 1, 2, \ldots; \tau_0 = 0)$ are independent positive random variables with distribution functions

$$\mathbf{P}\{\tau_1 \leq x\} = \hat{F}(x)$$

and

$$\mathbf{P}\{\tau_n - \tau_{n-1} \leq x\} = F(x) \qquad (n = 2, 3, \ldots).$$

Let us denote by $\nu(t)$ the number of events occurring in the time interval $(0, t]$. Thus $\nu(0) = 0$. The process $\{\nu(t), 0 \leq t < \infty\}$ is said to be a *recurrent process*.

If specifically $\hat{F}(x) = F(x)$ then we speak about the *Palm process*. The Poisson process forms a particular case of the Palm process. Furthermore we shall speak about the *Erlang process* if

$$(1) \qquad F(x) = \hat{F}(x) = \begin{cases} 1 - \displaystyle\sum_{j=0}^{m-1} e^{-\lambda x} \frac{(\lambda x)^j}{j!} & \text{if } x \geq 0, \\[2mm] & \text{if } x < 0, \end{cases}$$

and m is a positive integer. If $m = 1$ then the Erlang process reduces to the *Poisson process*.

If the mean of $F(x)$,

$$\mu = \int_0^\infty x \, dF(x),$$

is finite then let us define

$$(2) \qquad F^*(x) = \begin{cases} \dfrac{1}{\mu} \displaystyle\int_0^x [1 - F(y)] \, dy & \text{if } x \geq 0, \\[2mm] 0 & \text{if } x < 0. \end{cases}$$

If $\hat{F}(x) = F^*(x)$ then the recurrent process $\{\nu(t), 0 \leq t < \infty\}$ will be called a *homogeneous recurrent process*.

Let us introduce the following notation

$$\phi(s) = \int_0^\infty e^{-sx} \, dF(x),$$

$$\hat{\phi}(s) = \int_0^\infty e^{-sx} \, d\hat{F}(x),$$

$$\phi^*(s) = \int_0^\infty e^{-sx} \, dF^*(x).$$

Clearly

$$\phi^*(s) = \frac{1 - \phi(s)}{\mu s}.$$

Further let

$$\sigma^2 = \int_0^\infty (x - \mu)^2 \, dF(x)$$

provided that it exists.

The distribution of $\nu(t)$. Let $\mathbf{P}\{\nu(t) \leq n\} = W(t, n)$. Since $\nu(t) \leq n$ if and only if $t < \tau_{n+1}$, therefore

$$W(t, n) = \mathbf{P}\{t < \tau_{n+1}\} = 1 - \mathbf{P}\{\tau_{n+1} \leq t\} = 1 - \hat{F}(t) * F_n(t),$$

where $F_n(t)$ denotes the nth iterated convolution of the distribution function $F(t)$ with itself. $F_0(t) = 1$ if $t \geq 0$ and $F_0(t) = 0$ if $t \leq 0$. Here $\tau_{n+1} = \tau_1 + (\tau_2 - \tau_1) + \cdots + (\tau_{n+1} - \tau_n)$ is a sum of $n + 1$ independent random variables amongst which n have the distribution function $F(x)$ and one has the distribution function $\hat{F}(x)$.

The Laplace transform of $W(t, n)$ is given by

$$\int_0^\infty e^{-st} W(t, n) \, dt = \frac{1 - \hat{\phi}(s)[\phi(s)]^n}{s}$$

if $\Re(s) > 0$.

Let $\mathbf{E}\{[\nu(t)]^r\} = m_r(t)$ be the rth moment of the random variable $\nu(t)$. If $r = 1$ then let us write $m_1(t) = m(t)$. We have

$$m_r(t) = \sum_{n=0}^\infty n^r[W(t, n) - W(t, n - 1)]$$

$$= \sum_{n=0}^\infty [(n + 1)^r - n^r][1 - W(t, n)].$$

Hence

$$\mu_r(s) = \int_0^\infty e^{-st} \, dm_r(t) = \hat{\phi}(s) \sum_{j=1}^r \mathfrak{S}_r^j \frac{j![\phi(s)]^{j-1}}{[1 - \phi(s)]^j} \qquad (\Re(s) > 0)$$

where $\mathfrak{S}_r^j$ denotes the Stirling numbers of the second kind which are defined by the relation

$$x^r = \sum_{j=1}^r \mathfrak{S}_r^j j! \binom{x}{j},$$

which holds for every x. (Cf. *Ch. Jordan* [7], p. 168.)

Specifically

$$\mu(s) = \int_0^\infty e^{-st}\, dm(t) = \frac{\hat{\phi}(s)}{1 - \phi(s)} \qquad (\Re(s) > 0).$$

For $m(t)$ we have the following limit

$$\lim_{t \to \infty} \frac{m(t)}{t} = \frac{1}{\mu}.$$

(*S. Täcklind* [12].)

Let $d^2(t) = \mathbf{D}^2\{\nu(t)\}$ be the variance of $\nu(t)$, i.e. $d^2(t) = m_2(t) - [m_1(t)]^2$. If $\sigma^2 < \infty$ then we have

$$\lim_{t \to \infty} \frac{d^2(t)}{t} = \frac{\sigma^2}{\mu^3}.$$

(*W. L. Smith* [9].)

If $\sigma^2 < \infty$ then $\nu(t)$ has an asymptotic normal distribution as $t \to \infty$. We have

$$\lim_{t \to \infty} \mathbf{P}\left\{ \frac{\nu(t) - \dfrac{t}{\mu}}{\sqrt{\dfrac{\sigma^2 t}{\mu^3}}} \leq x \right\} = \frac{1}{\sqrt{2\pi}} \int_{-\infty}^{x} e^{-y^2/2}\, dy.$$

BLACKWELL'S THEOREM. *If $F(x)$ is not a lattice distribution and $\mu < \infty$ then*

$$(3) \qquad \lim_{t \to \infty} \frac{m(t+h) - m(t)}{h} = \frac{1}{\mu}$$

for every $h > 0$.

This theorem was proved by *D. Blackwell* [1] in the particular case when $\hat{F}(x) = F(x)$. The general case is an easy consequence of this special case. Let

$$\tilde{m}(t) = \sum_{n=0}^{\infty} F_n(t).$$

Then by Blackwell's theorem

$$\lim_{t \to \infty} \frac{\tilde{m}(t+h) - \tilde{m}(t)}{h} = \frac{1}{\mu}$$

for every $h > 0$. Since in the general case

$$m(t) = \int_0^t \tilde{m}(t - x) \, d\hat{F}(x),$$

therefore

$$m(t + h) - m(t) = \int_0^{t/2} [\tilde{m}(t + h - x) - \tilde{m}(t - x)] \, d\hat{F}(x)$$

$$+ \int_{t/2}^t [\tilde{m}(t + h - x) - \tilde{m}(t - x)] \, d\hat{F}(x) + \int_t^{t+h} \tilde{m}(t + h - x) \, d\hat{F}(x).$$

On the right-hand side the first term tends to h/μ if $t \to \infty$, the second term is non-negative and less than $[1 + \tilde{m}(h)] \left[\hat{F}(t) - \hat{F}\left(\dfrac{t}{2}\right) \right]$, which tends to 0 if $t \to \infty$ and the third term is non-negative and less than $\tilde{m}(h)[\hat{F}(t + h) - \hat{F}(t)]$, which tends to 0 if $t \to \infty$. This completes the proof of (3).

Denote by χ_t the distance between t and the instant of the next random event. The distribution function of χ_t is given by

(4) $$\mathbf{P}\{\chi_t \leqq x\} = \int_t^{t+x} [1 - F(t + x - u)] \, dm(u)$$

when $x \geqq 0$. For, the event $\chi_t \leqq x$ occurs if and only if there is at least one random event in the interval $(t, t + x]$. This event can occur in several mutually exclusive ways: the last event occurring in the time interval $(t, t + x]$ may be the 1st, 2nd, ..., nth, ... one. Thus by the theorem of total probability we have

$$\mathbf{P}\{\chi_t \leqq x\} = \sum_{n=1}^{\infty} \mathbf{P}\{t < \tau_n \leqq t + x < \tau_{n+1}\}$$

$$= \sum_{n=1}^{\infty} \int_t^{t+x} [1 - F(t + x - u)] \, d\mathbf{P}\{\tau_n \leqq u\}.$$

Since

$$m(u) = \sum_{n=1}^{\infty} \mathbf{P}\{\tau_n \leqq u\},$$

we get (4).

Now we shall prove the following

THEOREM 1. *If $F(x)$ is not a lattice distribution and its mean $\mu < \infty$, then the limiting distribution* $\lim\limits_{t \to \infty} \mathbf{P}\{\chi_t \leqq x\} = F^*(x)$ *exists and we have*

$$(5) \qquad F^*(x) = \begin{cases} \dfrac{1}{\mu} \displaystyle\int_0^x [1 - F(y)] \, dy & \text{if } x \geqq 0, \\[2ex] 0 & \text{if } x < 0. \end{cases}$$

This theorem is a particular case of the following fundamental theorem when we put

$$g(u) = \begin{cases} 1 - F(u) & \text{if } u \leqq x, \\ 0 & \text{if } u > x. \end{cases}$$

FUNDAMENTAL THEOREM. *If $g(u)$ has bounded variation in the interval $[0, \infty)$ and $F(x)$ is not a lattice distribution and its mean $\mu < \infty$, then we have*

$$(6) \qquad \lim_{t \to \infty} \int_0^t g(t - u) \, dm(u) = \frac{1}{\mu} \int_0^\infty g(u) \, du$$

provided that the integral on the right-hand side exists.

PROOF. Every function of bounded variation can be expressed as the difference of two non-increasing functions. Thus in proving this theorem we can restrict ourselves to the case when $g(t)$ is a non-negative and non-increasing function of t.

Let

$$T_1(t) = \int_0^{t/2} g(t - u) \, dm(u)$$

and

$$T_2(t) = \int_{t/2}^t g(t - u) \, dm(u).$$

We have evidently

$$0 \leqq T_1(t) \leqq g\left(\frac{t}{2}\right) m\left(\frac{t}{2}\right).$$

Since

$$\lim_{t \to \infty} \frac{t}{2} g\left(\frac{t}{2}\right) = 0$$

and

$$\lim_{t \to \infty} m\left(\frac{t}{2}\right) \bigg/ \frac{t}{2} = \frac{1}{\mu},$$

we get

(7) $$\lim_{t \to \infty} T_1(t) = 0.$$

Further we prove that

(8) $$\lim_{t \to \infty} T_2(t) = \frac{Q}{\mu},$$

where

$$Q = \int_0^\infty g(t)\, dt.$$

If $\epsilon > 0$ and $0 < h < \epsilon/g(0)$ then

$$0 < Q - h \sum_{n=1}^\infty g(nh) < hg(0) < \epsilon.$$

Choose t so large that

$$h \sum_{n=[t/2h]}^\infty g(nh) < \epsilon$$

and

$$\left| \frac{m(u+h) - m(u)}{h} - \frac{1}{\mu} \right| < \epsilon$$

if $u \geq t/2$. For such t values we have

$$\left(\frac{1}{\mu} - \epsilon\right) \left(h \sum_{n=1}^\infty g(nh) - \epsilon\right) < T_2(t) < \left(\frac{1}{\mu} + \epsilon\right) \left(h \sum_{n=1}^\infty g(nh)\right).$$

Hence

$$\left(\frac{1}{\mu} - \epsilon\right) (Q - 2\epsilon) < T_2(t) < \left(\frac{1}{\mu} + \epsilon\right) (Q + \epsilon)$$

if t is large enough. Since $\epsilon > 0$ is arbitrary this proves (8). Finally

$$\lim_{t \to \infty} \int_0^t g(t - u)\, dm(u) = \lim_{t \to \infty} [T_1(t) + T_2(t)] = \frac{Q}{\mu},$$

which was to be proved.

THE ERLANG PROCESS. If we consider a Poisson process of density λ and we take into account only every mth event then we arrive at the Erlang process. Denote by $\xi(t)$ the number of events occurring in the Poisson process during the time interval $(0, t]$ and denote by $\nu(t)$ the number of events occurring in the Erlang process during the time interval $(0, t]$. We have $v(t) = \left[\dfrac{\xi(t)}{m} \right]$. The process $\{v(t), 0 \leqq t < \infty\}$ is not a Markov process. But if we introduce an auxiliary variable $\xi(t) - mv(t)$ which assumes the values $0, 1, 2, \ldots, m - 1$ then the vector process $\{v(t), \xi(t) - mv(t)\}$ will be a Markovian one.

THE HOMOGENEOUS RECURRENT PROCESS. In this case $\hat{F}(x) = F^*(x)$ defined by (2). Denote by $v^*(t)$ the number of events which occur in the homogeneous process in the time interval $(0, t]$.

Let $\mathbf{P}\{v^*(t) \leqq n\} = W^*(t, n)$. Then we have

$$W^*(t, n) = 1 - F^*(t) * F_n(t),$$

whence

$$\int_0^\infty e^{-st} W^*(t, n) \, dt = \frac{1}{s} - \frac{[1 - \phi(s)][\phi(s)]^n}{\mu s^2} \qquad (\Re(s) > 0).$$

Let $m_r^*(t) = \mathbf{E}\{[v^*(t)]^r\}$ be the rth moment of the random variable $v^*(t)$. We have

$$m_r^*(t) = \sum_{n=0}^\infty [(n + 1)^r - n^r][1 - W^*(t, n)]$$

and its Laplace-Stieltjes transform is

$$\int_0^\infty e^{-st} \, dm_r^*(t) = \frac{1}{\mu s} \sum_{j=1}^r \mathfrak{S}_r^j \frac{j![\phi(s)]^{j-1}}{[1 - \phi(s)]^{j-1}}.$$

In particular we have for the expectation $m^*(t) = m_1(t)$ that

$$m^*(t) = \sum_{n=0}^\infty [1 - W^*(t, n)] = \frac{t}{\mu}.$$

If χ_t^* denotes the distance between t and the instant of the next random event, then

$$\mathbf{P}\{\chi_t^* \leqq x\} = F^*(x)$$

for every t. If $\sigma^2 < \infty$ then

$$\mathbf{E}\{\chi_t^*\} = \int_0^\infty x \, dF^*(x) = \frac{\sigma^2 + \mu^2}{2\mu}.$$

REMARK 1. Let us consider the Palm process, when $\hat{F}(x) = F(x)$. If $F(x)$ is known then the distribution, the asymptotic distribution, and moments of $\nu(t)$ can easily be determined. However, in many cases $F(x)$ is not known or is too complicated to determine, but the average function $m(t)$ which denotes the expectation of the number of events occurring in the time interval $(0, t]$ can easily be obtained. In this case $F(x)$ can be calculated from $m(t)$, and after that the method mentioned may be used to determine the distributions and moments in question. Since in this case

$$\mu(s) = \int_0^\infty e^{-st}\,dm(t) = \frac{\phi(s)}{1 - \phi(s)} \quad (\Re(s))$$

the Laplace-Stieltjes transform of $F(x)$ is given by

$$\phi(s) = \frac{\mu(s)}{1 + \mu(s)}.$$

In particular, the Laplace transform of $\mathbf{P}\{\nu(t) \leqq n\} = W(t, n)$ is given by

$$\int_0^\infty e^{-st} W(t, n)\,dt = \frac{1}{s} - \frac{1}{s}\left[\frac{\mu(s)}{1 + \mu(s)}\right]^{n+1}$$

and for the homogeneous process $\{\nu^*(t)\}$ the Laplace transform of $\mathbf{P}\{\nu^*(t) \leqq n\} = W^*(t, n)$ is given by

$$\int_0^\infty e^{-st} W^*(t, n)\,dt = \frac{1}{s} - \frac{1}{\mu s^2}\frac{[\mu(s)]^n}{[1 + \mu(s)]^{n+1}}.$$

4. General theorems

THEOREM OF TOTAL PROBABILITY. If $A_0, A_1, \ldots, A_n, \ldots$ is a complete system of events (i.e. mutually exclusive and exhaustive), then for an arbitrary event B we have

$$\mathbf{P}\{B\} = \sum_{n=0}^\infty \mathbf{P}\{A_n\}\mathbf{P}\{B\,|\,A_n\}.$$

THEOREM OF TOTAL EXPECTATION. If η is a real-valued random variable and $\mathbf{E}\{\xi|\eta\}$ denotes the conditional expectation of ξ given η, then

$$\mathbf{E}\{\xi\} = \int_{-\infty}^{\infty} \mathbf{E}\{\xi|\eta = x\}\, d\mathbf{P}\{\eta \leq x\}$$

provided that the expectations exist.

JORDAN'S THEOREM. Let us suppose that the random variable ξ assumes only non-negative integer values. Let $P_k = \mathbf{P}\{\xi = k\}$ $(k = 0, 1, 2, \ldots)$. The rth binomial moment of ξ is defined by

$$B_r = \mathbf{E}\left\{\binom{\xi}{r}\right\} = \sum_{k=r}^{\infty} \binom{k}{r} P_k.$$

If the moments B_r $(r = 0, 1, 2, \ldots)$ determine $\{P_k\}$ uniquely, then we have

$$P_k = \sum_{r=k}^{\infty} (-1)^{r-k} \binom{r}{k} B_r.$$

(Cf. [10].)

WALD'S THEOREM. Let $\{\xi_n\}$ be a sequence of identically distributed, independent random variables with finite expectation $\mathbf{E}\{\xi_1\}$ and let ν be a random variable which assumes non-negative integer values and for which $\mathbf{E}\{\nu\} < \infty$. If the event $\nu = n$ and the random variables $\xi_{n+1}, \xi_{n+2}, \ldots$ are independent then

$$\mathbf{E}\{\xi_1 + \xi_2 + \cdots + \xi_\nu\} = \mathbf{E}\{\nu\}\mathbf{E}\{\xi_1\}.$$

If $\nu = 0$ then the empty sum is equal to zero. (Cf. *N. L. Johnson* [6].)

A COMBINATORIAL LEMMA. If $\nu_1, \nu_2, \ldots, \nu_n$ are exchangeable random variables which assume non-negative integer values then for $0 \leq k \leq n$ we have

(9) $\mathbf{P}\{\nu_1 + \cdots + \nu_r < r$ for $r = 1, 2, \ldots, k | \nu_1 + \cdots + \nu_n = k\}$

$$= 1 - \frac{k}{n}.$$

PROOF. The random variables $\nu_1, \nu_2, \ldots, \nu_n$ are called exchangeable if for every r and $1 \leqq i_1 < i_2 < \cdots < i_r \leqq n$ the joint distribution of $(\nu_{i_1}, \nu_{i_2}, \ldots, \nu_{i_r})$ agrees with the joint distribution of $(\nu_1, \nu_2, \ldots, \nu_r)$. In this case we have

$$\mathbf{E}\{\nu_i | \nu_1 + \cdots + \nu_n = k\} = \frac{k}{n} \qquad (i = 1, 2, \ldots, n).$$

For, $\mathbf{E}\{\nu_i | \nu_1 + \cdots + \nu_n = k\}$ is independent of i and

$$\sum_{i=1}^{n} \mathbf{E}\{\nu_i | \nu_1 + \cdots + \nu_n = k\}$$
$$= \mathbf{E}\{\nu_1 + \cdots + \nu_n | \nu_1 + \cdots + \nu_n = k\} = k.$$

We shall prove by induction that (9) is true for every pair (n, k) where $0 \leqq k \leqq n$. The lemma is evidently true for the pairs $(1, 0)$ and $(1, 1)$. Supposing that it is true for the pairs $(1, 0)$, $(1, 1)$, $\ldots$, $(n - 1, 0)$, $\ldots$, $(n - 1, n - 1)$, we shall prove that it is also true for the pair (n, k) where $0 \leqq k \leqq n$. If $k = n$ then (9) is trivially true. Let $k < n$. If $0 \leqq j \leqq k$ then

$$\mathbf{P}\{\nu_1 + \cdots + \nu_r < r \text{ for } r = 1, 2, \ldots, k | \nu_1 + \cdots + \nu_k = j,$$
$$\nu_1 + \cdots + \nu_n = k\} = \mathbf{P}\{\nu_1 + \cdots + \nu_r < r \text{ for }$$
$$r = 1, 2, \ldots, j | \nu_1 + \cdots + \nu_k = j\} = 1 - \frac{j}{k},$$

because, by assumption, (9) is true for the pair (k, j). Thus by the theorem of total probability we get

$$\mathbf{P}\{\nu_1 + \cdots + \nu_r < r \text{ for } r = 1, 2, \ldots, k | \nu_1 + \cdots + \nu_n = k\}$$
$$= \sum_{j=0}^{k} \left(1 - \frac{j}{k}\right) \mathbf{P}\{\nu_1 + \cdots + \nu_k = j | \nu_1 + \cdots + \nu_n = k\}$$
$$= 1 - \frac{1}{k} \mathbf{E}\{\nu_1 + \cdots + \nu_k | \nu_1 + \cdots + \nu_n = k\} = 1 - \frac{k}{n}$$

because

$$\mathbf{E}\{\nu_1 + \cdots + \nu_k | \nu_1 + \cdots + \nu_n = k\}$$
$$= \sum_{i=1}^{k} \mathbf{E}\{\nu_i | \nu_1 + \cdots + \nu_n = k\} = \frac{k^2}{n}.$$

CRAMÉR-LÉVY'S THEOREM. Let $\{F_n(x)\}$ be a sequence of distribution functions and let $\phi_n(\omega) = \int_{-\infty}^{\infty} e^{i\omega x} dF_n(x)$ be the characteristic function of $F_n(x)$. A necessary and sufficient condition for the convergence of the sequence $\{F_n(x)\}$ to a distribution function $F(x)$ at every point of continuity of $F(x)$ is that for every ω, the sequence $\{\phi_n(\omega)\}$ converges to a limit $\phi(\omega)$, which is continuous for $\omega = 0$. When this condition is satisfied, the limit $\phi(\omega)$ is identical with the characteristic function of the limiting distribution function $F(x)$. (Cf. *H. Cramér* [2] p. 96.)

ZYGMUND'S THEOREM. Let $\{F_n(x)\}$ be a sequence of distribution functions all vanishing for $x \leqq 0$ and let $\phi_n(\omega) = \int_0^{\infty} e^{i\omega x} dF_n(x)$, $-\infty < \omega < \infty$. If the functions $\phi_n(\omega)$ tend to a limit in an interval around $\omega = 0$, and if the limiting function is continuous at $\omega = 0$, then there is a distribution function $F(x)$ such that $F_n(x)$ tends to $F(x)$ at every point of continuity of $F(x)$. (Cf. *A. Zygmund* [15].)

HELLY-BRAY THEOREM. If $g(x)$ is bounded and continuous when $-\infty < x < \infty$ and the sequence of distribution functions $F_n(x)$ converges to a distribution function $F(x)$ in every continuity point of $F(x)$, then

$$\lim_{n \to \infty} \int_{-\infty}^{\infty} g(x) \, dF_n(x) = \int_{-\infty}^{\infty} g(x) \, dF(x).$$

(Cf. *M. Loève* [8].)

ABEL'S THEOREM. If

$$\lim_{n \to \infty} a_n = a$$

then

$$\lim_{x \to 1-0} (1 - x) \sum_{n=0}^{\infty} a_n x^n = a.$$

TAUBER'S THEOREM. If

$$\lim_{x \to 1-0} (1 - x) \sum_{n=0}^{\infty} a_n x^n = a$$

and

$$\lim_{n \to \infty} n(a_n - a_{n-1}) = 0,$$

then

$$\lim_{n \to \infty} a_n = a.$$

AN ABELIAN THEOREM. If for some non-negative number γ

$$\lim_{t \to \infty} \frac{m(t)}{t^\gamma} = \frac{C}{\Gamma(\gamma + 1)}$$

and

$$\mu(s) = \int_0^\infty e^{-st}\, dm(t),$$

then

$$\lim_{s \to +0} s^\gamma \mu(s) = C.$$

(Cf. *D. V. Widder* [13] p. 182.)

A TAUBERIAN THEOREM. If $m(t)$ is non-decreasing and such that the integral

$$\mu(s) = \int_0^\infty e^{-st}\, dm(t)$$

converges for $\Re(s) > 0$, and if for some non-negative number γ

$$\lim_{s \to 0} s^\gamma \mu(s) = C,$$

then

$$\lim_{t \to \infty} \frac{m(t)}{t^\gamma} = \frac{C}{\Gamma(\gamma + 1)}.$$

(Cf. *D. V. Widder* [13], p. 192.)

ROUCHÉ'S THEOREM. If $f(z)$ and $g(z)$ are regular inside and on a closed contour C, and $|g(z)| < |f(z)|$ on C, then $f(z)$ and $f(z) + g(z)$ have the same number of zeros inside C.

LAGRANGE'S THEOREM. Let $f(z)$ and $\phi(z)$ be regular on and inside a closed contour C surrounding a point a, and let w be such that the inequality

$$|w\phi(z)| < |z - a|$$

is satisfied at all points z on the perimeter of C. Then the equation

$$\zeta = a + w\phi(\zeta),$$

regarded as an equation in ζ, has one root in the interior of C; and further any function of ζ regular on and inside C can be expanded as a power series in w by the formula

$$f(\zeta) = f(a) + \sum_{n=1}^{\infty} \frac{w^n}{n!} \frac{d^{n-1}}{da^{n-1}} \{f'(a)[\phi(a)]^n\}.$$

(Cf. [14] pp. 132–3.)

Bibliography

[1] *D. Blackwell:* A renewal theorem. Duke Math. J. 15 (1948) 145–50.

[2] *H. Cramér:* Mathematical Methods of Statistics. Princeton University Press, Princeton, 1946.

[3] *J. L. Doob:* Stochastic Processes. John Wiley and Sons, New York, 1953.

[4] *W. Feller:* An Introduction to Probability Theory and its Applications. John Wiley and Sons, New York, 1950. Second edition, 1957.

[5] *F. G. Foster:* On the stochastic matrices associated with certain queueing processes. Ann. Math. Statist. 24 (1953) 355–60.

[6] *N. L. Johnson:* A proof of Wald's theorem on cumulative sums. Ann. Math. Statist. 30 (1959) 1245–7.

[7] *Ch. Jordan:* Calculus of Finite Differences. Budapest, 1939. Second edition, Chelsea, New York, 1947.

[8] *M. Loève:* Probability Theory. D. Van Nostrand, New York, 1955. Second edition, 1960.

[9] *W. L. Smith:* Renewal theory and its ramifications. J. Roy. Statist. Soc. Ser. B. 20 (1958) 243–302.

[10] *L. Takács:* On a general probability theorem and its applications in the theory of the stochastic processes. Proc. Cambridge Philos. Soc. 54 (1958) 219–24.

[11] *L. Takács:* Stochastic Processes. Methuen, London, and John Wiley and Sons, New York, 1960.

[12] *S. Täcklind:* Elementare Behandlung vom Erneuerungsproblem. Skand. Aktuarietidsk. 27 (1944) 1–15.

[13] *D. V. Widder:* The Laplace Transform. Princeton University Press, Princeton, 1946.

[14] *E. T. Whittaker and G. N. Watson:* A Course of Modern Analysis. Cambridge University Press, Cambridge, 1952.

[15] *A. Zygmund:* A remark on characteristic functions. Proc. Second Berkeley Symposium on Math. Stat. and Prob., Berkeley and Los Angeles, University of California Press (1951) 369–72.

SOLUTIONS OF THE PROBLEMS

1. *Chapter 1*

PROBLEM 1. We have

$$\mathbf{P}\{\zeta^*(t) \leq -c \,|\, \nu_1(t) = a, \nu_2(t) = b\} = \frac{\binom{a+b}{a+c}}{\binom{a+b}{a}} \qquad (c = 0, 1, \ldots, b).$$

The right-hand side is the probability that in the case of symmetric random walk on the x axis a particle, starting from the origin and moving $a + b$ unit steps, among which a is taken in the positive direction and b is taken in the negative direction, reaches the point $x = -c$. Hence if $\xi(0) = i$ is fixed then

$$\mathbf{P}\{\xi(t) \geq k \,|\, \nu_1(t) = a, \nu_2(t) = b\} = \begin{cases} 1 & \text{if } k \leq i + a - b, \\[2ex] \dfrac{\binom{a+b}{a-k}}{\binom{a+b}{a}} & \text{if } k > i + a - b, \end{cases}$$

and unconditionally

$$\mathbf{P}\{\xi(t) \geq k\} = \sum_{k-i \leq a-b} e^{-\lambda t} \frac{(\lambda t)^a}{a!} e^{-\mu t} \frac{(\mu t)^b}{b!}$$

$$+ \sum_{k-i > a-b} \frac{\binom{a+b}{a-k}}{\binom{a+b}{a}} e^{-\lambda t} \frac{(\lambda t)^a}{a!} e^{-\mu t} \frac{(\mu t)^b}{b!}.$$

237

Now we introduce

$$I_r(x) = \sum_{\nu=0}^{\infty} \frac{(x/2)^{r+2\nu}}{\nu!(r+\nu)!},$$

the modified Bessel function of order r; then we can write that

$$\mathbf{P}\{\xi(t) \geqq k\} = e^{-(\lambda+\mu)t} \left\{ \sum_{\nu=k-i}^{\infty} \left(\frac{\lambda}{\mu}\right)^{\nu/2} I_\nu(2\sqrt{\lambda\mu}\,t) \right.$$

$$\left. + \sum_{\nu=i+k+1}^{\infty} \left(\frac{\lambda}{\mu}\right)^{k-\nu/2} I_\nu(2\sqrt{\lambda\mu}\,t) \right\} \quad \text{if } k \geqq i$$

and

$$\mathbf{P}\{\xi(t) \geqq k\} = 1 - e^{-(\lambda+\mu)t} \left\{ \sum_{\nu=k-i+1}^{\infty} \left(\frac{\lambda}{\mu}\right)^{-\nu/2} I_\nu(2\sqrt{\lambda\mu}\,t) \right.$$

$$\left. - \sum_{\nu=i+k-1}^{\infty} \left(\frac{\lambda}{\mu}\right)^{k-\nu/2} I_\nu(2\sqrt{\lambda\mu}\,t) \right\} \quad \text{if } k < i.$$

Thus for fixed $\xi(0) = i$ we have

$$\mathbf{P}\{\xi(t) = k\} = \mathbf{P}\{\xi(t) \geqq k\} - \mathbf{P}\{\xi(t) \geqq k+1\}$$

$$= e^{-(\lambda+\mu)t} \left\{ \left(\frac{\lambda}{\mu}\right)^{(k-i)/2} I_{k-i}(2\sqrt{\lambda\mu}\,t) \right.$$

$$+ \left(\frac{\lambda}{\mu}\right)^{(k-i+1)/2} I_{k+i+1}(2\sqrt{\lambda\mu}\,t)$$

$$\left. + \left(1 - \frac{\lambda}{\mu}\right)\left(\frac{\lambda}{\mu}\right)^k \sum_{r=i+k+2}^{\infty} \left(\frac{\lambda}{\mu}\right)^{-(r/2)} I_r(2\sqrt{\lambda\mu}\,t) \right\},$$

which is in agreement with (4).

PROBLEM 2. The probabilities $P_{ik}(t)$ satisfy the following system of differential equations

(1) $P'_{i0}(t) = -\lambda P_{i0}(t) + \mu P_{i1}(t)$

(2) $P'_{ik}(t) = \lambda P_{i,k-1}(t) - (\lambda + \mu)\,P_{ik}(t) + \mu P_{i,k+1}(t)$

$$(k = 1, 2, \ldots),$$

and the initial condition is

$$P_{ik}(0) = \begin{cases} 1 & \text{if } k = i, \\ 0 & \text{if } k \neq i. \end{cases}$$

Forming the Laplace transforms of (1) and (2) we get the following system of linear equations

(3) $$-\lambda \pi_{i0}(s) + \mu \pi_{i1}(s) = s\pi_{i0}(s) - \delta_{i0}$$

and

(4) $$\lambda \pi_{i,k-1}(s) - (\lambda + \mu)\pi_{ik}(s) + \mu \pi_{i,k+1}(s) = s\pi_{ik}(s) - \delta_{ik}$$

$$(k = 1, 2, \ldots),$$

where $\delta_{ik} = 1$ if $i = k$ and $\delta_{ik} = 0$ if $i \neq k$.

Let us introduce the generating function

$$G_i(z, s) = \sum_{k=0}^{\infty} \pi_{ik}(s)z^k;$$

then by (3) and (4) we obtain

$$G_i(z, s) = \frac{\mu(1 - z)\pi_{i0}(s) - z^{i+1}}{\lambda z^2 - (\lambda + \mu + s)z + \mu}.$$

$G_i(z, s)$ is a regular function of z if $|z| < 1$ and $\Re(s) > 0$. The denominator has one root in the circle $|z| < 1$, namely $z = \Gamma(s)$, where

$$\Gamma(s) = \frac{(\lambda + \mu + s) - \sqrt{(\lambda + \mu + s)^2 - 4\lambda\mu}}{2\lambda}.$$

This must be a root of the numerator too. Hence

$$\pi_{i0}(s) = \frac{[\Gamma(s)]^{i+1}}{\mu[1 - \Gamma(s)]}$$

in agreement with (32) of Section 2, Chapter 1. Thus

$$G_i(z, s) = \frac{(1 - z)[\Gamma(s)]^{i+1} - z^{i+1}[1 - \Gamma(s)]}{[1 - \Gamma(s)][\lambda z^2 - (\lambda + \mu + s)z + \mu]}.$$

If specifically $i = 0$ then

$$G_0(z, s) = \frac{\Gamma(s)}{[1 - \Gamma(s)][\mu - z\lambda\Gamma(s)]},$$

whence

$$\pi_{0k}(s) = \left(\frac{\lambda}{\mu}\right)^k \frac{[\Gamma(s)]^{k+1}}{\mu[1 - \Gamma(s)]}.$$

PROBLEM 3. The sequence of random variables $\{\xi_n\}$ forms an irreducible and aperiodic Markov chain. Thus $\lim_{n\to\infty} \mathbf{P}\{\xi_n = k\} = P_k$ $(k = 0, 1, 2, \ldots)$ always exists. There are two possibilities. Either $P_k > 0$ for every k and $\{P_k\}$ is a probability distribution, or $P_k = 0$ for every k. If ρ denotes the expected number of the services in a busy period, that is, ρ is the mean recurrence time of the state E_0, then $P_0 = 1/\rho$. Now evidently

$$\rho\frac{1}{\lambda} = \rho\frac{1}{\mu} + \frac{1}{\lambda}.$$

Hence $\rho = 1 \Big/ \left(1 - \frac{\lambda}{\mu}\right)$ if $\lambda < \mu$ and $\rho = \infty$ if $\lambda \geqq \mu$. Consequently $\{P_k\}$ is a probability distribution if and only if $\lambda < \mu$. In this case there is only one stationary distribution and it agrees with $\{P_k\}$. To determine $\{P_k\}$ let us suppose that $\lambda < \mu$ and that $\{\xi_n\}$ is a stationary Markov chain. Then $\mathbf{P}\{\xi_n = k\} = P_k$ $(k = 0, 1, 2, \ldots)$ and if we introduce the generating function

$$G(z) = \sum_{k=0}^{\infty} P_k z^k,$$

we obtain by (17) of Section 2, Chapter 1 that

$$(z - q)\, G(z) = pz^2 G(z) - (1 - z)q^2 G(q),$$

where

$$p = \frac{\lambda}{\lambda + \mu} \quad \text{and} \quad q = \frac{\mu}{\lambda + \mu}.$$

Thus

$$G(z) = \frac{q^2 G(q)}{q - pz}.$$

Since $G(1) = 1$ we obtain finally

$$G(z) = \frac{q - p}{q - pz},$$

whence

$$P_k = \left(1 - \frac{p}{q}\right)\left(\frac{p}{q}\right)^k \qquad (k = 0, 1, 2, \ldots).$$

PROBLEM 4. If we suppose that $\{\eta_n\}$ is stationary and introduce the notation $\mathbf{P}\{\eta_n \leqq x\} = W(x)$,

$$\Omega(s) = \mathbf{E}\{e^{-s\eta_n}\} = \int_0^\infty e^{-sx} \, dW(x) \qquad (\Re(s) \geqq 0)$$

and

$$\mathbf{P}\{\eta_n = 0\} = P_0,$$

then by (46) of Section 2, Chapter 1 we have

$$(\lambda - s)\Omega(s) = \frac{\lambda\mu}{(\mu + s)} \Omega(s) - sP_0,$$

whence

$$\Omega(s) = P_0 \frac{\mu + s}{(\mu - \lambda + s)}.$$

Since $\Omega(0) = 1$, therefore $P_0 = 1 - \frac{\lambda}{\mu}$ and consequently stationary distribution cannot exist if $\mu \leqq \lambda$. If $\lambda < \mu$ then

$$\Omega(s) = \left(1 - \frac{\lambda}{\mu}\right)\frac{\mu + s}{\mu - \lambda + s},$$

whence

$$W(x) = \begin{cases} 1 - \dfrac{\lambda}{\mu} e^{-(\mu-\lambda)x} & \text{if } x \geqq 0, \\ 0 & \text{if } x < 0. \end{cases}$$

Thus if $\lambda < \mu$ then there exists one and only one stationary distribution $W(x)$.

PROBLEM 5. The sequence of random variables $\{\xi_n\}$ forms an irreducible and aperiodic Markov chain. Let $\lim_{n \to \infty} \mathbf{P}\{\xi_n = k\} = P_k$ $(k = 0, 1, \ldots)$. Denote by α the average service time. Now we shall show that if $\lambda\alpha < 1$ then $\{P_k\}$ is a probability distribution with positive elements, whereas if $\lambda\alpha \geqq 1$ then $P_k = 0$ for every k. Evidently $P_0 = 1/\rho$ where ρ is the mean recurrence time of the state E_0. It is easy to see that

$$\rho \frac{1}{\lambda} = \rho\alpha + \frac{1}{\lambda}.$$

Thus $\rho = 1/(1 - \lambda\alpha)$ if $\lambda\alpha < 1$ and $\rho = \infty$ if $\lambda\alpha \geqq 1$, whence $P_0 = 1 - \lambda\alpha$ if $\lambda\alpha < 1$ and $P_0 = 0$ if $\lambda\alpha \geqq 1$. Accordingly the Markov chain $\{\xi_n\}$ has a stationary distribution if and only if $\lambda\alpha < 1$ and this agrees with the limiting distribution $\{P_k\}$. Let

$$U(z) = \sum_{k=0}^{\infty} P_k z^k.$$

Then by (62) of Section 3, Chapter 1, we have that

$$U(z) = \psi(\lambda(1 - z)) \left[\frac{U(z) - P_0}{z} + P_0 \right],$$

whence

$$U(z) = P_0 \frac{(1 - z)\psi(\lambda(1 - z))}{\psi(\lambda(1 - z)) - z}.$$

Since $U(1) = 1$ and $\psi'(0) = -\alpha$ we get $P_0 = 1 - \lambda\alpha$. This shows at once that a stationary distribution cannot exist if $\lambda\alpha \geqq 1$. If $\lambda\alpha < 1$ then

$$U(z) = (1 - \lambda\alpha) \frac{(1 - z)\psi(\lambda(1 - z))}{\psi(\lambda(1 - z)) - z}.$$

If $\chi_n \equiv \alpha$ (constant), then $\psi(s) = e^{-s\alpha}$ and

$$U(z) = \frac{(1 - \lambda\alpha)e^{-\lambda\alpha(1-z)}}{1 - \dfrac{1 - e^{-\lambda\alpha(1-z)}}{1 - z}},$$

whence

$$P_k = (1 - \lambda\alpha) \left\{ \sum_{j=0}^{k} (-1)^{k-j} e^{j\lambda\alpha} \frac{(j\lambda\alpha)^{k-j}}{(k - j)!} \right.$$
$$\left. + \sum_{j=0}^{k-1} (-1)^{k-j} e^{j\lambda\alpha} \frac{(j\lambda\alpha)^{k-j-1}}{(k - j - 1)!} \right\}.$$

If $\mathbf{P}\{\chi_n \leqq x\} = 1 - e^{-x/\alpha}$ $(x \geqq 0)$, then $\psi(s) = 1/(1 + \alpha s)$ and

$$U(z) = \frac{1 - \lambda\alpha}{1 - \lambda\alpha z},$$

whence

$$P_k = (1 - \lambda\alpha)(\lambda\alpha)^k \qquad (k = 0, 1, 2, \ldots).$$

PROBLEM 6. Let $\mathbf{P}\{\eta_n \leqq x\} = W(x)$ and $\mathbf{P}\{\eta_n = 0\} = P_0$ and introduce the Laplace-Stieltjes transform

$$\Omega(s) = \mathbf{E}\{e^{-s\eta_n}\} = \int_0^\infty e^{-sx}\,dW(x).$$

By (25) of Section 3, Chapter 1, we have

$$(\lambda - s)\Omega(s) = \lambda\Omega(s)\psi(s) - sP_0,$$

whence

$$\Omega(s) = P_0 \frac{s}{s - \lambda[1 - \psi(s)]}.$$

Since $\Omega(0) = 1$ and $\psi'(0) = -\alpha$ we get that $P_0 = 1 - \lambda\alpha$. Thus if $\lambda\alpha \geqq 1$ then a stationary distribution does not exist. If $\lambda\alpha < 1$ then

$$(1) \quad \Omega(s) = \frac{(1 - \lambda\alpha)}{1 - \lambda\dfrac{1 - \psi(s)}{s}} = (1 - \lambda\alpha) \sum_{j=0}^\infty (\lambda\alpha)^j \left(\frac{1 - \psi(s)}{\alpha s}\right)^j.$$

If

$$H^*(x) = \begin{cases} \dfrac{1}{\alpha} \displaystyle\int_0^x [1 - H(y)]\,dy & \text{when } x \geqq 0, \\[2mm] 0 & \text{when } x < 0, \end{cases}$$

then

$$\int_0^\infty e^{-sx}\,dH^*(x) = \frac{1 - \psi(s)}{\alpha s}$$

and by (1) we get that

$$W(x) = (1 - \lambda\alpha) \sum_{j=0}^\infty (\lambda\alpha)^j H_j^*(x),$$

where $H_j^*(x)$ denotes the jth iterated convolution of $H^*(x)$ with itself.

If $\chi_n \equiv \alpha$ (constant) then $\psi(s) = e^{-s\alpha}$, and if $\lambda\alpha < 1$ we have

$$W(x) = (1 - \lambda\alpha) \sum_{j=0}^{[x/\alpha]} (-1)^j e^{\lambda(x-j\alpha)} \frac{\lambda^j(x - j\alpha)^j}{j!}.$$

If $\mathbf{P}\{\chi_n \leq x\} = 1 - e^{-x/\alpha}$ $(x \geq 0)$, then $\psi(s) = 1/(1 + \alpha s)$ and

$$\Omega(s) = \frac{(1 - \lambda\alpha)(1 + \alpha s)}{(1 - \lambda\alpha + \alpha s)},$$

whence

$$W(x) = \begin{cases} 1 - \lambda\alpha e^{-(1-\lambda\alpha)x/\alpha} & \text{if } x \geq 0, \\ 0 & \text{if } x < 0. \end{cases}$$

PROBLEM 7. Denote by $G_{nk}(x)$ the probability that the busy period consists of at least n services, the total service time of the first n customers is at most x, and at the end of the nth service k customers are present in the queue. Then evidently

$$\tilde{G}_n(x) = G_{n0}(x).$$

If we write

$$\Gamma_{nk}(s) = \int_0^\infty e^{-sx} \, dG_{nk}(x)$$

then

$$\Gamma_n(s) = \Gamma_{n0}(s).$$

Now by the theorem of total probability we can write that

$$G_{1k}(x) = \int_0^x e^{-\lambda y} \frac{(\lambda y)^k}{k!} \, dH(y)$$

and

$$G_{nk}(x) = \sum_{r=1}^{k+1} \int_0^x G_{n-1,r}(x - y)e^{-\lambda y} \frac{(\lambda y)^{k+1-r}}{(k + 1 - r)!} \, dH(y)$$

$$(n = 2, 3, \ldots).$$

Forming Laplace-Stieltjes transforms we get

$$\Gamma_{1k}(s) = \int_0^\infty e^{-(\lambda+s)y} \frac{(\lambda y)^k}{k!} \, dH(y)$$

and

$$\Gamma_{nk}(s) = \sum_{r=1}^{k+1} \Gamma_{n-1,r}(s) \int_0^\infty e^{-(\lambda+s)y} \frac{(\lambda y)^{k+1-r}}{(k + 1 - r)!} \, dH(y).$$

If we introduce the generating functions

$$C_n(s, z) = \sum_{k=0}^{\infty} \Gamma_{nk}(s) z^k \qquad (n = 1, 2, \ldots),$$

then we have

$$C_1(s, z) = \psi(s + \lambda(1 - z))$$

and

$$z C_n(s, z) = \psi(s + \lambda(1 - z)) [C_{n-1}(s, z) - \Gamma_{n-1}(s)].$$

Hence

$$(1) \quad \sum_{n=1}^{\infty} C_n(s, z) w^n = w\psi(s + \lambda(1 - z)) \frac{z - \sum_{n=1}^{\infty} \Gamma_n(s) w^n}{z - w\psi(s + \lambda(1 - z))}.$$

The left-hand side of (1) is a regular function of z if $|z| < 1$, $\Re(s) \geqq 0$ and $|w| < 1$. In this domain the denominator of the right-hand side has exactly one root $z = \gamma(s, w)$. This must also be a root of the numerator, that is,

$$(2) \quad \sum_{n=1}^{\infty} \Gamma_n(s) w^n = \gamma(s, w)$$

for $|w| < 1$ where $\gamma(s, w)$ is defined by (3) of Section 3, Chapter 1. By using the continuity of (2) it follows that (2) is true also for $|w| = 1$.

If $\chi_n \equiv \alpha$ then

$$\gamma(s, w) = w \sum_{j=1}^{\infty} \frac{(\lambda \alpha j w)^{j-1}}{j!} e^{-(\lambda + s)\alpha j},$$

whence

$$\Gamma_n(s) = \frac{(\lambda \alpha n)^{n-1}}{n!} e^{-(\lambda + s)\alpha n}$$

and thus

$$\tilde{G}_n(x) = \begin{cases} e^{-\lambda \alpha n} \dfrac{(\lambda \alpha n)^{n-1}}{n!} & \text{if } x \geqq n\alpha, \\ 0 & \text{if } x < n\alpha. \end{cases}$$

REMARK. In the general case we have

$$\tilde{G}_n(x) = \frac{\lambda^{n-1}}{n!} \int_0^x e^{-\lambda u} u^{n-1} \, dH_n(u),$$

where $H_n(x)$ denotes the nth iterated convolution of $H(x)$ with itself.

This formula can be proved as follows. Let us suppose that a busy period starts at the arrival of a customer and it consists of n services. Denote by $\chi_1, \chi_2, \ldots, \chi_n$ the lengths of the successive service times and $\nu_1, \nu_2, \ldots, \nu_n$ the number of customers joining the queue during the 1st, 2nd, $\ldots$, nth service time respectively. Then $\nu_1 \geqq 1$, $\nu_1 + \nu_2 \geqq 2, \ldots, \nu_1 + \cdots + \nu_{n-1} \geqq n - 1$, $\nu_1 + \cdots + \nu_n = n - 1$ must hold. Thus we have

$$\tilde{G}_n(x) = \mathbf{P}\{\chi_1 + \cdots + \chi_n \leqq x, \nu_1 \geqq 1, \nu_1 + \nu_2 \geqq 2, \ldots,$$

$$\nu_1 + \cdots + \nu_{n-1} \geqq n - 1, \nu_1 + \cdots + \nu_n = n - 1\}.$$

Now for $u > 0$ we have

$$\mathbf{P}\{\nu_1 \geqq 1, \nu_1 + \nu_2 \geqq 2, \ldots, \nu_1 + \cdots + \nu_{n-1} \geqq n - 1 \,|$$

$$\nu_1 + \cdots + \nu_n = n - 1, \chi_1 + \cdots + \chi_n = u\} = \frac{1}{n} \cdot$$

For, if $\chi_1 + \cdots + \chi_n = u$ then $\nu_1, \nu_2, \ldots, \nu_n$ are exchangeable random variables and we can apply the combinatorial lemma in the Appendix if we put $k = n - 1$ in it. Since

$$\mathbf{P}\{\nu_1 + \cdots + \nu_n = n - 1 | \chi_1 + \cdots + \chi_n = u\} = e^{-\lambda u} \frac{(\lambda u)^{n-1}}{(n - 1)!}$$

and

$$\mathbf{P}\{\chi_1 + \cdots + \chi_n \leqq u\} = H_n(u),$$

we obtain $\tilde{G}_n(x)$ by the theorem of total probability.

If, in particular, $H(x) = 1 - e^{-\mu x}$ $(x \geqq 0)$ then all the $\binom{2n - 2}{n - 1}$ possible arrangements of the $n - 1$ arrivals and $n - 1$ departures, following the first arrival, have the same probability, and $\frac{1}{n}\binom{2n - 2}{n - 1}$ arrangements satisfy the requirement that at any time the total number of arrivals is not less than the total number of departures.

PROBLEM 8. The sequence of random variables $\{\xi_n\}$ forms an irreducible and aperiodic Markov chain. Therefore if $\{\xi_n\}$ has a stationary distribution then it is unique. Denote by $\{P_k\}$ the stationary distribution, provided that it exists, and let

$$U(z) = \sum_{k=0}^{\infty} P_k z^k.$$

By (61) of Section 4, Chapter 1, we have

$$\xi_{n+1} = [\xi_n - m]^+ + \nu_{m+1},$$

where $\{\nu_n\}$ is a sequence of identically distributed, independent random variables with distribution

$$\mathbf{P}\{\nu_n = j\} = p_j = \int_0^\infty e^{-\lambda x} \frac{(\lambda x)^j}{j!} \, dH(x).$$

The generating function of $\{p_j\}$ is given by

$$\sum_{j=0}^\infty p_j z^j = \psi(\lambda(1 - z)),$$

where $\psi(s)$ is the Laplace-Stieltjes transform of $H(x)$. Thus we have

$$U(z) = \psi(\lambda(1 - z)) \left[\frac{U(z) - \sum_{k=0}^{m-1} P_k z^k}{z^m} + \sum_{k=0}^{m-1} P_k \right],$$

whence

$$U(z) = \frac{\psi(\lambda(1 - z)) \sum_{k=0}^{m-1} P_k(z^m - z^k)}{z^m - \psi(\lambda(1 - z))}.$$

If α denotes the expectation of the service time then we get

$$U(1) = \frac{\sum_{k=0}^{m-1} P_k(m - k)}{m - \lambda\alpha}.$$

Since $U(1) = 1$ should hold, consequently $\lambda\alpha < m$ also must hold. If $\lambda\alpha \geqq m$ then the existence of a stationary distribution is impossible. Let us suppose that $\lambda\alpha < m$ then $z^m = \psi(\lambda(1 - z))$ has exactly $m - 1$ roots $\omega_1, \omega_2, \ldots, \omega_{m-1}$ in the unit circle $|z| < 1$ and $\omega_m = 1$ is also a root of this equation. $U(z)$ is a bounded function of z if $|z| \leqq 1$ and thus $\omega_1, \omega_2, \ldots, \omega_m$ must be roots of the numerator of $U(z)$ too. That is,

$$\sum_{k=0}^{m-1} P_k(z^m - z^k) = C \prod_{r=1}^m (z - \omega_r),$$

where C is a constant. Hence

$$\sum_{k=0}^{m-1} P_k \frac{(z^m - z^k)}{(z-1)} = C \prod_{r=1}^{m-1} (z - \omega_r),$$

and if $z \to 1$ then we get

$$m - \lambda\alpha = C \prod_{r=1}^{m-1} (1 - \omega_r)$$

because $U(1) = 1$. That is,

$$\sum_{k=0}^{m-1} P_k(z^m - z^k) = m\left(1 - \frac{\lambda\alpha}{m}\right)(z-1) \prod_{r=1}^{m-1} \left(\frac{z - \omega_r}{1 - \omega_r}\right)$$

and finally

$$U(z) = m\left(1 - \frac{\lambda\alpha}{m}\right) \frac{(z-1) \prod_{r=1}^{m-1} \left(\dfrac{z - \omega_r}{1 - \omega_r}\right)}{z^m - \psi(\lambda(1-z))} \psi(\lambda(1-z)).$$

PROBLEM 9. Let us denote by $W(x)$ the stationary distribution of η_n provided that it exists. Let

$$\Omega(s) = \int_0^\infty e^{-sx} \, dW(x) \qquad (\Re(s) \geqq 0).$$

By (54) of Section 4, Chapter 1, we can write that

$$(\lambda - s)^m \Omega(s) = \lambda^m \psi(s)\Omega(s) - sC_{m-1}(s),$$

where $C_{m-1}(s)$ is a polynomial of degree $m - 1$. Hence

$$\Omega(s) = \frac{sC_{m-1}(s)}{\lambda^m \psi(s) - (\lambda - s)^m}.$$

If we suppose that $\lambda\alpha < m$ then the denominator of $\Omega(s)$ has exactly $m - 1$ roots $\lambda(1 - \omega_1), \lambda(1 - \omega_2), \ldots, \lambda(1 - \omega_{m-1})$ in the domain $\Re(s) > 0$ and $s = 0$ is also a root of the denominator. Since $\Omega(s)$ is a bounded function of s if $\Re(s) \geqq 0$, therefore these roots must be roots of the numerator too, that is,

$$C_{m-1}(s) = C \prod_{r=1}^{m-1} [s - \lambda(1 - \omega_r)],$$

where C is a constant. Evidently $\lim_{s \to 0} \Omega(s) = 1$ and hence

$$C = m\left(1 - \frac{\lambda\alpha}{m}\right)(-1)^{m-1}\Big/ \prod_{r=1}^{m-1}(1 - \omega_r).$$

Finally

$$\Omega(s) = \left(1 - \frac{\lambda\alpha}{m}\right)\frac{m s \lambda^{m-1} \prod_{r=1}^{m-1}\left(1 - \dfrac{s}{\lambda(1 - \omega_r)}\right)}{\lambda^m \psi(s) - (\lambda - s)^m}.$$

If $\lambda\alpha \geqq m$ then a stationary distribution does not exist.

REMARK. We have the obvious relation

$$P_j = \int_0^\infty e^{-\lambda x}\frac{(\lambda x)^j}{j!}\,d[W(x) * H(x)],$$

whence

$$U(z) = \Omega(\lambda(1 - z))\psi(\lambda(1 - z)).$$

PROBLEM 10. Let us denote by $\{P_k\}$ the stationary distribution of the Markov chain $\{\xi_n\}$ and let

$$U(z) = \sum_{k=0}^\infty P_k z^k.$$

We have

(1) $$\xi_{n+1} = [\xi_n + 1 - \nu_n]^+,$$

where $\{\nu_n\}$ is a sequence of identically distributed, independent random variables with distribution

$$\mathbf{P}\{\nu_n = j\} = p_j = \int_0^\infty e^{-\mu x}\frac{(\mu x)^j}{j!}\,dF(x) \qquad (j = 0, 1, 2, \ldots).$$

The generating function of the probability distribution $\{p_j\}$ is

$$\sum_{j=0}^\infty p_j z^j = \phi(\mu(1 - z)),$$

where $\phi(s)$ is the Laplace-Stieltjes transform of $F(x)$.

If $|z| = 1$ then by (1) we get

$$U(z) = z\phi\left(\mu\left(1 - \frac{1}{z}\right)\right) U(z) + \sum_{j=0}^{\infty} C_j\left(1 - \frac{1}{z^j}\right),$$

where

$$C_j = \mathbf{P}\{\xi_n + 1 - \nu_n = -j\}.$$

Hence

(2) $$U(z) = \frac{\displaystyle\sum_{j=0}^{\infty} C_j\left(1 - \frac{1}{z^j}\right)}{1 - z\phi\left(\mu\left(1 - \frac{1}{z}\right)\right)}$$

if $|z| = 1$. $U(z)$ is a regular function of z if $|z| \leq 1$. Now let us define $U(z)$ also for $|z| > 1$ by (2). Thus $U(z)$ has singularities only at the zeros of the denominator of (2) outside the unit circle. These zeros evidently agree with the reciprocal values of the roots of $z = \phi(\mu(1 - z))$ inside the unit circle. If $\mu\beta \leq 1$ then there is no such root. If $\mu\beta > 1$ then there is one root $z = 1/\delta$.

If we suppose that $\mu\beta > 1$ and define

$$V(z) = U(z)\left(z - \frac{1}{\delta}\right),$$

then $V(z)$ will be a regular function of z on the whole complex plane. Since obviously

$$\lim_{|z| \to \infty} \frac{V(z)}{|z|} = 0,$$

therefore $V(z)$ is a constant, that is,

$$U(z) = \frac{C}{1 - \delta z}.$$

Since $U(1) = 1$, we get finally

$$U(z) = \frac{1 - \delta}{1 - \delta z},$$

whence

$$P_k = (1 - \delta)\delta^k.$$

If $\mu\beta \leqq 1$ then $U(z)$ is a regular function of z on the whole complex plane. Since

$$\lim_{|z|\to\infty} U(z) = 0,$$

therefore $U(z) \equiv 0$. Thus in this case a stationary distribution does not exist.

PROBLEM 11. If η_n denotes the waiting time of the nth customer, then we have

(1)
$$\eta_n = \sum_{i=1}^{\xi_n} \chi_i,$$

where $\chi_1, \chi_2, \ldots, \chi_n, \ldots$ are independent random variables with distribution function $H(x) = 1 - e^{-\mu x}$ $(x \geqq 0)$. If $\mathbf{P}\{\eta_n \leqq x\} = W(x)$ and

$$\Omega(s) = \mathbf{E}\{e^{-s\eta_n}\} = \int_0^\infty e^{-sx}\, dW(x),$$

then by (1) we get

$$\Omega(s) = \sum_{k=0}^\infty P_k \left(\frac{\mu}{\mu + s}\right)^k,$$

where $\{P_k\}$ is the stationary distribution of $\{\xi_n\}$. Hence

$$\Omega(s) = \frac{(1 - \delta)}{\left(1 - \delta\,\dfrac{\mu}{\mu + s}\right)}.$$

By inversion we get

$$W(x) = 1 - \delta e^{-\mu(1-\delta)x}$$

if $x \geqq 0$.

PROBLEM 12. The sequence $\{\xi_n\}$ forms an irreducible and aperiodic Markov chain. If a stationary distribution exists then it is unique. Denote by $\{P_k\}$ the stationary distribution and let

$$U(z) = \sum_{k=0}^\infty P_k z^k.$$

We have

(1)
$$\xi_{n+1} = [\xi_n + m - \nu_n]^+,$$

where $\{\nu_n\}$ is a sequence of identically distributed, independent random variables with distribution

$$\mathbf{P}\{\nu_n = j\} = p_j = \int_0^\infty e^{-\mu x} \frac{(\mu x)^j}{j!}\, dF(x) \qquad (j = 0, 1, 2, \ldots).$$

The generating function of $\{p_j\}$ is given by

$$\sum_{j=0}^\infty p_j z^j = \phi(\mu(1 - z)),$$

where $\phi(s)$ is the Laplace-Stieltjes transform of $F(x)$.

By (1) we have for $|z| = 1$ that

$$U(z) = z^m \phi\left(\mu\left(1 - \frac{1}{z}\right)\right) U(z) + \sum_{j=0}^\infty C_j\left(1 - \frac{1}{z^j}\right),$$

where

$$C_j = \mathbf{P}\{\xi_n + m - \nu_n = -j\} \qquad (j = 0, 1, 2, \ldots).$$

Hence

(2)
$$U(z) = \frac{\displaystyle\sum_{j=0}^\infty C_j\left(1 - \frac{1}{z^j}\right)}{1 - z^m \phi\left(\mu\left(1 - \frac{1}{z}\right)\right)}$$

if $|z| = 1$. By definition $U(z)$ is a regular function of z if $|z| \leq 1$. Now let us define $U(z)$ also for $|z| > 1$ by (2). Thus $U(z)$ has singularities only at the zeros of the denominator of (2) outside the unit circle. These zeros evidently agree with the reciprocal values of the roots of $z^m = \phi(\lambda(1 - z))$ inside the unit circle. If we suppose that $\mu\beta > m$ then $z^m = \phi(\mu(1 - z))$ has exactly m roots: $\delta_1, \delta_2, \ldots, \delta_m$ in the unit circle $|z| < 1$. If we define

$$V(z) = U(z) \prod_{r=1}^m \left(z - \frac{1}{\delta_r}\right)$$

then $V(z)$ will be a regular function of z on the whole complex plane. Since obviously

$$\lim_{|z|\to\infty} \frac{V(z)}{|z|} = 0,$$

therefore $V(z)$ is a constant, that is,

$$U(z) = \frac{C}{\prod_{r=1}^{m} (1 - \delta_r z)}.$$

Since $U(1) = 1$ we get finally

$$U(z) = \prod_{r=1}^{m} \left(\frac{1 - \delta_r}{1 - \delta_r z} \right),$$

where $\delta_1, \delta_2, \ldots, \delta_m$ are the m roots of the equation $z^m = \phi(\mu(1 - z))$ inside the unit circle.

It is to be remarked that in the above solution we did not exploit the fact that the roots $\delta_1, \delta_2, \ldots, \delta_m$ are distinct. If we use that the roots $\delta_1, \delta_2, \ldots, \delta_m$ are distinct, then we can write that

$$P_k = \sum_{j=1}^{m} (1 - \delta_j)\delta_j^{k+m-1} \prod_{r \neq j} \left(\frac{1 - \delta_r}{\delta_j - \delta_r} \right).$$

If $\mu\beta \leqq m$ then $z^m = \phi(\mu(1 - z))$ has only $m - 1$ roots: $\delta_1, \delta_2, \ldots, \delta_{m-1}$ inside the unit circle. Then

$$V_1(z) = U(z) \prod_{r=1}^{m-1} \left(z - \frac{1}{\delta_r} \right)$$

will be a regular function of z on the whole complex plane. Since obviously

$$\lim_{|z| \to \infty} V_1(z) = 0,$$

therefore $V_1(z) \equiv 0$ and consequently $U(z) \equiv 0$. In this case a stationary distribution does not exist.

PROBLEM 13. Denote by $\Gamma_n(s)$ the Laplace-Stieltjes transform of $\tilde{G}_n(x)$, that is,

$$\Gamma_n(s) = \int_0^\infty e^{-sx} d\tilde{G}_n(x)$$

if $\Re(s) \geqq 0$.

Now let us suppose that the queue size is j at the arrival of a batch and under this assumption denote by $G_{j,n}(x)$ the joint probability that the server will be idle for the first time after $nm + j$ services and that the total time of these $nm + j$ services is at most x. Write

$$\Gamma_{j,n}(s) = \int_0^\infty e^{-sx}\, dG_{j,n}(x).$$

Clearly $\tilde{G}_n(x) = G_{0n}(x)$ and $\Gamma_n(s) = \Gamma_{0n}(s)$.

By the theorem of total probability we can write that

$$G_{j,1}(x) = \mu \int_0^x e^{-\mu y}\frac{(\mu y)^{j+m-1}}{(j+m-1)!}\,[1 - F(y)]\, dy$$

and

$$G_{j,n+1}(x) = \sum_{i=0}^{j+m-1}\int_0^x e^{-\mu y}\frac{(\mu y)^i}{i!}\, G_{j+m-i,n}(x - y)\, dF(y)$$

$$(n = 1, 2, \ldots).$$

Hence

$$(1) \qquad \Gamma_{j,1}(s) = \mu \int_0^\infty e^{-(s+\mu)x}\frac{(\mu x)^{j+m-1}}{(j+m-1)!}\,[1 - F(y)]\, dy$$

and

$$(2) \qquad \Gamma_{j,n+1}(s) = \sum_{i=0}^{j+m-1}\Gamma_{j+m-i,n}(s)\int_0^\infty e^{-(s+\mu)x}\frac{(\mu x)^i}{i!}\, dF(x).$$

Introducing the generating function

$$\Omega_n(s,\, z) = \sum_{j=0}^\infty \Gamma_{jn}(s) z^j$$

which is convergent if $\Re(s) \geqq 0$ and $|z| \leqq 1$, we obtain by (1) that

$$z^m \Omega_1(s,\, z) = z\mu \left\{ \frac{1 - \phi(s + \mu(1 - z))}{s + \mu(1 - z)} \right.$$

$$\left. - \sum_{r=0}^{m-2} z^r \int_0^\infty e^{-\mu y}\frac{(\mu y)^r}{r!}\,[1 - F(y)]\, dy \right\}$$

and by (2) that

$$z^m \Omega_{n+1}(s,\, z) = \phi(s + \mu(1 - z)) \left\{ [\Omega_n(s,\, z) - \Gamma_n(s)] \right.$$

$$\left. - \sum_{r=1}^{m-1} z^r \Gamma_{r,n}(s) \sum_{\nu=0}^{m-1-r} z^\nu \int_0^\infty e^{-(s+\mu)y}\frac{(\mu y)^\nu}{\nu!}\, dF(y) \right\}.$$

Hence

$$(3) \quad \sum_{n=1}^{\infty} \Omega_n(s, z)w^n = \frac{1}{[z^m - w\phi(s + \mu(1 - z))]}$$

$$\cdot \left\{ z\mu w \left[\frac{1 - \phi(s + \mu(1 - z))}{s + \mu(1 - z)} \right] - w\phi(s + \mu(1 - z)) \sum_{n=1}^{\infty} \Gamma_n(s)w^n \right.$$

$$\left. - \sum_{r=1}^{m-1} z^r C_r(s, w) \right\},$$

where $C_r(s, w)$ $(r = 1, 2, \ldots, m - 1)$ are suitable abbreviations. Write

$$C_m(s, w) = \sum_{n=1}^{\infty} \Gamma_n(s)w^n.$$

The left-hand side of (3) is a regular function of z if $|z| < 1$, $|w| < 1$ and $\Re(s) \geqq 0$. In this domain the denominator of the right-hand side of (3) has m roots $\delta_j(s, w)$ $(j = 1, 2, \ldots, m)$. These must also be roots of the numerator, that is,

$$\sum_{r=1}^{m} [\delta_j(s, w)]^r C_r(s, w) = \mu w \delta_j(s, w) \frac{1 - \dfrac{[\delta_j(s, w)]^m}{w}}{s + \mu[1 - \delta_j(s, w)]}$$

if $j = 1, 2, \ldots, m$. In other words

$$[s + \mu(1 - z)] \sum_{r=1}^{m} C_r(s, w)z^r = \mu z(w - z^m)$$

if $z = \delta_j(s, w)$ $(j = 1, 2, \ldots, m)$. Hence

$$(4) \quad [s + \mu(1 - z)] \sum_{r=1}^{m} C_r(s, w)z^r - \mu z(w - z^m)$$

$$= C(s, w)z \prod_{j=1}^{m} [z - \delta_j(s, w)],$$

where the unknown $C(s, w)$ can be determined by putting $z = 1 + \dfrac{s}{\mu}$

in the above equation. So we get

$$C(s, w) = \frac{\mu \left[w \left(\dfrac{\mu}{\mu + s} \right)^m - 1 \right]}{\prod\limits_{j=1}^{m} \left[1 - \dfrac{\mu}{\mu + s} \delta_j(s, w) \right]}.$$

Comparing the coefficients of z^{m+1} in both sides of (4), we get

$$C_m(s, w) = 1 - \frac{C(s, w)}{\mu},$$

that is,

$$\sum_{n=1}^{\infty} \Gamma_n(s) w^n = 1 - \frac{1 - w \left(\dfrac{\mu}{\mu + s} \right)^m}{\prod\limits_{j=1}^{m} \left[1 - \dfrac{\mu}{\mu + s} \delta_j(s, w) \right]}.$$

2. Chapter 2

PROBLEM 14. In this special case $\{\xi(t)\}$ forms a homogeneous Markov process. Define $P_{ik}(t) = \mathbf{P}\{\xi(t) = k \,|\, \xi(0) = i\}$. We have

$$P_{ik}(\Delta t) = a_{ik} \, \Delta t + o(\Delta t) \qquad \text{if } k \neq i$$

and

$$P_{ii}(\Delta t) - 1 = a_{ii} \, \Delta t + o(\Delta t),$$

where

$$a_{i,i+1} = \lambda \qquad (i = 0, 1, 2, \ldots)$$

$$a_{i,i-1} = \delta_i \mu \qquad (i = 0, 1, 2, \ldots)$$

$$a_{ii} = -(\lambda + \delta_i \mu)$$

and $\delta_i = \min \, (i, m)$. Accordingly if a stationary distribution $\{P_k^*\}$ exists then $P_{ik}(t) = P_k^*$ for every t and $\{P_k^*\}$ satisfies the following system of linear equations

(1) $$\sum_{j=0}^{\infty} P_j^* a_{jk} = 0 \qquad (k = 0, 1, \ldots)$$

and

(2) $$\sum_{j=0}^{\infty} P_j^* = 1.$$

Thus by (1)

$$\lambda P_{k-1}^* - \delta_k \mu P_k^* = \lambda P_k^* - \delta_{k+1} \mu P_{k+1}^* \qquad (k = 0, 1, \ldots)$$

whence

$$\lambda P_{k-1}^* - \delta_k \mu P_k^* = 0 \qquad (k = 0, 1, \ldots)$$

and

$$P_k^* = \frac{\left(\dfrac{\lambda}{\mu}\right)^k}{\delta_1 \delta_2 \ldots \delta_k} P_0^* \qquad (k = 1, 2, \ldots)$$

or

(3) $\qquad P_k^* = \begin{cases} \dfrac{\left(\dfrac{\lambda}{\mu}\right)^k}{k!} P_0^* & \text{if } k = 0, 1, \ldots, m, \\[4mm] \dfrac{\left(\dfrac{\lambda}{\mu}\right)^k}{m! m^{k-m}} P_0^* & \text{if } k = m+1, m+2, \ldots, \end{cases}$

and P_0^* is determined by the requirement (2). $\{P_k^*\}$ is a probability distribution if and only if $\lambda < m\mu$.

PROBLEM 15. The sequence of random variables $\{\xi_n\}$ forms a homogeneous, irreducible, and aperiodic Markov chain. A unique stationary distribution exists if and only if the Markov chain $\{\xi_n\}$ is ergodic, that is, if $m\mu > \lambda$. If $\{P_k\}$ denotes the stationary distribution, then by (27) and (28) of Section 1, Chapter 2, we have

$$\lambda P_{k-1} = \begin{cases} k\mu P_k^* & \text{if } k = 1, 2, \ldots, m, \\ m\mu P_k^* & \text{if } k = m, m+1, \ldots, \end{cases}$$

where $\{P_k^*\}$ is defined by (3). In this case we have

$$\lambda P_{k-1}^* = \begin{cases} k\mu P_k^* & \text{if } k = 1, 2, \ldots, m, \\ m\mu P_k^* & \text{if } k = m, m+1, \ldots, \end{cases}$$

and hence

$$P_k = P_k^* \qquad (k = 0, 1, 2, \ldots).$$

3. *Chapter 3*

PROBLEM 16. Define

$$(1) \qquad \gamma_k(s) = \int_0^\infty e^{-sx}\, dG_k(x) = \frac{D_k(s)}{D_{k+1}(s)}$$

where $D_0(s) = 1$. We shall determine $D_r(s)$ $(r = 1, 2, \ldots)$. We note that if we write $D_r(s)$ in the following form

$$(2) \qquad D_r(s) = \sum_{j=0}^{r} \binom{r}{j} \Delta^j D_0(s)$$

where $\Delta^j D_0(s)$ is the jth difference of $D_r(s)$ at $r = 0$, i.e.

$$\Delta^j D_0(s) = \sum_{i=0}^{j} (-1)^{j-i} \binom{j}{i} D_i(s),$$

then $D_r(s)$ is uniquely determined by its differences.

By the theorem of total probability we can write

$$(3) \quad G_r(x) = \int_0^x \sum_{j=0}^{r} \binom{r}{j} e^{-j\mu y}(1 - e^{-\mu y})^{r-j} G_{j+1}(x - y) * \cdots$$
$$* \, G_r(x - y)\, dF(y)$$

if $r = 0, 1, 2, \ldots$ where the empty convolution product is equal to 1. Let us consider the instant of a transition $E_{r-1} \to E_r$ and measure time from this instant. Then $G_r(x)$ is the probability that the next transition $E_r \to E_{r+1}$ occurs in the time interval $(0, x]$. This event may occur in the following mutually exclusive ways: the first customer in the time interval $(0, x]$ arrives at the instant y $(0 < y \leq x)$ and he finds state E_j $(j = 0, 1, \ldots, r)$, the probability of which is

$$\binom{r}{j} e^{-j\mu y}(1 - e^{-\mu y})^{r-j},$$

further in the time interval $(y, x]$ a transition $E_r \to E_{r+1}$ occurs, the probability of which is

$$G_{j+1}(x - y) * \cdots * G_r(x - y).$$

Introduce the notation

$$q_{r,j}(s) = \binom{r}{j} \int_0^\infty e^{-sx} e^{-j\mu x} (1 - e^{-\mu x})^{r-j} \, dF(x)$$

and form the Laplace-Stieltjes transform of (3). Then we get

$$\gamma_r(s) = \sum_{j=0}^r q_{r,j}(s) \prod_{i=j+1}^r \gamma_i(s) \qquad (r = 0, 1, 2, \ldots),$$

where the empty product is 1. Now using (1) we obtain

$$D_r(s) = \sum_{j=0}^r q_{r,j}(s) D_{j+1}(s) \qquad (r = 0, 1, 2, \ldots).$$

This is already a recurrence formula for the determination of $D_r(s)$ $(r = 0, 1, 2, \ldots)$ but the coefficients can be simplified even more.

If we form

$$\Delta^j D_0(s) = \sum_{l=0}^j (-1)^{j-l} \binom{j}{l} D_l(s)$$

where $D_l(s)$ is replaced by (2) and take into consideration that

$$\sum_{l=i}^j (-1)^{j-l} \binom{j}{l} q_{l,i}(s) = (-1)^{j-i} \binom{j}{i} \phi(s + j\mu)$$

then we obtain

$$\Delta^j D_0(s) = \phi(s + j\mu) \sum_{i=0}^j (-1)^{j-i} \binom{j}{i} D_{i+1}(s)$$

$$= \phi(s + j\mu)[\Delta^{j+1} D_0(s) + \Delta^j D_0(s)],$$

whence

$$\Delta^{j+1} D_0(s) = \frac{[1 - \phi(s + j\mu)]}{\phi(s + j\mu)} \Delta^j D_0(s) \qquad (j = 0, 1, 2, \ldots).$$

Thus finally

$$\Delta^j D_0(s) = \prod_{\nu=0}^{j-1} \left(\frac{1 - \phi(s + \nu\mu)}{\phi(s + \nu\mu)} \right)$$

and

$$D_r(s) = \sum_{j=0}^r \binom{r}{j} \Delta^j D_0(s).$$

PROBLEM 17. Now similarly to (3) in Problem 16, we can write that

$$(1) \quad \Gamma_r = q_{r,0}(\Gamma_1 + \Gamma_2 + \cdots + \Gamma_r) + \ldots$$

$$+ q_{r,r-2}(\Gamma_{r-1} + \Gamma_r) + q_{r,r-1}\Gamma_r + 1,$$

where

$$q_{r,j} = \binom{r}{j} \int_0^\infty e^{-j\mu x}(1 - e^{-\mu x})^{r-j} \, dF(x) \qquad (j = 0, 1, \ldots, r).$$

Let $\Gamma_0 = 1$ and introduce the notation $T_0 = 0$ and $T_{r+1} = \Gamma_0 + \Gamma_1 + \cdots + \Gamma_r$ $(r = 0, 1, \ldots)$. Then (1) can be written as follows

$$T_r = \sum_{k=0}^r q_{r,k} T_{k+1} - 1.$$

If we form

$$\Delta^j T_0 = \sum_{r=0}^j (-1)^{j-r} \binom{j}{r} T_r \qquad (j = 0, 1, \ldots)$$

and take into consideration that

$$\sum_{r=k}^j (-1)^{j-r} \binom{j}{r} q_{r,k} = (-1)^{j-k} \binom{j}{k} \phi(j\mu),$$

then we obtain for $j \geqq 1$

$$\Delta^j T_0 = \phi(j\mu) \sum_{k=0}^j (-1)^{j-k} \binom{j}{k} T_{k+1} = \phi(j\mu)(\Delta^{j+1} T_0 + \Delta^j T_0).$$

Hence

$$\Delta^{j+1} T_0 = \frac{1 - \phi(j\mu)}{\phi(j\mu)} \Delta^j T_0 \qquad (j = 1, 2, \ldots).$$

By applying this formula repeatedly and using $\Delta T_0 = \Gamma_0 = 1$, we obtain

$$\Delta^j \Gamma_0 = \Delta^{j+1} T_0 = \prod_{\nu=1}^j \left(\frac{1 - \phi(\nu\mu)}{\phi(\nu\mu)} \right).$$

Finally

$$\Gamma_r = \sum_{j=0}^r \binom{r}{j} \Delta^j \Gamma_0 = \sum_{j=0}^r \binom{r}{j} \prod_{\nu=1}^j \left(\frac{1 - \phi(\nu\mu)}{\phi(\nu\mu)} \right).$$

4. Chapter 4

PROBLEM 18. In this case $\{\zeta(t)\}$ forms a homogeneous Markov process. If we write $P_{ik}(t) = \mathbf{P}\{\zeta(t) = k \,|\, \zeta(0) = i\}$ then we have

$$P_{ik}(\Delta t) = a_{ik}\,\Delta t + o(\Delta t) \qquad \text{if } i \neq k,$$

and

$$P_{ii}(\Delta t) - 1 = a_{ii}\,\Delta t + o(\Delta t),$$

where $a_{i,i+1} = \lambda$ $(i = 0, 1, \ldots, m-1)$, $a_{i,i-1} = i\mu$ $(i = 1, 2, \ldots, m)$, $a_{ii} = -(\lambda + i\mu)$ $(i = 0, 1, \ldots, m-1)$, $a_{mm} = -m\mu$ and $a_{ik} = 0$ if $|i - k| > 1$.

If we introduce the matrix notation $\mathbf{P}(t) = \| P_{ik}(t) \|$ $(i, k = 0, 1, \ldots, m)$ and $\mathbf{A} = \| a_{ik} \|$ $(i, k = 0, 1, \ldots, m)$, then we have the following differential equation

(1) $$\mathbf{P}'(t) = \mathbf{A}\mathbf{P}(t) = \mathbf{P}(t)\mathbf{A}$$

where

$$\mathbf{A} = \begin{Vmatrix} -\lambda & \lambda & 0 & 0 & \cdots & 0 & 0 \\ \mu & -(\lambda+\mu) & \lambda & 0 & \cdots & 0 & 0 \\ 0 & 2\mu & -(\lambda+2\mu) & \lambda & \cdots & 0 & 0 \\ \cdot & \cdot & \cdot & \cdot & \cdots & \cdot & \cdot \\ 0 & 0 & \cdot & \cdot & \cdots & -(\lambda+(m-1)\mu) & \lambda \\ 0 & 0 & \cdot & \cdot & \cdots & m\mu & -m\mu \end{Vmatrix}.$$

Let

$$\pi_{ik}(s) = \int_0^\infty e^{-st} P_{ik}(t)\,dt \qquad (\Re(s) > 0)$$

and $\Pi(s) = \| \pi_{ik}(s) \|$ $(i, k = 0, 1, \ldots, m)$. Then by (1) we get

$$s\Pi(s) - \mathbf{I} = \mathbf{A}\Pi(s) = \Pi(s)\mathbf{A}$$

where $\mathbf{I} = \| \delta_{ik} \|$ $(i, k = 0, 1, \ldots, m)$ is the unit matrix $(\delta_{ik} = 1$ if $i = k$ and $\delta_{ik} = 0$ if $i \neq k)$. Hence

$$\Pi(s) = [\mathbf{A} - s\mathbf{I}]^{-1},$$

provided that the inverse exists. Now we have

$$|\mathbf{A} - s\mathbf{I}| = (-1)^{m+1} \sum_{j=0}^{m} \binom{m}{j} \lambda^{m-j} s(s + \mu) \ldots (s + j\mu)$$

and thus

$$\pi_{0m}(s) = \frac{\lambda^m}{\displaystyle\sum_{j=0}^{m} \binom{m}{j} \lambda^{m-j} s(s + \mu) \ldots (s + j\mu)}.$$

PROBLEM 19. In this case we may suppose that every holding time consists of s phases the lengths of which are independent random variables with distribution function $1 - e^{-\mu x}$ if $x \geq 0$. Let us denote by $\nu_1(t), \nu_2(t), \ldots, \nu_s(t)$ the number of holding times in phase $1, 2, \ldots, s$ respectively at time t. The vector process $\{\nu_1(t), \nu_2(t), \ldots, \nu_s(t)\}$ is a Markov process and it is easy to see that the limit

$$(1) \qquad \lim_{t \to \infty} \mathbf{P}\{\nu_1(t) = j_1, \nu_2(t) = j_2, \ldots, \nu_s(t) = j_s\} = P_{j_1, j_2, \ldots, j_s}$$

exists and is independent of the initial distribution. Further $P_{j_1, j_2, \ldots, j_s}$ satisfies the following system of linear equations

$$\mu \sum_{k=1}^{s} (j_k + 1) P_{j_1, \ldots, j_k+1, j_{k+1}-1, \ldots, j_s} + \lambda P_{j_1-1, j_2, \ldots, j_s}$$

$$= \mu \sum_{k=1}^{s} j_k P_{j_1, \ldots, j_k, \ldots, j_s} + \begin{cases} \lambda P_{j_1, \ldots, j_k, \ldots, j_s} & \text{if } \sum_{k=1}^{s} j_k < m \\[2em] 0 & \text{if } \sum_{k=1}^{s} j_k = m \end{cases}$$

and

$$\sum_{j_1 + \cdots + j_s \leq m} P_{j_1, \ldots, j_s} = 1.$$

The solution of this system is

$$P_{j_1, j_2, \ldots, j_s} = \frac{C}{j_1! j_2! \ldots j_s!} \left(\frac{\lambda}{\mu}\right)^{j_1 + j_2 + \cdots + j}$$

where C is a constant to be determined.

The number of the busy lines is evidently $\zeta(t) = \nu_1(t) + \nu_2(t) + \cdots + \nu_s(t)$ and by (1) $\lim\limits_{t\to\infty} \mathbf{P}\{\zeta(t) = k\} = P_k^*$ exists and we have

$$P_k^* = \sum_{j_1+\cdots+j_s=k} P_{j_1,j_2,\ldots,j_s} = C\left(\frac{\lambda s}{\mu}\right)^k \frac{1}{k!} = C\frac{(\lambda\alpha)^k}{k!}.$$

Since

$$\sum_{k=0}^{m} P_k^* = 1$$

we get finally

$$P_k^* = \frac{\dfrac{(\lambda\alpha)^k}{k!}}{\displaystyle\sum_{j=0}^{m} \frac{(\lambda\alpha)^j}{j!}} \qquad (k = 0, 1, \ldots, m),$$

which is in agreement with (2) of Section 3, Chapter 4.

5. *Chapter 5*

PROBLEM 20. Let us denote by A_{m+1} the expected length of the waiting time of a machine. The time difference between two successive breakdowns of a machine consists of a waiting time, a service time, and a working time, the expectations of whose lengths are A_{m+1}, β, and $1/\mu$ respectively. Thus the expected number of the breakdowns during a time interval of length t is

$$\frac{t}{A_{m+1} + \beta + \dfrac{1}{\mu}}.$$

On the other hand this expectation can be given also as follows

$$\frac{(1 - Q_{m+1}^*)t}{m + 1} = \frac{\beta\mu t}{Q_m + (m + 1)\beta\mu}.$$

If we compare these two formulas we get

$$A_{m+1} = m\beta - \frac{1}{\mu}(1 - Q_m),$$

which is in agreement with (34) of Section 1, Chapter 5.

PROBLEM 21. In this case $\{\xi(t)\}$ forms a homogeneous Markov process. Let $Q_{ik}(t) = \mathbf{P}\{\xi(t) = k \,|\, \xi(0) = i\}$ $(i, k = 0, 1, \ldots, m + r)$. Then we have

$$Q_{ik}(\Delta t) = a_{ik}\,\Delta t + o(\Delta t) \qquad \text{if } i \neq k,$$

$$Q_{ii}(\Delta t) - 1 = a_{ii}\,\Delta t + o(\Delta t),$$

where $a_{i,i+1} = \beta^{-1} \min(r, m + r - i)$, $a_{i,i-1} = i\mu$, $a_{ii} = -a_{i,i+1} - a_{i,i-1}$, $a_{ik} = 0$ if $|i - k| > 1$. The limiting distribution $\lim_{t \to \infty} Q_{ik}(t) = Q_k^*$ $(k = 0, 1, \ldots, m + r)$ always exists and satisfies the following system of linear equations

$$\sum_{i=0}^{m+r} a_{ik} Q_i^* = 0 \qquad (k = 0, 1, \ldots, m + r)$$

whose solution is

$$Q_k^* = Q_0^* \frac{r^k}{k!(\mu\beta)^k} \qquad\qquad (k \leq m)$$

$$Q_k^* = Q_0^* \frac{r!\,r^m}{(m + r - k)!\,k!(\mu\beta)^k} \qquad (k \geq m)$$

where Q_0^* is determined by

$$\sum_{k=0}^{m+r} Q_k^* = 1.$$

6. Chapter 6

PROBLEM 22. We have

$$W(t, n) = 1 - F(t) * R_n(t),$$

where

$$F(t) = \begin{cases} 1 - e^{-\lambda t} & \text{if } t \geq 0, \\ 0 & \text{if } t < 0, \end{cases}$$

and $R_n(t)$ is the nth iterated convolution of

$$R(t) = \begin{cases} 1 - e^{-\lambda(t-\alpha)} & \text{if } t \geq \alpha, \\ 0 & \text{if } t < \alpha, \end{cases}$$

with itself. Thus

$$\int_0^\infty e^{-st} W(t, n)\, dt = \frac{1 - \phi(s)[\rho(s)]^n}{s},$$

where $\phi(s) = \lambda/(\lambda + s)$ and

$$\rho(s) = \frac{\lambda e^{-s\alpha}}{\lambda + s}.$$

By inversion we get

$$W(t, n) = \begin{cases} \sum_{j=0}^n e^{-\lambda(t-n\alpha)} \dfrac{\lambda^j (t - n\alpha)^j}{j!} & \text{if } n\alpha \leqq t, \\ 0 & \text{if } n\alpha > t. \end{cases}$$

PROBLEM 23. We have

$$\int_0^\infty e^{-st} W(t, n)\, dt = \frac{1 - \phi(s)[\rho(s)]^n}{s},$$

where $\phi(s) = \lambda/(\lambda + s)$ and by (2) of Section 3, Chapter 6,

$$\rho(s) = \frac{\lambda e^{-\alpha(\lambda + s)}}{s + \lambda e^{-\alpha(\lambda + s)}}.$$

Thus

$$W(t, n) = 1 - (-1)^{n-1} \sum_{j=n}^{[t/\alpha]} \binom{j-1}{n-1} e^{-j\lambda\alpha}$$
$$\cdot \left[e^{-\lambda(t - j\alpha)} - \sum_{\nu=0}^j (-1)^\nu \frac{\lambda^\nu (t - j\alpha)^\nu}{\nu!} \right].$$

PROBLEM 24. Let us denote by $R(x)$ the distribution function of the distances between the arrivals of successive registered particles. The Laplace-Stieltjes transform of $R(x)$ is given by

$$\rho(s) = \frac{\lambda(\lambda p + s) e^{-(\lambda p + s)\alpha}}{(\lambda + s)(s + \lambda p e^{-(\lambda p + s)\alpha})}.$$

Hence the mean of $R(x)$ is

$$A = \frac{e^{\lambda p \alpha} + p - 1}{\lambda p}$$

and its variance is

$$B^2 = \frac{e^{\lambda p \alpha}(e^{\lambda p \alpha} - 2\lambda p \alpha) + p^2 - 1}{(\lambda p)^2}.$$

If ν_t denotes the number of the particles registered in the time interval $(0, t]$, then

$$\lim_{t \to \infty} \mathbf{P} \left\{ \frac{\nu_t - \dfrac{t}{A}}{\sqrt{\dfrac{B^2 t}{A^3}}} \leq x \right\} = \frac{1}{\sqrt{2\pi}} \int_{-\infty}^{x} e^{-y^2/2} \, dy.$$

INDEX